Fundamentals of **carpentry**

*Carpentry is an ancient and proud craft.
There is pride and dignity in being a safe and
competent workman.*

Fundamentals of carpentry
practical construction
volume 2

by **WALTER E. DURBAHN**

Chairman Emeritus, Vocational Department
Highland Park High School, Highland Park, Illinois

FOURTH EDITION

Revised by **ELMER W. SUNDBERG**

Administrative Assistant for Curriculum
Washburne Trade School, Chicago

AMERICAN TECHNICAL SOCIETY

Chicago, U.S.A. 60637

Preface

The basic purpose of this book is to delineate the fundamental areas of knowledge, and to teach the practical procedures, which should form the background of every competent carpenter. The arrangement in previous editions of using particular examples and then generalizing from them to broader applications has been retained in this edition. The method is again used of following the progress of a house from the first study of the blueprints to the laying out of the excavation, and continuing step by step until the interior finish is applied to the completed structure.

Walter Durbahn, who was an inspiration to so many men who benefitted from his teaching skill, used this method in his work. His students actually constructed houses and other buildings in order to learn each step. The revising author, as a teacher of carpenter apprentices and as head of the curriculum department at the Washburne Trade School in Chicago, has helped to direct a program in which the school work parallels the on-the-job experience as much as possible, both in shop and in related class work.

One of the best ways of demonstrating certain fundamentals is to use a specific house as an example. This serves the purpose of providing problems to be solved, and also serves as a point of departure for expanding the subject. For this edition a practical contemporary house with wide regional acceptance has been designed by architects Ekroth, Martorano and Ekroth.

Information on new materials and their application has been introduced several times. Developments that have taken place in recent years in the basic structure of buildings have been included. Architects have made many innovations in design, and it has become the responsibility of the carpenter to solve in a practical way the problems that have resulted. Careful attention has been given to the subject of trends and variations in building that are due to regional differences.

Individual builders and carpenters may find items with which they do not completely agree. Many problems are solved daily on the job by procedures that differ between tradesmen in the same area, and differ even more between tradesmen in various parts of the country. The intention of the author has been to make this book a useful tool in the hands of carpentry students who must begin with the fundamentals of practical construction. But wherever possible several alternative solutions to carpentry problems have been given.

There are many people who have been helpful in preparing this revision. For their invaluable help the authors particularly wish to thank Mr. Charles W. Barillier, Coordinator, Building Trades Department, Los Angeles Trade-Technical College; Mr. C. M. Sanford, Director, Carpenters Joint Apprenticeship Fund for Southern California; and Mr. William Woltjes, Coordinator, Woodworking Trades, Los Angeles City Schools.

The authors gratefully acknowledge the cooperation of trade organizations and manufacturers who have been generous in supplying information. The staff of American Technical Society has been devoted to the cause of preparing a book worthy to be called *Fundamentals of Carpentry*.

ELMER W. SUNDBERG

Contents

Chapter

To build a sound and attractive home requires the knowledge and skills of well trained carpenters. *(Top:* Western Red Cedar Lumber Assoc. *Bottom:* Western Pine Assoc.)

Preparing for the Job

The term *carpentry* refers to the art or science of cutting, fitting, and assembling wood or related materials in the construction of buildings, bridges, piers, and many other structures made from such materials. Throughout many successive periods of history, carpentry has maintained a prominent position in the construction of buildings, and still remains one of the most important areas of the building trades. Many new materials have taken their places along with wood in construction work, and are installed by carpenters. Carpentry has had to expand to include skills and techniques which were not even thought of by builders a generation ago. Architects and engineers have developed structures which have challenged the ingenuity of builders, and carpenters have had to find ways to build them.

The *carpenter* is involved in al-most every phase of erecting a home or other building. He provides the formwork for the footings and foundations; he builds a sound, basic structure, including the roof; he builds or installs stairs, and built-in cabinets; and he also trims the house inside and out. He takes care of hundreds of details in the process. He has the job of preparing the way for other craftsmen and then working closely with them. He knows his materials and is able to shape them with precision using hand and power tools.

Knowledge of Construction Methods. In addition to his knowledge of materials and products, the carpenter must have a wide background in building methods. He must know about good construction, and why certain jobs should be done in certain ways. Since methods of construction differ from one job to another, and are very much different in

1

various parts of the country, the carpenter comes to understand that in many instances there may be no one best method. There are, however, some underlying principles of good, safe, economical construction that are relatively basic. The methods discussed in this book have been devised to teach fundamentals that are widely accepted and that provide a sound background for expansion into new practices. The capable and progressive mechanic will try to find as many ways of doing a job as he can and will then choose the one that he thinks is best.

The carpenter has a special role of working with others. It is the job of the carpenter to work closely with the architect in carrying out his ideas in the most practical way. Once the basic design has been made, except for a certain amount of supervision which is done by the architect, the carpenter assumes the responsibility of working out many details so that the building will fulfill the wishes of the owner. The carpenter must also coordinate his efforts with the work of the plumber, the sheet metal worker, the electrician, and men from other trades.

Specialization. The carpenter. must meet the challenge of specialization and mass production. Carpenters who work on big jobs often find themselves doing the same work day after day. This is inevitable in the present day business world because the division of labor brings about great efficiency and more economy. In addition, technical developments in the field of home construction have resulted in the manufacture of building components by mass production in factories and their delivery to the job site ready for installation.

The carpenter need not view these developments with dismay, but should stand firm in the conviction that a carpenter is an all-round man who has many skills and a vast background of knowledge to contribute to the building industry. He must be constantly alert to changes which are taking place in his field and be ready for them. Labor leaders, employment counselors, and educators agree that the successful person in any occupation will require a greater degree of versatility in the future.

Reading Plans: A First Step

The person who intends to become a carpenter should learn about the tools of his trade and how to use them with skill. He should also learn about the many materials that a carpenter handles and how they are

Fig. 1. The HOUSE PLAN A (Front and Rear Perspective Views): The HOUSE PLAN A is used extensively in the book to bring out problems in carpentry as they apply to a contemporary residence. The working drawings by architects Ekroth, Martorano and Ekroth, which are included in this chapter, were the basis for the artist's renderings of the HOUSE PLAN A.

applied. These areas of information are covered in FUNDAMENTALS OF CARPENTRY, VOLUME I—*Tools, Materials, and Practices.* This book, VOLUME II—*Practical Construction,* deals with the application of skill and know-how to many problems in the construction field. Houses which are referred to as the HOUSE PLAN A, the HOUSE PLAN B, and the HOUSE PLAN C will be used as a means of

studying these problems. (This book may be used as a general textbook without reference to the example houses.)

The HOUSE PLAN A Fig. 1 is a typical two-story frame building which is adaptable to all climates. It is complex enough to bring out many problems that must be solved by the carpenter. It is the basis for the detailed study of framing in this book.

3

The HOUSE PLAN B, Figs.1 and 2, Chapter III, is a one-floor contemporary dwelling laid out on a modular scale. This type of house has been accepted in all climates, but has special usefulness in warmer climates. It is particularly valuable in this book as a means of working out details on foundation work and for the study of trends in panel construction.

The HOUSE PLAN C, Fig. 110, Chapter IV, is a tri-level house which poses two problems that the carpenter may be required to solve—the support of floors at different levels and the use of post and beam construction. This type of house is frequently used where the lot is on sloped ground. It is also used to advantage in cities where land value is great and lots are small.

In addition to the skillful use of his tools and equipment, the carpenter must thoroughly understand how to use architectural drawings or working drawings. The blueprints in this chapter are copies of architectural plans, and are similar to those used by builders in the construction of homes in different parts of the country.

Construction really begins with the study of the blueprints and building specifications. Since all details cannot be shown on the drawings, a word picture of the work to be done and the materials required must be available to the builder in the form of written specifications. The information thus provided, together with the blueprints, will help both the builder and the owner to have the same mental picture of the finished house before the actual construction begins. Specifications may be defined as instructions to the builder, and as such they must be clear, simple, and complete. They are a supplement to, and an explanation of, the blueprints. Their function is to make perfectly explicit every item that cannot be clearly indicated on the blueprints. See p. 12.

Read this chapter carefully. Study all the information given on the blueprints and in the specifications. Then try to answer the questions at the end of the chapter. The importance of knowing how to follow the instructions and directions for building the HOUSE PLAN A will become apparent. Notice particularly the complete and detailed instructions given in the specifications. Reading such precise statements as these will help you see the importance of your obligations and responsibilities as a carpenter.

After studying this chapter, you should have a better understanding than you had before of what the work of the carpenter involves and how it must be coordinated with the work of other skilled craftsmen on the job. It is essential for all craftsmen, each doing the work assigned to them, to cooperate in bringing together materials, supplies, and equipment, along with the necessary skills to build the building. Such cooperation and harmony in working together are needed if the construction of the HOUSE PLAN A, or of any other house, is to be a success.

Finally, as a beginning carpenter you should be aware of the hazards of construction work before starting your first job, and should develop the attitude of always being safety conscious. There is some danger in almost every occupation, but there is much more danger in an industry where heavy materials are moved about, where many men work in the same area, each doing a different type of work, and where some of them are required to work at a considerable height.[1]

A carpenter can work without fear of mishap if he is alert, knows what he is doing, and keeps his surroundings shipshape.

Blueprint Reading

The beginner in carpentry learns very early how essential it is to be able to read working drawings (blueprints). When he has acquired this skill, he becomes a part of a team, working out a series of construction problems. Each man must know how to "take off" dimensions accurately so that all of the partitions, windows and doors will be placed exactly according to plan. The beginner must learn to recognize all of the conventions that represent materials, all of the symbols for equipment and fixtures, and all of the abbreviations and notations.[2] He should know about the items which involve other trades so that he can make provision for their work as he frames out the house. For instance, he should know where heating ducts occur in the walls, and where the plumbing fixtures are located in the bathroom, so that he may place the studs and joists to allow for them.

The ability to read blueprints can be acquired in several ways. The trainee should use every opportunity to study plans on the job and to see how the building is progressing step by step. Experienced men will often help to point out special details and show the beginner how to anticipate problems. Where a student does not have an opportunity to get first hand information, he can learn how to read blueprints by home study, using a set of plans like those in this

---

1. See Durbahn's *Fundamentals of Carpentry Vol. I*, Chapter 2, for a detailed description of accident prevention.
2. See Durbahn's *Fundamentals of Carpentry, Vol. I*, Appendix E, pages 325-341.

chapter. By means of a systematic study of these plans he will gain a basic knowledge of one building; and by studying more complex structures he will eventually acquire the ability to read all of the blueprints that apply to his work.

Visualizing the *House Plan A*

A set of working drawings of the HOUSE PLAN A, is included in this chapter. When you look at these plans, you will notice that they seem complicated and confusing because of the amount of detail. Yet an ex-perienced builder can look at them, and in the course of a few minutes can interpret them correctly. He will not only know what the building will look like when it is finished, but will be able to tell if there are any special problems involved that will be difficult and costly to execute. Perhaps the stairs do not have enough headroom, or bearing partitions do not line up with supporting members. He is then responsible for passing on this information to the architect and owner. However, you must first learn how to read the blueprints thor-

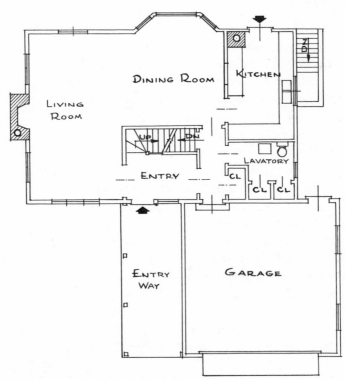

Fig. 2. First floor plan, the HOUSE PLAN A. Trace a path from the front door through the entry and hall to the rear door. Notice the location of the stairs.

oughly before venturing into a critical study of the carpentry problems involved.

The following procedure will be helpful in studying blueprints. When examining a set of plans, forget all of the details at first, and instead try to get a picture of how the house is laid out and what it looks like. (Figs. 2, 3, 4 and 5 are simplified schematic drawings made to bring out this idea.) Look at the first floor plan to see the room arrangement (Fig. 2). The plan view looks as if you were viewing a horizontal slice taken through the building about five or six feet above the floor level. Try to imagine coming into the house through the front door and then going from room to room. After becoming familiar with the layout of the first floor, study the basement plan (Fig. 3) and then the second floor plan (Fig. 4). Several questions can now be answered. How many bedrooms are there? Can you get to the basement directly from the outside? Where are the bathrooms located?

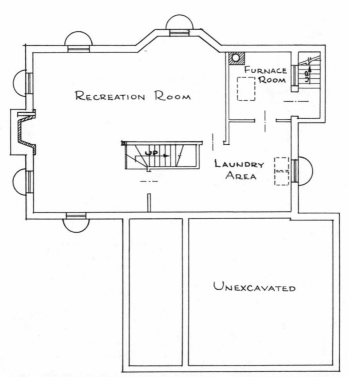

Fig. 3. Basement plan, the **HOUSE PLAN A.** Trace the path from the exterior stairs to the recreation room. Notice the arrangement of utility and recreation areas.

7

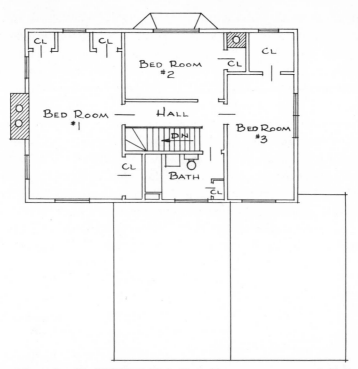

Fig. 4. Second floor plan, the **HOUSE PLAN A**. Study the room arrangement. Notice how the closets fit in. See how the windows provide cross ventilation.

Fig. 5. The **HOUSE PLAN A**. Study the general appearance of the house. Roof, door, windows, siding, etc. Take note of the grade and floor levels.

The next thing to do is to look at the front elevation (Fig. 5). Elevation drawings are easy to read because they look like pictures of the house taken from points directly opposite the center of that side of the house. Now more questions can be answered. Does the house have a gable or a hip roof? What do the windows look like? Is the first floor level close to the grade level or several feet above grade? A general idea of what the house is like is essential before beginning to examine it in detail.

Using Working Drawings

While the terms *blueprints*, *plans*, and *working drawings* are used interchangeably, *working drawings* is the correct term. (Plans should be limited to floor plans. Blueprints are reproductions of the architect's working drawings in blueprint form.) After gaining a general idea of what the working drawings include, analyze them in detail in order to use them intelligently.

Perhaps the easiest way to study its parts is to follow the steps used in building the house. Review the vertical section through the house first, because it gives basic information about the foundation (see Sheet No. 8). Then look at the basement plan (see Sheet No. 1) to study the footings and foundations in detail, noticing the dimensions and problems that develop at the fireplace,

the points where the garage fastens to the house, and the rear exterior stairs. Go back to the section drawing and study the structure of the walls and supporting members for floors and roof. Wall sheathing, insulation, and interior wall finish would be next in order. Items having to do with stairs, interior trim and exterior trim would follow. Now carefully study the windows and doors in the plan views and elevations, and then read all notations and notes, to round out the picture.

It is important to be able to take dimensions from the plans with absolute accuracy and to learn how to check the work as it progresses. You must also remember that although plans are very complex they still do not contain all of the information needed to build the house. The architect trusts you, the carpenter, to do many things which cannot possibly be shown on the plans. You must frame the openings for stairwells, put in the proper headers over openings, lay out all of the rafters for the roof, and do many other things that are vital to the safety, strength and beauty of the house. The real challenge in your work begins after you have read the plans, and begin to use them in the construction phase.

Scaling Working Drawings

The matter of scaling a working drawing is a point that should be considered. Occasionally a dimension is missing, and the temptation is to scale the drawing. Do not scale a plan except as a last resort. Sometimes the information may be obtained by studying the plans to see if the dimension is shown elsewhere. A partition may be continuous and common to several rooms and the dimension may be shown in another room. At times the dimension may be found by adding a series of dimensions and subtracting it from an overall dimension to find the remainder. If the architect is still involved in the building of the house, he will supply missing dimensions or other desired information upon request. The main reason it is not good practice to scale a drawing is that drawings are not always made to scale. If last minute changes by the owner were to make it necessary to redraw the plans completely to bring them into accurate scale again, time and cost might not permit this to be done. Changes in dimensions would be made instead. If you follow and check the dimensions shown in the working drawings carefully, few mistakes will occur.

The Specifications

A house would have to be a very simple structure indeed if all of the information about its construction and the materials to be used could be shown on the working drawings. Plans for the HOUSE PLAN A, for instance, would become so complicated that they would be very difficult to read. The architect or designer who is responsible for preparing the working drawings finds it necessary to cover most of this information in a document called the *Specifications*, which explains many details about the house. First of all it gives general information about legal responsibility, guarantees of performance, who will obtain and pay for permits, how the work will be supervised, when inspections are to be made, and so on. Then it takes up the work of each trade or sub-contractor and describes what materials are to be used and how the work is to be done. Suppliers of lumber, roofing, insulation, etc., are able to determine the kind and grade of materials to be used in each application. When they study the plans in order to find the quantities needed, they can estimate the cost with great accuracy. Equipment suppliers are asked to bid on specific bathroom fixtures, cabinets, the furnace, etc. There is no chance left for argument if the specification is correctly written. The specification for each trade also tells the sub-contractor exactly how the material is to be used in the house. From previous experience he has a very good idea of how long it will take him to do the work. Using the information in the specifications and his knowledge of labor costs, he can make an estimate that will give him a profit and be fair to the owner as well. The arrangement of *Specifications* may vary, but the following list is typical:

1. Excavating, Filling and Grading
2. Concrete
3. Masonry
4. Carpentry and Millwork
5. Wall Finish
6. Sheet Metal and Roofing
7. Glass and Glazing
8. Painting
9. Hardware
10. Heating
11. Plumbing
12. Electrical

The purposes served by *Specifications* fall into four groups: (1) *Scope* —the specifications tell each tradesman exactly how much of the work he is responsible for; (2) *Materials* —they give the suppliers instructions as to the type of materials and equipment required; (3) *Application*—they give detailed instructions as to how the materials are to be applied; and (4) *Guarantees*—they state the quality standards to be maintained and specify how long the contractor is responsible for defects in workmanship or material after the job is finished.

The specifications are neither more nor less important than the working drawings. Each supplements the other, and both must be studied by the tradesman.

Carpentry Specifications. A carpenter should be interested in the whole set of specifications, which includes the work of all of the trades. Your particular concern, however, is with the specifications written for carpentry.[3] The part of the general specifications dealing with carpentry for the HOUSE PLAN A follows this section. First read the opening paragraph, which tells about the scope of the work. Then study each item beginning with *Lumber and Framing.* Each paragraph describes the type and grade of lumber or material to be used, the sizes and spacing of members (unless this information is in the plan), and how the work is to be done where special problems are anticipated. Near the end of the specifications is a paragraph requiring the carpenter to return to the building to ease doors and windows. The last paragraph requires a guarantee of the work against defects in workmanship and material for a twelve month period.

Specifications should be studied with great care to avoid mistakes

3. It is assumed that the student will not be familiar with all of the things mentioned in the specification at this point. However, he will gain an idea of the purpose of the specifications. Frequent reference to this section should be made as each topic is discussed in the book.

and to help the contractor stay within the limits of the scope of work which the contract calls for. A conscientious effort to do a quality job will be reflected in the fact that the carpenter need not be called back to correct costly errors.

FROM THE SPECIFICATIONS FOR THE *HOUSE—PLAN A*

CARPENTRY SPECIFICATIONS

1. <u>SCOPE OF WORK</u>: This Contractor shall furnish all materials and labor for the erection and construction of the following:

All lumber	Carpentry labor
Millwork	Stairs
Furring	Insulation
Finished flooring	Medicine cases
Caulking	Combination screens
Weather stripping	and storm windows
doors	Hardware

2. <u>LUMBER & FRAMING</u>: All lumber shall be sound, well seasoned, free from large, loose, or dead knots or other imperfections liable to impair the strength or durability of the timber. All shall be #2 Douglas Fir or Yellow Pine or equal, except joists, rafters, foundation plates and sills which shall be #1 Douglas Fir or Yellow Pine. For sizes of framing members see plans and sections.

All floor joists must be sized to widths and set crowning edge upward. All joists, studding, rafters and other framing timbers shall be set 16 inches on centers unless where otherwise mentioned on drawings. Frame double-headers and trimmer joists well spiked together, chimney breasts, etc. All joists under partitions shall be set double and triple. Bearing partitions shall be cross-bridged. All door and window studs shall be set double; truss over all openings in bearing partitions in a substantial manner. Angles of rooms shall be made solid. All joists shall be well cross-bridged with good sound material, well fitted at the angles and put in as soon as joists are levelled. Frame horizontal collar beams to rafters above the upper ceiling joists, well spiked to long rafters. All furring, blocks, grounds, etc., shall be worked according to plans to provide solid base for fixtures and trim.

All wood framing construction shall be at least 2 inches away from chimney masonry and the space between the floor framing and the chimney masonry shall be completely filled with fire resistant material to form a firestop.

Carpenter Contractor shall do all cutting and chasing

16. (a) How many risers are there in the stairs from first to second floor? (b) How many risers in the interior stairs to the basement? (c) Do both stairs have winders?

17. (a) Where do you find the size of the doors to be used? (b) Is there a light (i.e. glass) in the front door?

18. (a) List the different types of windows. (b) Where do you find the sizes of the windows?

19. (a) What items of trim are shown full size on the working drawings? (b) What flooring is used in the bedrooms?

PLASTERING AND TILE

20. (a) What kind of ceiling is there in the garage? (b) What kind of tile is used on the bathroom walls and floor?

CARPENTRY SPECIFICATIONS

21. What do the carpentry specifications say about spacing joists and studding?

22. What kind of insulation shall be used?

23. What material shall be used for kitchen cabinets?

24. (a) Who shall select the hardware? (b) Is the carpenter responsible for installing it?

25. The carpenter-contractor must guarantee his work for what period of time?

ELECTRICAL SYMBOLS

○ CEILING OUTLET
Ⓛps LAMP HOLDER WITH PULL SWITCH
S WALL SWITCH
S₃ THREE-WAY SWITCH
⊖ DUPLEX CONVENIENCE OUTLET
◑ WALL BRACKET
◀ TELEPHONE
□ PUSH BUTTON
▷ DOOR CHIMES (or BUZZER)

FIN FL
ROUGH FL

2"×10"-16" O C

METAL TIE

FRAMING DETAIL at STEEL BEAM
SCALE 1½"=1'-0"

PUBLISHER'S NOTE: THIS DRAWING WAS ORIGINALLY DRAWN TO THE SCALE SHOWN. THE DRAWING WAS REDUCED TO FIT THE PAGE AND CAN NO LONGER BE SCALED.

NOTE: ALL BASEMENT WINDOWS TO BE STEEL SASH, 2'-8½"×1'-10⅝" COMPLETE WITH SCREENS.

MATERIAL SYMBOLS

CONCRETE   FIRE BRICK
FACE BRICK   WOOD
COMMON BRICK ENDS OF LUMBER AND BLOCKING
STUDS, GYPSUM LATH AND PLASTER

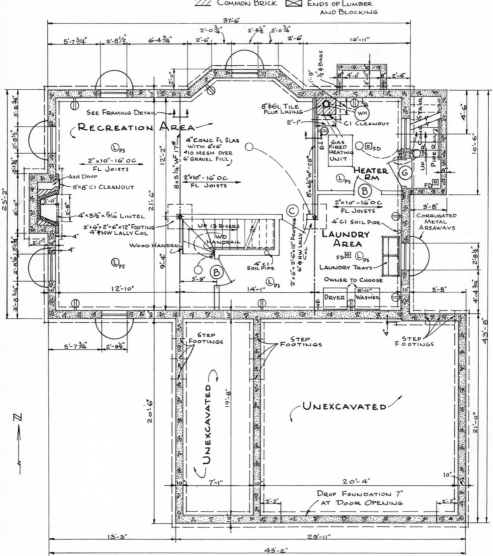

RECREATION AREA

See Framing Detail
Ⓛps
2"×10"-16" OC FL JOISTS
Ash Drop
8"×8" CI CLEANOUT
4"×3½"×5/16 LINTEL
2'-6"×2'-6"×12" FOOTING
4"Φ HW LALLY COL
4"
Ⓛps
Wood Handrail
12'-10"
Ⓛps

4" CONC FL SLAB WITH 6"×6" #10 MESH OVER 6" GRAVEL FILL
2"×10"-16" OC FL JOISTS
8×5¼"-WF 17#
UP 13 RISERS
WD HANDRAIL
Ⓑ
3'-9"
4" CI SOIL PIPE
14'-1"
Ⓛps

8"Φ GL TILE FLUE LINING
2'-1"
CI Cleanout
GAS FIRED HEATING UNIT
6×5¼"-WF-28#
HEATER RM
Ⓛps
Ⓑ
2"×10"-16" OC FL JOISTS
2'-6"×2'-6"×12" FOOTING
4"Φ HW LALLY COL
4" CI SOIL PIPE
LAUNDRY AREA
FD Ⓛps
LAUNDRY TRAYS
OWNER TO CHOOSE
DRYER WASHER

UP CONC STAIR
WH
FD
Ⓖ
PIPE RAIL
3'-8"
Corrugated Metal Areaways
5'-8"
10"

23'-2"
37'-6"
4'-6"
10'-6"
2'-8½"
4'-4¾"
43'-8"
21'-0"

STEP FOOTINGS
STEP FOOTINGS
STEP FOOTINGS

UNEXCAVATED
19'-8"
7'-1"

UNEXCAVATED
20'-4"
DROP FOUNDATION 7" AT DOOR OPENING
2'-2"
2'-2"
10"

20'-6"
13'-3"
29'-11"
43'-2"

N

DOOR SCHEDULE

MARK	SIZE	AM'T REQ'D	REMARKS	MARK	SIZE	AM'T REQ'D	REMARKS
A	3'-0"×6'-8"×1¾"	1	EXTERIOR FLUSH DOOR	D	2'-4"×6'-8"×1⅜"	4	FLUSH DOORS
B	2'-8"×6'-8"×1¾"	7	FLUSH DOORS 1-SLIDING 1-METAL COVER'D	D₁	2'-4"×6'-8"×1⅜"	1	LOUVERED
				E	1'-3"×6'-8"×1⅜"	1	BI-FOLD LOUVERED
C	2'-6"×6'-8"×1⅜"	4	FLUSH DOORS	F	2'-10"×6'-8"×1¾"	2	EXTERIOR 2-LIGHTS
C₁	2'-6"×6'-8"×1⅜"	2	LOUVERED	G	2'-8"×6'-8"×1¾"	1	EXTERIOR 2-LIGHTS

NOTE: ALL EXTERIOR WALL DIMENSIONS ARE TO OUTSIDE FACE OF STUDS AND CENTERLINES OF WINDOWS AND DOORS. INTERIOR DIMENSIONS ARE TO CENTERLINES OF PARTITIONS.

PUBLISHER'S NOTE: THIS DRAWING WAS ORIGINALLY DRAWN TO THE SCALE SHOWN. THE DRAWING WAS REDUCED TO FIT THE PAGE AND CAN NO LONGER BE SCALED.

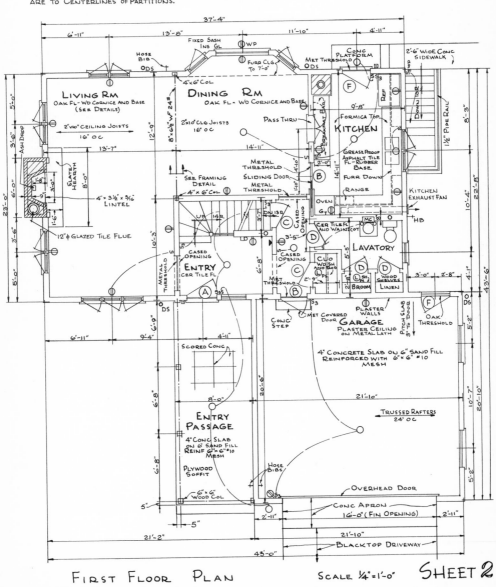

FIRST FLOOR PLAN   SCALE ¼"=1'-0"   SHEET 2

19

BATHROOM ELEVATION

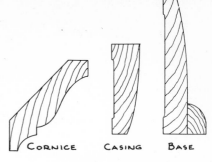

CORNICE   CASING   BASE

TYPICAL TRIM - FULL SIZE

NOTE: ALL EXTERIOR WALL DIMENSIONS ARE TO OUTSIDE FACE OF STUDS

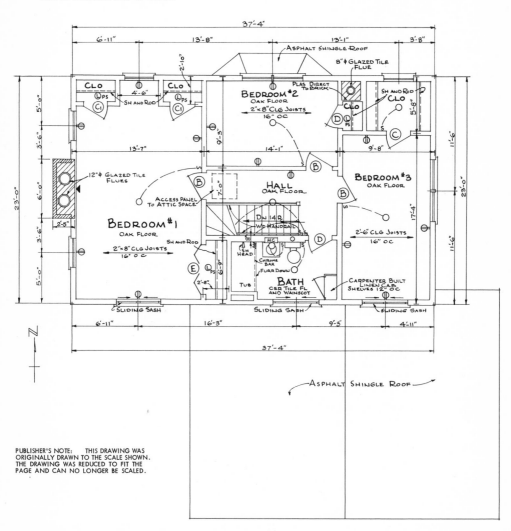

PUBLISHER'S NOTE: THIS DRAWING WAS ORIGINALLY DRAWN TO THE SCALE SHOWN. THE DRAWING WAS REDUCED TO FIT THE PAGE AND CAN NO LONGER BE SCALED.

SECOND FLOOR PLAN   SCALE ¼"=1'-0"

SHEET 3

Preparing for the Job

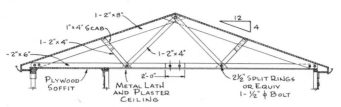

1 - 2" x 8"
1" x 4" Scab
1 - 2" x 4"
- 2" x 6"
1 - 2" x 4"
12
4

Plywood Soffit
Metal Lath and Plaster Ceiling
2'-0"
2½" Split Rings or Equiv
1 - ½" ∅ Bolt

Trussed Rafter Detail for Garage
Scale ¼" = 1'-0"

PUBLISHER'S NOTE: THIS DRAWING WAS
ORIGINALLY DRAWN TO THE SCALE SHOWN.
THE DRAWING WAS REDUCED TO FIT THE
PAGE AND CAN NO LONGER BE SCALED.

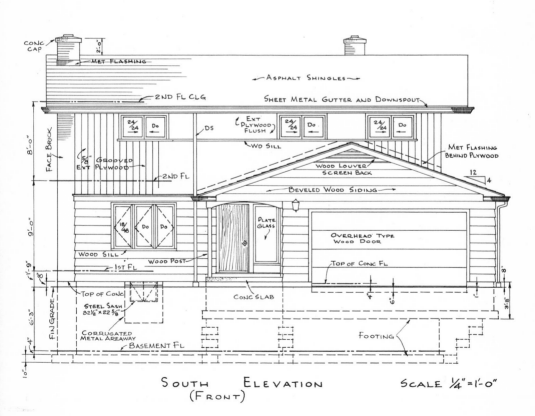

Conc Cap
Met Flashing
2'-0"
2nd Fl Clg
Asphalt Shingles
Sheet Metal Gutter and Downspout
8'-0"
Face Brick
24/24   Do
DS
Ext Plywood Flush
24/24   Do
24/24   Do
Met Flashing Behind Plywood
5/8" Grooved Ext Plywood
Wd Sill
2nd Fl
Wood Louver Screen Back
12
4
Beveled Wood Siding
9'-0"
18/40   Do   Do
Plate Glass
Overhead Type Wood Door
Wood Sill
Wood Post
Top of Conc Fl
1st Fl
1'-9"
8"
Top of Conc
Conc Slab
8"
Fin Grade
Steel Sash 32½" x 22 5/8"
6'-3"
Corrugated Metal Areaway
Basement Fl
Footing
4"
3'-8"
0"

South   Elevation
(Front)

Scale ¼" = 1'-0"

Sheet 4

PUBLISHER'S NOTE: THIS DRAWING WAS
ORIGINALLY DRAWN TO THE SCALE SHOWN.
THE DRAWING WAS REDUCED TO FIT THE
PAGE AND CAN NO LONGER BE SCALED.

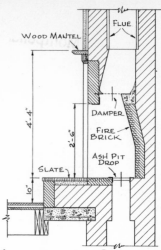

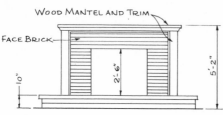

FIREPLACE ELEVATION
SCALE ½" = 1'-0"

SECTION THRU FIREPLACE
SCALE ¾" = 1'-0"

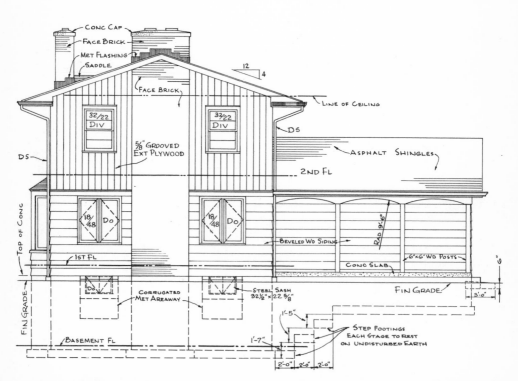

WEST ELEVATION   SCALE ¼" = 1'-0"   SHEET 5

22

PUBLISHER'S NOTE: THIS DRAWING WAS ORIGINALLY DRAWN TO THE SCALE SHOWN. THE DRAWING WAS REDUCED TO FIT THE PAGE AND CAN NO LONGER BE SCALED.

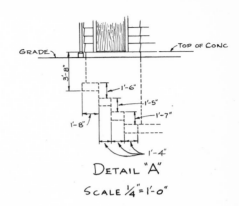

DETAIL "A"

SCALE ¼"=1'-0"

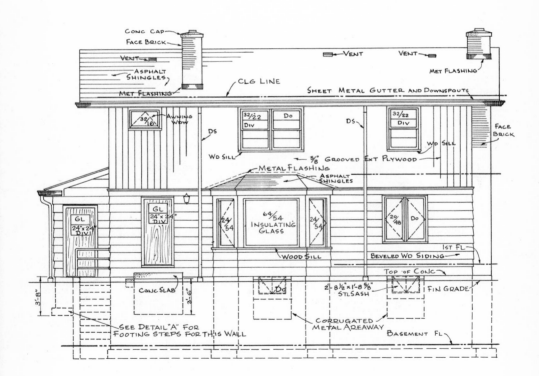

NORTH ELEVATION   SCALE ¼"=1'-0"

SHEET 6

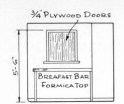

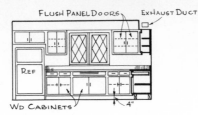

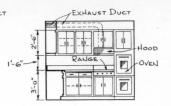

3/4" PLYWOOD DOORS

5'-6"

BREAFAST BAR
FORMICA TOP

FLUSH PANEL DOORS

EXHAUST DUCT

REF

WD CABINETS

4"

EXHAUST DUCT

2'-6"

1'-6"

3'-0"

RANGE

HOOD

OVEN

KITCHEN ELEVATIONS   SCALE 1/4"=1'-0"

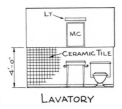

LT.

MC

CERAMIC TILE

4'-0"

LAVATORY

SCALE 1/4"=1'-0"

PUBLISHER'S NOTE: THIS DRAWING WAS
ORIGINALLY DRAWN TO THE SCALE SHOWN
THE DRAWING WAS REDUCED TO FIT THE
PAGE AND CAN NO LONGER BE SCALED.

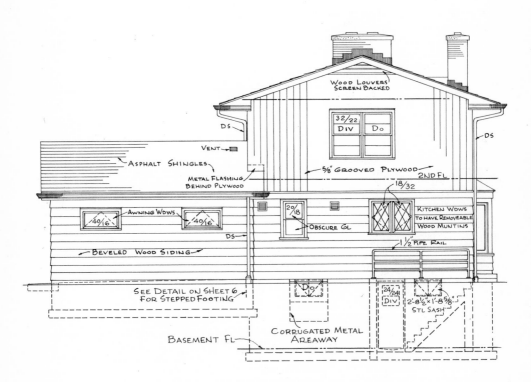

WOOD LOUVERS
SCREEN BACKED

DS

32/22
DIV   DO

DS

VENT

ASPHALT SHINGLES

METAL FLASHING
BEHIND PLYWOOD

5/8" GROOVED PLYWOOD

2ND FL

18/32

AWNING WDWS

40/16   40/16

20/18

OBSCURE GL

KITCHEN WDWS
TO HAVE REMOVEABLE
WOOD MUNTINS

1 1/2" PIPE RAIL

BEVELED WOOD SIDING

DS

SEE DETAIL ON SHEET 6
FOR STEPPED FOOTING

DO

24/24
DIV

2-8 1/2 x 1-8 5/8
STL SASH

BASEMENT FL

CORRUGATED METAL
AREAWAY

EAST SIDE ELEVATION

SCALE 1/4"=1'-0"

SHEET 7

24

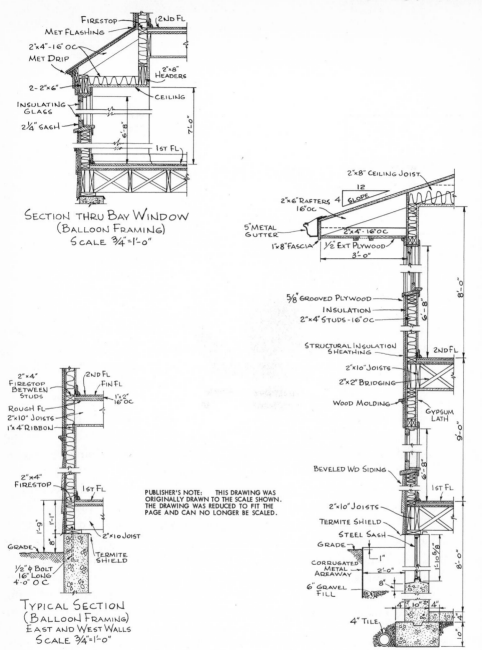

SECTION THRU BAY WINDOW
(BALLOON FRAMING)
SCALE ¾"=1'-0"

Firestop
Met Flashing
2"x4"-16"OC
Met Drip
2-2"x6"
Insulating Glass
2¼" Sash
2ND FL
2"x8" Headers
Ceiling
1st Fl
7'-0"
6'-8"

2"x8" Ceiling Joist
2"x6" Rafters 16"OC
12
4 Slope
5"Metal Gutter
1"x8"Fascia
2"x4"-16"OC
½" Ext Plywood
3'-0"
5/8" Grooved Plywood
Insulation
2"x4" Studs-16"OC
Structural Insulation Sheathing
2"x10"Joists
2"x2" Bridging
Wood Molding
Gypsum Lath
2ND FL
8'-0"
6'-8"
9'-0"
Beveled Wd Siding
1st Fl
6'-8"
2"x10" Joists
Termite Shield
Steel Sash
Grade
Corrugated Metal Areaway
6" Gravel Fill
4" Tile
1"
2'-0"
8"
8'-0"
1'-10 5/8"
4" 10" 4"
10"

TYPICAL SECTION
(PLATFORM OR WESTERN FRAMING)
NORTH AND SOUTH WALLS
SCALE ¾"=1'-0"

2"x4" Firestop Between Studs
Rough Fl
2"x10" Joists
1"x4" Ribbon
2ND FL
Fin Fl
1"x2" 16"OC
2"x4" Firestop
1st Fl
1'-9"
1'-1"
8"
Grade
½" ∅ Bolt 16" Long 4'-0" OC
2"x10 Joist
Termite Shield

PUBLISHER'S NOTE: THIS DRAWING WAS
ORIGINALLY DRAWN TO THE SCALE SHOWN.
THE DRAWING WAS REDUCED TO FIT THE
PAGE AND CAN NO LONGER BE SCALED.

TYPICAL SECTION
(BALLOON FRAMING)
EAST AND WEST WALLS
SCALE ¾"=1'-0"

SHEET 8

2 Leveling Instruments

A carpenter has the responsibility of laying out foundations, establishing grades, and performing other layout jobs which must be done with a high degree of accuracy. A builder's level, or even better, a transit-level is essential for this work. It is important that the carpenter be aware of all of the uses of these instruments and be conscious of the rules regarding their care.

The builder's level is used:

1. To establish levels in relation to a base point called a datum point.
2. To determine elevations.
3. To run straight lines and establish points on a line.
4. To lay out or measure angles of any degree.
5. To lay out building lines.
6. To level flooring.

The transit-level can be used for *all* of the above operations and also:

1. To set stakes at grade.
2. To establish slopes for tile and drainage.
3. To plumb walls and uprights.
4. To measure vertical angles.

The importance of accurate work in laying out the footings and the foundation of a building cannot be over-emphasized. A level, square, straight foundation with accurate dimensions will give the carpenters and other tradesmen an opportunity to do their best work. Laying floor joists and erecting walls and partitions is simplified and valuable time is saved. The application of trim, the installation of cabinets, and the hanging of doors are all done with greater ease if the walls are plumb and true. When pre-built components are used, or when the architect has planned the building using modular standards, it becomes even more important that angles, dimensions, and levels be strictly according to plan.

The mathematics involved in laying out building lines and establishing levels is the simple arithmetic needed to add and subtract feet, inches and fractions of an inch. An understanding of measuring angles in degrees and parts of degrees is also essential. See Table I.

Table I   Measurement of a Circle

A CIRCLE HAS 360°(DEGREES)
1°(DEGREE) HAS 60′(MINUTES)
1′(MINUTE) HAS 60″(SECONDS)
1/4 OF A CIRCLE IS 1 QUADRANT OR 90°
AN ARC IS ANY PART OF A CIRCLE

The Builder's Level

The builder's level (Fig. 1) is more common than the transit-level (Fig. 2) because it is relatively inexpensive and can perform most of the operations required in the work of the carpenter. The transit-level is basically the same instrument with the added advantage that it can operate in a vertical plane as well as a horizontal plane. The builder's level will be discussed in detail first.

Many builders use a builder's level (Fig. 1) because it serves all of the basic needs in establishing levels and

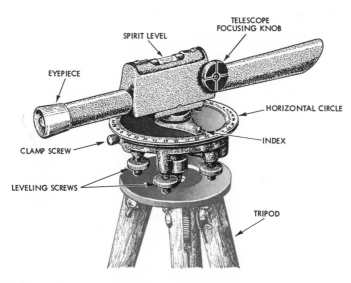

Fig. 1. The builder's level is an accurate instrument used for determining points in a horizontal plane. (David White Instruments, Div. of Realist, Inc.)

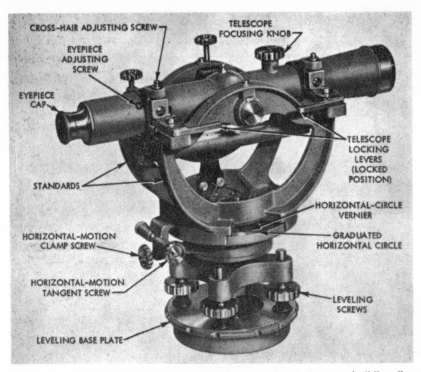

CROSS-HAIR ADJUSTING SCREW

TELESCOPE FOCUSING KNOB

EYEPIECE ADJUSTING SCREW

EYEPIECE CAP

STANDARDS

TELESCOPE LOCKING LEVERS (LOCKED POSITION)

HORIZONTAL-CIRCLE VERNIER

HORIZONTAL-MOTION CLAMP SCREW

GRADUATED HORIZONTAL CIRCLE

HORIZONTAL-MOTION TANGENT SCREW

LEVELING SCREWS

LEVELING BASE PLATE

Fig. 2. The transit-level is valuable for establishing grades, laying out building lines and foundations, plumbing walls, and lining up stakes. (David White Instruments, Div. of Realist, Inc.)

laying out building lines. The essential parts are the telescope, the spirit level, the horizontal circle and the leveling screws. The more expensive levels and transit-levels have a leveling base plate which is a part of the instrument itself. The inexpensive levels require the use of a special tripod which is equipped with a steel ring which serves as a base plate.

The telescope is a fine optical instrument provided with a cross hair arrangement so that it can be aimed precisely toward an object and focused. An inexpensive builder's level will usually be equipped with a 12 power telescope which means that objects will seem 12 times closer than if viewed without the instrument. Very fine instruments are as high as 32 power.

Four leveling screws are provided

so that delicate adjustments may be made to bring the instrument into a perfectly level position. See Fig. 1. The spirit level is the indicator which tells when the adjustments are correct. The telescope frame or support is made so that the instrument can revolve on a horizontal circle marked in degrees. Some horizontal circles are divided into four quadrants of 0° to 90° others into two half circles of 0° to 180°. An indicator inside of the horizontal circle serves as a pointer or index for angular measurements. By taking note of the reading at the index point and then revolving the telescope through the desired number of degrees, accurate angles may be determined. The better instruments are equipped with one other important feature called a vernier which increases the precision greatly. A vernier is a scale which lines up with the degree markings on the horizontal circle in a way which provides a means to measure angles to the nearest 5 minute divisions ($\frac{1}{12}$ of a degree).

A plumb bob is suspended directly below the center of the horizontal circle of the tripod. The instrument is moved until the plumb bob is directly over the center of the measuring point on the ground, usually crossed lines on a stake.

Setting Up the Builder's Level

In setting up any leveling instrument the tripod must first be placed so as to provide a firm solid base. The legs should be spread about three feet apart and firmly pressed into the ground. If the tripod is to be placed on a paved surface extra care must be taken to make sure that the points hold securely. Some tripods have adjustable legs so that they may be used on sloped or irregular ground.

Remove the level from its case or container lifting it by its frame or base rather than by the telescope. Loosen the clamp screw and screw the instrument on to the tripod so that the plumb bob hook hangs through the tripod head. Lightly tighten the leveling screws.

If the level is to be set up over a point on a stake, fasten the plumb bob on a cord and suspend it so that it is very near the level of the top of the stake. It may be necessary to relocate the instrument and tripod so that the plumb bob is not more than $\frac{1}{4}$ inch horizontally away from the point. To get the plumb bob directly over the point loosen two *adjacent* leveling screws and shift the instrument on the leveling base plate to the desired position.

Leveling the Builder's Level

The accurate leveling of the instrument is a delicate operation. Too much pressure will do damage to the screws or the base plate. First loosen two *adjacent* leveling screws to free both pairs of opposite screws. Turn

29

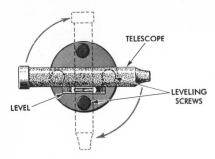

Fig. 3. The instrument is leveled by adjusting opposite leveling screws.

the telescope so that it is directly over two *opposite* leveling screws (Fig. 3). Use thumb and forefinger of each hand to turn the screws. By turning one of these opposite screws clockwise and the other screw counterclockwise and observing the bubble in the spirit level, bring the instrument into a level position. Turn the telescope through a 90° arc and level the instrument in the same manner by adjusting the other pair of *opposite* leveling screws. Continue to swing the telescope between the first and second position adjusting the screws until the bubble indicates that it is perfectly level. The final adjustment should be made with a slightly firmer tightening of the screws. The spirit bubble should now remain centered when the telescope is revolved in a complete circle.

Sighting the Builder's Level

With the clamp screw released, revolve the telescope and line it up with the object by sighting along the top of the barrel. Look through the eyepiece and adjust the telescope focusing knob until the object becomes clear. When lining up stakes tighten the clamp screw so that the telescope remains in a fixed position. When laying out or measuring angles, release the clamp screw and take readings on the horizontal circle as indicated by the index.

The Transit-Level

The transit-level is a much more versatile instrument than the builder's level because the telescope can swing in the vertical plane as well as the horizontal plane. The instrument shown in Figs. 2 and 4 has several features which add to its precision. The verniers help in measuring angles and the tangent screws permit very fine adjustments.

Setting Up the Transit-Level

Set up the tripod with the legs spread and firmly planted in the ground. Remove the transit-level carefully from the case by taking hold of the base plate rather than the telescope. Mount and level the instrument in the same manner as the builder's level.

The telescope locking levers must

be engaged in order to keep the telescope in a fixed horizontal position during the leveling operation.

Sighting the Transit-Level

The eyepiece may need focusing to meet the needs of the person doing the sighting. Do this by turning the eyepiece until the cross hairs show up sharply.

When the instrument is used as a level loosen the horizontal-motion clamp screw and horizontal-motion tangent screw but leave the telescope locking levers in a locked position. The telescope now has free movement in a horiontal plane. To find the object to be sighted, first aim the telescope by looking along the top of the barrel, then look into the eyepiece and turn the telescope focusing knob to bring the object into

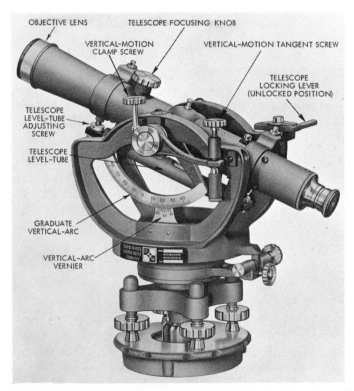

Fig. 4. The transit-level can be used to line up stakes or to plumb walls when adjusted in the transit position. The angle of elevation from a horizontal plane can be measured. (David White Instruments, Div. of Realist, Inc.)

clear focus. If the transit-level is to be used in a fixed position or to measure angles tighten the horizontal-motion clamp screw and use the horizontal-motion tangent screw to bring the cross hairs into perfect bearing on the target.

To use the transit-level as a transit (Fig. 4) leave the horizontal-motion clamp and tangent screws in a fixed position and release the telescope locking levers to permit the telescope to point upward or downward. If you wish to determine angles in a vertical plane, use the vertical-motion clamp screw and vertical-motion tangent screw for fine adjustment.

Rules to Remember in Using Leveling Instruments

A leveling instrument is a delicate precision instrument. Although constructed to withstand handling on the job, certain precautions should be taken to safeguard the instrument. Careful consideration of the following rules for its maintenance and operation will insure its continued usefulness.

1. Study the instructions which come with the instrument to find out about its features and care.

2. Keep the instrument clean, lubricated, dry, and in a carrying case when not in use.

3. Keep a cover available in case of rain.

4. Move the instrument carefully in and out of the carrying case, lifting it by the leveling base plate.

5. Set leveling screws snug and firm, but not too tight. (Setting them too tight may spring the instrument.)

6. Set the tripod on firm ground with the leveling base as level as possible. Position tripod legs about 3 to 3½ feet apart, more if is windy. Seat the legs firmly.

7. When using the instrument on a smooth floor, provide a base that will prevent tripod legs from sliding.

8. Do not touch the tripod legs when sighting. Do not straddle a leg if it can be avoided.

9. Engage the mounting screws carefully to prevent cross-threading.

10. Permit the instrument to reach air temperature before using.

11. The bubble is inaccurate when the vial is unevenly heated. Keep the instrument as cool as possible.

12. Check the spirit level each time before taking readings.

13. Clean the lens occasionally with a camel's-hair brush or lens paper.

14. Carry the instrument in front of you, and not over your shoulder, when walking through doorways, under trees or scaffolds. (Normally, however, it may be carried over the shoulder.)

Reading the Circle Scale and Vernier

The horizontal circle (Fig. 5) is always divided into degrees. The inexpensive levels have a pointer or index which indicates the exact reading (Fig. 6). A measurement of an angle is determined by recording the reading when the instrument is lined up on one point and then noting the reading when the instrument is swung to line up with the second

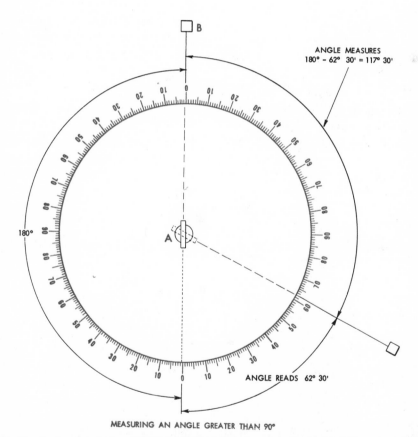

MEASURING AN ANGLE GREATER THAN 90°

Fig. 5. The horizontal circle of 360° is divided into four quadrants of 90° each. An angle of less than 90° is read directly from the circle. An angle greater than 90° but less than 180° (see illustration) is determined by subtracting the reading on the circle from 180°. For an angle between 180° and 270°, the reading on the circle is added to 180°. For an angle over 270° but less than 360°, the reading is subtracted from 360°.

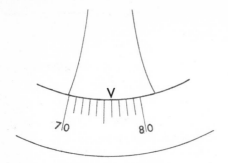

Fig. 6. The pointer or index indicates which degree on the circle is to be read.

to measure angles with great precision. Through their use it is possible to measure divisions as small as one twelfth of a degree or 5 minutes. The vernier is a scale which lines up with the horizontal circle. (A twelve unit arc on the vernier is made equivalent to an eleven degree arc on the circle.) When an angle measures a whole degree with no fraction the index on the vernier which is also the pointer for the arc will coincide with the degree line. In this case no *other vernier line will line up with a degree line* except at the two ends of the vernier (Fig. 7).

point. By subtracting the one from the other the angle may be found.

Better instruments are equipped with moveable horizontal circles so that readings may begin at 0°. They also have vernier scales which help

There are two types of vernier scales in use. One type (Fig. 7, 8, and 9) has a vernier scale in which the

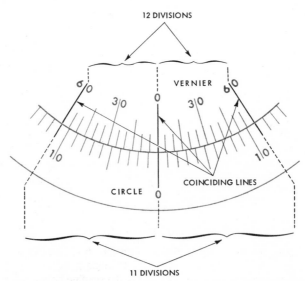

Fig. 7. A vernier scale is designed to find parts of a degree in 5 minute intervals. This scale is set at 0 degrees, 0 minutes.

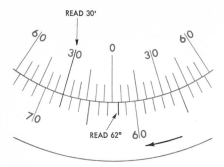

Fig. 8. This shows a reading of 62°-30'. A mark on the vernier indicates the number of minutes when it lines up with a mark on the circle scale. Read in the direction of ascending degrees.

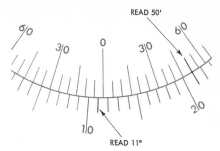

Fig. 9. This shows a reading of 11°-50'.

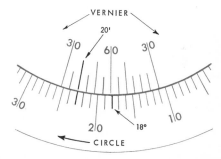

Fig. 10. This shows a reading of 18°-20'. Use the 60' mark on the vernier scale as the pointer.

index is indicated by a pointer or a figure "0" with 12 spaces on each side of the "0" and with designations representing 30 and 60 minutes. Each small space represents five minutes. The reading is always taken in the direction of the rising number of degrees. (See arrow Fig. 8.) In Fig. 8 the index point "0" is between 62° and 63°. To read the fraction of a degree, note the vernier lines and find the one which coincides with a degree line. (Reading in the direction of the arrow again.) It will be found to be the 30' line. Thus the reading will be 62°-30'.

Fig. 9 is another example but is to be read in the opposite direction. The index indicates that the angle is between 11° and 12°. The vernier scale shows that the 50' line coincides with a degree line. Thus the reading is 11°-50'.

The other type of vernier has an index at the center of the scale

marked "60." This is actually the vernier zero. In Fig. 10 if this index line had lined up exactly with the degree mark the reading would be 18°-0'. However, the index points to a position slightly more than 18°. Counting 5' for each small space on the vernier from the index (to the left) it will be noted that the fourth line coincides with a degree line. Thus the angle reading is 18°-20'. (Always read the vernier in the direction of the rising number of degrees.)

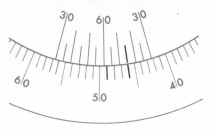

Fig. 11. This shows a reading of 49°-45'.

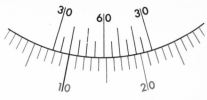

Fig. 12. Care must be taken to read the number of degrees as well as the vernier scale in the direction of rising number of degrees. This shows a reading of 14°-40'.

Fig. 11 shows a reading of between 49° and 50°. None of the vernier lines to the left of the index coincides with a degree line but one of the lines to the right of the index does. Reading the number of minutes is done in the following manner. Counting from the index "60" (actually "0") to the end of the scale to the left will give 30 minutes. Beginning over again at the far right of the vernier scale 15 minutes more are added to reach a line which coincides with a degree line. Thus the angle reading is 49°-45'.

Fig. 12 shows a reading between 14 and 15 degrees. (Always notice the direction of rising number of degrees. This time it is toward the right.) None of the vernier lines to the right of the index coincide with a degree line but one of the lines to the left does. Reading the number of minutes is done in the following manner. Counting from the index "60" to the end of the scale to the right gives 30 minutes. Beginning over again at the far left on the vernier scale, two spaces or 10 minutes are added to find a line which coincides with a degree line. The angle measures 14°-40'.

Leveling Rods and Targets

When sighting long distances (150 feet or more), a leveling rod is necessary (see Fig. 13). The carpenter, however, will generally use a "ripping" for shorter distances (see Fig. 14). He will mark the various heights for the first floor elevation, porch height, etc., in relation to the H.I. (height of instrument). The carpenter who is doing the sighting (levelman) can turn his instrument to bear on other corners where the ripping can be held in the same way. One method is to hold a rule against a stick so that inches may be read through the instrument. It is impor-

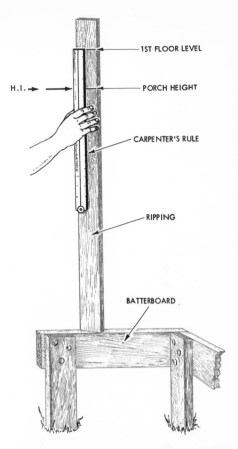

Fig. 13. A leveling rod must be held firmly in a vertical position.

1ST FLOOR LEVEL

H.I. →

PORCH HEIGHT

CARPENTER'S RULE

RIPPING

BATTERBOARD

Fig. 14. The carpenter will mark a ripping in relation to the H.I. (Height of Instrument). The points are transferred to other corners.

tant that the piece of wood be held in a vertical position.

Leveling rods are used to measure the difference in elevation between the station point where the level is located and the place where the rod is held. The height of the instrument at the station point is designated H.I. Some rods are called self-reading. The measurement is read by the person operating the level (the levelman). Other rods have targets that permit the man holding the rod (the rodman) to read the measurement. Rods are graduated in two ways. Some rods are divided into feet, inches and eighths of an inch. Other rods are divided into feet, and tenths and hundredths of a foot. It is important that a person who uses a rod be aware of its divisions.

37

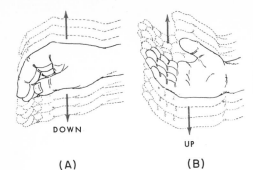

Fig. 15. Hand signals are used by the level-man to tell the rodman to raise or lower the target.

Fig. 16. When the target is on-grade, the levelman will signal by holding his hand in a level position.

Fig. 17. The signal to lower the target.

Fig. 18. The signal to raise the target.

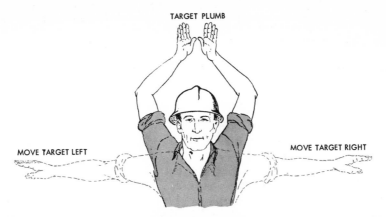

Fig. 19. Signals used to tell the rodman how to get the target on the proper plumb line. To indicate that the target should move sideways an arm is extended and the other arm held at the side. The target moves in the direction the arm points.

Fig. 20. Arms extended level is the signal that the target is on grade.

Signals. When rodman and levelman are comparatively close together, hand signals A and B (Fig. 15) can be used. Signals A and B are made with a rapid motion up and down from the wrist, the motion becoming slower as the target approaches the horizontal hairline. Hand straight out indicates the target is "on grade" (Fig. 16).

Arm signals are necessary when the distance is over 150 feet. Figs. 17 and 18 show how the arm is moved closer to the horizontal as the target approaches the horizontal hairline. Fig. 19 shows the levelman's arm motions for proper rod placement. When one arm is extended sideways the other arm hangs at his side. Both arms extended horizontally indicate "on grade" (Fig. 20).

39

Use of the Level or Transit-Level

For many simple operations, either the level or transit-level may be employed. The transit-level is more versatile, however. It can not only perform more operations, but it can also do some basic operations with greater speed and accuracy.

Leveling

Finding the difference in grade between several points and the transfer of the same level from one point to another is called leveling. The transit-level is very useful in transferring the level established at the datum point (which is a point of reference on a sidewalk or a stake) to the point where it will help determine the elevation of the first floor, the top of the footings, levels of batterboards, etc. To transfer a level from one point to another, the instrument is set up at some intermediate point and adjusted as outlined in previous sections. A rod is held at one of the points and a reading is made through the telescope. A rod is held at the other point and another reading is made. The difference between the two readings will be the difference in elevation. See Fig. 21.

When the distance from the high-

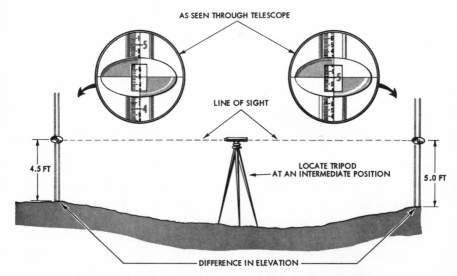

AS SEEN THROUGH TELESCOPE

LINE OF SIGHT

4.5 FT

LOCATE TRIPOD
AT AN INTERMEDIATE POSITION

5.0 FT

DIFFERENCE IN ELEVATION

Fig. 21. When transferring an elevation from one point to another, the instrument is placed at an intermediate location. The elevation of the ground to the left is ½ foot higher than the ground to the right. (Note that the rod is divided into tenths of a foot.)

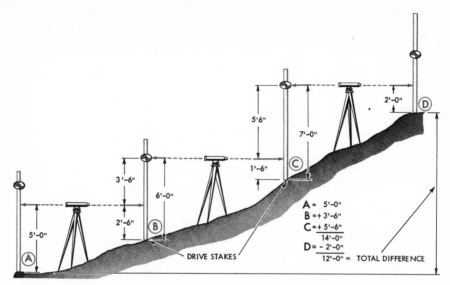

A = 5'-0"
B = + 3'-6"
C = + 5'-6"
14'-0"
D = - 2'-0"
12'-0" = TOTAL DIFFERENCE

DRIVE STAKES

Fig. 22. When the rise from one elevation to another cannot be sighted from one position, the instrument may have to be moved several times.

est to the lowest point cannot be sighted from one position, the tripod should be relocated as many times as necessary. It must be set up carefully each time and the successive readings added or subtracted accurately. See Fig. 22. Note that the rod is not moved until the tripod has been set up at a new position and an accurate reading on the rod has been taken.

When stakes or batterboards are to be erected, the tripod should be set up in a central location on the building site unless prevented by construction operations. See Fig. 23. If distances *A*, *B*, *C*, *D*, *E*, and *F* are as nearly equal as possible, it will minimize the need of focusing. A slight error in adjustment will be

multiplied if the distance is very great to one point. When the instrument has been leveled and the telescope locked in a horizontal position, the elevation established at any one corner can be transferred quickly to all the other corners by revolving the telescope and sighting each one in turn. If the problem were to establish the height of a concrete footing at the various corners, a ripping and ruler could be used in a manner similar to that in Fig. 14.

Determining Elevations

Every federal and state public works has a bench mark and every city has a city datum point. These are markers made of concrete, a

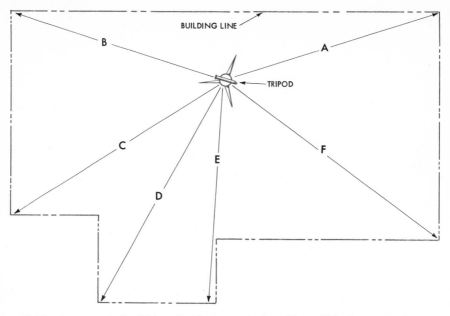

Fig. 23. The instrument should be placed at a central position within the excavation.

notch on a building, or other fixed points. They are usually related to sea level. These points are used both for the establishment of elevations and for making horizontal measurements to locate other datum points in the immediate vicinity of the building project. Once the datum point at the building is established, the architect arbitrarily designates the elevation to be 100.00'. An elevation of 110'-0" would be 10 feet above the datum point and an elevation of 95'-0" would be 5 feet below the datum point.

To establish an elevation in relation to a benchmark or datum point the instrument is set up over it and adjusted to be perfectly level. The telescope is brought to bear on a stake, batterboard or ripping fixed so that it can be used as a point of reference. By adding the height of the instrument and the amount needed to make the desired height above the benchmark or datum point the new elevation can be established precisely. (See Fig. 14.)

When steep hillside lots are encountered, two or more position settings may have to be made with the instrument (same principle used as in Fig. 22). When the transit level is set up on succeeding days, the readings are taken off of the batterboard. When there is a building in the way between the benchmark and the location of the new datum point it is necessary to place the instrument at an intermediate point and establish a secondary hub (or point of reference) from which a final sighting may be made. A licensed surveyor usually is called upon to provide the service of establishing the datum point near the lot.

Laying Out Building Lines

When the transit-level is used for laying out building lines it proves to be a fast and accurate means for doing the job. It will be used as a level to establish the elevation at each corner of the building (the corner stakes are called *hubs*) and to determine accurate right angle corners. It

will be used as a transit to locate the points on the hubs.

Let us assume that a building 100 feet by 190 feet is to be laid out on a particular lot. See Fig. 24. Establish the first hub at point *A* by measuring the required distances of 20 feet and 30 feet from the lot lines. Set up and level the transit level over the datum point and with the telescope locking levers engaged sight a pole held on the top of hub *A*. Drive the stake in the ground until the required elevation is established. (If the lot is flat it may not be necessary to establish the elevations at this time provided that care is taken that the other hubs are driven to approximately the same elevation.) Measure the distance from the lot lines again

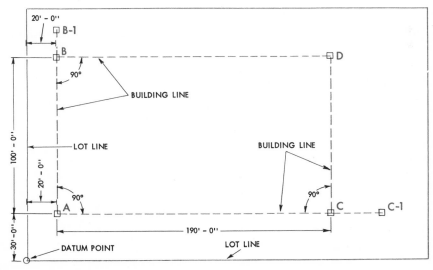

Fig. 24. A problem in laying out building lines is solved with a transit-level.

and make a cross on top of hub *A* indicating the exact point.

Set the instrument up over the point on hub *A*. See Fig. 25. Far down the lot have the rodman drive a temporary stake *B-1* 20 feet from the lot line and make a mark on the stake. Hold the end of a steel tape on the mark on hub *A* and have the rodman measure 100 feet and drive a stake in line with hub *A* and stake *B-1*. The elevation of this new stake, which is hub *B*, should be made equal to the elevation of hub *A* by driving it further into the ground. With the telescope locking lever in a fixed position sight a rod or a line and plumb

bob held by the rodman over the mark on stake *B-1*. Tighten the horizontal motion clamp screw and release the telescope locking levers. Depress the telescope so that the mark on stake *B-1* is seen, then depress it further to bear on hub *B*. See Fig. 25, detail. The rodman will mark a line on hub *B* as directed by hand signals. By checking the 100 feet measurement again from the point on hub *A* the rodman will mark a cross on hub *B* which will locate a corner of the house.

To establish hub *C* a right angle must be measured. With the telescope still set and leveled over point

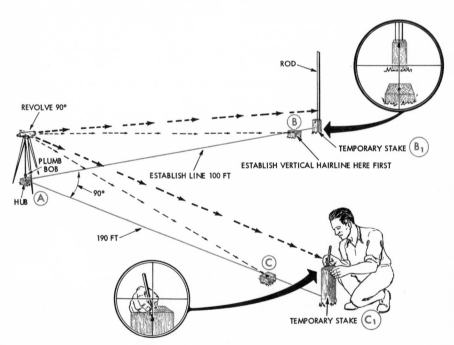

Fig. 25. The transit-level is used to advantage in laying out the corners of a lot or foundation.

A and with the locking levers engaged, sight a line and plumb bob held over the point at hub B. It should still be correct from the previous sighting. Adjust the graduated horizontal circle so that the index will read 0°. Release the horizontal motion clamp screw and turn the telescope clockwise to read exactly 90°. The rodman holds a rod so that it is beyond the required distance and so that he can locate the position of a temporary stake C-1 which he will drive into the earth. Using a line and plumb bob and observing hand signals from the levelman, he will establish a point on stake C-1. See Fig. 25. Use the same procedure to establish the position and elevation of hub C as used for hub B. The rodman marks the point indicating the location of the corner of the building on hub C.

To locate the last hub D set up the instrument directly over the point on hub C. With the telescope locking levers engaged sight a line and plumb bob held over the point on hub A. Then tighten the horizontal motion clamp screw and adjust the horizontal circle to read 0°. Release the horizontal motion clamp screw and move the telescope clockwise to read exactly 90°. Tighten the horizontal motion clamp screw again. Hold a tape on the point on hub C while the rodman locates a point 100 feet away to drive the hub D. The hub should be driven to the proper elevation corresponding to that of hubs A, B and

C. The rodman should measure the 100 feet distance again and mark the hub. Release the telescope locking levers and depress the telescope to bear on the hub. The rodman, directed by hand signals, will then mark the point establishing the corner of the house at D.

Taking one end of the steel tape, with the rodman holding the other end, check sides AC and BD to see that they are exactly 190 feet. Then check sides AB and CD to see that they are 100 feet in length. Then measure the diagonals AD and BC to see that they are equal.

The 6-8-10 Method. After stakes have been located which determine the location of two corners of a building, the 6-8-10 method may be used to set up the angles. It is based on the geometrical fact that a triangle with sides of 3, 4, and 5 or multiples of these numbers will contain a right triangle.

Assume a building with dimensions AB and AD (Fig. 26) is to be laid out. Establish corners A and B by measurement and stretch a line between them. Measure a distance of 6 feet from point A and drive a stake to locate point X. With a radius of 10 feet from point X and 8 feet from point A, locate point Y. Drive a stake at point Y. Extend line AY and measure distance AD. Drive a stake at point D.

Angle XAY is a right triangle. Points A, B and D have been lo-

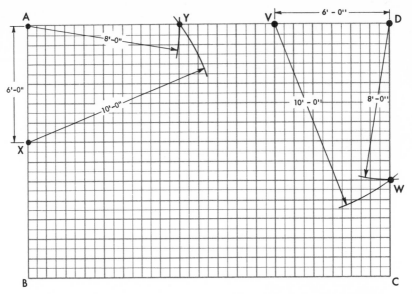

Fig. 26. The 6-8-10 method may be used to lay out the right angles of a building.

cated. Two methods may be used to locate point *C*.

(1) Use two steel tapes, one fastened to stake *B* and the other fastened to stake *D*, and with measurements equal to *AD* and *AB* respectively locate point *C*. Drive a stake and mark the point.

(2) With point *D* as the apex of a right triangle, locate and mark point *V* on line *AD* 6 feet from point *D*. Using two tapes, with a measurement of 10 feet from point *V* and 8 feet from point *D*, locate point *W*. Extend a line from point *D* through point *W*. Measure a distance equal to *AB* on this line, drive a stake and locate point *C*. Line *BC* should equal line *AD* if the work has been done accurately.

To check the layout measurements, *AB* should equal *DC*, line *AD* should equal *BC*, and the diagonals *AC* and *BD* should be equal. If the building were larger, 12-16-20 or 30-40-50 could have been used instead of 6-8-10.

Every carpenter should be familiar with this method because it has other applications. However, it takes much time and must be done with great care in order to have any degree of accuracy. When a builder's level is available it is much to be preferred because of time and accuracy factors.

Irregular Shaped Buildings. When buildings have an irregular shape as shown in Fig. 27, first lay out lines *A*, *B*, *C*, and *D*, then complete offsets and wings. Chapter III

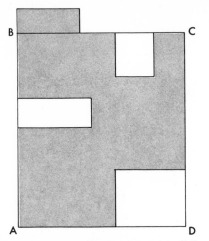

Fig. 27. An irregularly shaped building should be laid out from a large rectangle. Offsets and wings should be laid out later.

will explain how the HOUSE PLAN A is laid out.

Running Lines. The instrument is in a "transit" position when the telescope is locked for horizontal motion but is free to move in a vertical plane. It is then useful for setting a series of stakes in a straight line or for plumbing walls and columns.

Set up the transit-level directly over a hub or point of reference. After the instrument has been leveled, release the telescope and tilt it until you see a stake set in the line of sight in the distance. See Fig. 28. Tighten the horizontal clamp screw so that the telescope cannot move except in a vertical plane. By depressing or elevating the telescope any number of intermediate points may be found. All of them will be exactly on the line of sight.

Plumbing Walls or Columns. When a building wall or other vertical line is to be checked, set up and level the instrument at some convenient distance away. Release the locking levers and swing the telescope so that it bears on the line or point. Tighten the horizontal clamp screw and make fine adjustments with the horizontal tangent screw so that the vertical cross hair lines up exactly with the point. As the telescope is rotated in a vertical plane all of the points (which constitute the corner of the building or vertical member) are sighted on a plumb line. Set up

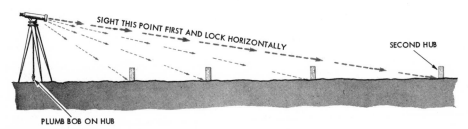

SIGHT THIS POINT FIRST AND LOCK HORIZONTALLY

SECOND HUB

PLUMB BOB ON HUB

Fig. 28. A transit-level can be used to set out a row of stakes in a line.

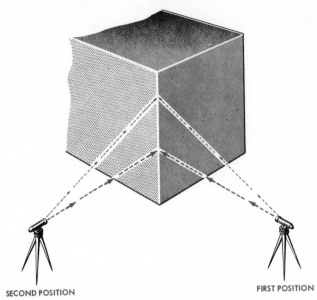

SECOND POSITION   FIRST POSITION

Fig. 29. A vertical line may be plumbed when the instrument is used in a transit position.

the instrument in a position about 90° from the first position and about as far away. Repeat the operation to determine that the line is truly vertical. (See Fig. 29.)

Measuring Vertical Angles. On rare occasions, a carpenter may have need for measuring an angle in a vertical plane. Other craftsmen, particularly those dealing with pipe and who use angle fittings, have considerable use of this feature of the transit-level. The operation is identical to

that of measuring angles in a horizontal plane. The instrument is brought to a perfectly level position and sighted on the base point (whatever it might be). The telescope locking levers are released and the telescope elevated or depressed and a reading taken on the vertical arc. By tightening the vertical motion clamp screw and using the vertical motion tangent screw, fine adjustments are made before reading the angle.

Checking On Your Knowledge

The following questions give you the opportunity to check up on yourself. If you have read the chapter carefully, you should be able to answer the questions. If you have any difficulty, read the chapter over once more so that you have the information well in mind before you go on with your reading.

DO YOU KNOW

1. What is the basic difference between a builder's level and a transit-level?

2. What instructions are important in setting up a tripod?

3. What steps are used to level a builder's level?

4. What is the purpose of a vernier?

5. How should you carry a mounted instrument through trees and around scaffolding?

6. What general types of rods are there regarding divisions and how are they used?

7. How is the elevation of a floor determined in relation to a datum point?

8. What is the 6-8-10 method?

9. How would you set out stakes in a line using a transit-level?

10. Why must an instrument be transferred to a second position to plumb a column?

3 Foundation Formwork

Concrete formwork is a distinct area of the work of the carpenter. Some craftsmen spend all of their lives in this area and find it satisfying and challenging. The forming for concrete work on a residence requires a certain amount of precision and "know how." The carpenter must be able to read plans, must know about concrete and its properties, and be aware of such limitations as hot and cold weather and frost. He must understand the engineering principles involved in the building of the forms and must be able to adapt his materials to make a safe, strong structure to retain the concrete in the desired shape until it sets. As the formwork gains in complexity his skill and knowledge must increase also. The building of reinforced con-

crete commercial structures, bridges, dams, municipal projects, such as sewage disposal plants, water filtration plants, tanks, silos and other large projects are examples which test his ability. Architects and engineers are constantly designing projects which are strikingly imaginative and carpenters must meet the problem of forming them.

The care required in the construction of the footings and foundations of homes cannot be over emphasized. If the footing is not laid correctly on firm earth, cracks will develop in the foundation wall, and it will be very difficult to make the foundation waterproof. If the foundation is not square, if the dimensions are not accurate, and if the top is not exactly according to grade requirements, adjustments must be made in the structure of the building that will affect many aspects of the work to be done later.

Regional Variations

The problems encountered by the carpenter are very different in various parts of the country. In the North many people want houses with basements; others want slab-at-grade houses. Almost all soil contains moisture from rain or snow which will freeze during cold weather. Frozen ground expands and tends to rise above its normal elevation settling back when the frost is out of the ground. In order to overcome this force footings and foundation walls must extend below the frost line. This line is determined locally and usually extends three or four feet below grade. Slab-at-grade houses require, on the other hand, carefully placed edge insulation in the North.

In the South and West houses are generally built on the ground or with crawl spaces. Because frost conditions are not anticipated, simple low foundation walls or slab on ground foundations without edge insulation are used. Each type has its particular forming problems. Building code retrictions, which have been adopted to protect the buying public, often make requirements that are very exacting for the man who does the work.

The actual forming is done differently in various areas of the country. In rural areas or where only one building is to be built, forms are made of boards and 2 × 4 members. After the forms are stripped, the lumber is used for rough flooring, sheathing, and structural purposes. Contractors building a number of houses have forms made in modular 4 × 8 foot panels (or other sizes) using 2 × 4 inch frames and sheathing or plywood for face material. These forms are used over again many times. Many contractors use manufactured form panels which are designed for durability and to provide fast, efficient erection. In larger cities, forms may be rented or purchased from companies that make a specialty of concrete products and building forms.

Two distinct problems will be discussed in detail in this chapter. A house without a basement, the HOUSE PLAN B (Figs. 1 and 2), has been chosen to show how simple forming is done for a low foundation wall in a warm climate. The second problem in forming concerns the HOUSE PLAN A, which has a full basement, and is to be built in a northern climate. See Chapter 1 for working drawings. Panel forms will be used for the HOUSE PLAN A. Other problems that will be discussed include wall footings for slab-at-grade construction, concrete stairs, and the use of patent forms.

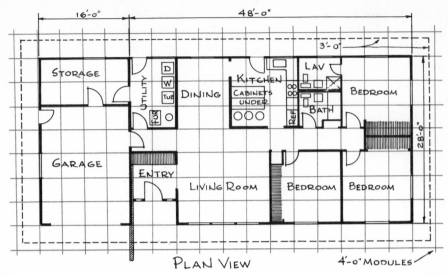

Fig. 1. The HOUSE PLAN B. The plan view of this ranch house is laid out on a modular grid.

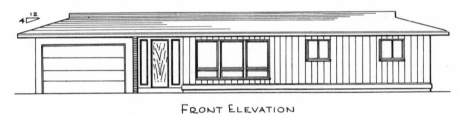

FRONT ELEVATION

Fig. 2. The HOUSE PLAN B. The front elevation of the ranch house is laid out with modular openings.

Concrete as a Material

It is important that the carpenter have an understanding of concrete as a material, because he must build forms strong enough to hold it in place until it sets. When forms fail, the time spent in erecting them is lost and much material is expended. On the other hand, labor and forming material can be wasted if the forms are made strong beyond sensible safe limits. The method and equipment used to place the concrete also has a bearing on how the forms should be designed.

Loads on a foundation wall are generally considered as hydraulic loadings that result in lateral pressure. In other words, the concrete acts as though it were in a liquid state pushing sideways against the forms.

Concrete itself is a mixture of cement, water, sand, gravel and in some cases additives which give it special properties. Cement is made up of some form of lime, silica sand, iron oxide, and alumina which are heated in a rotary kiln to a high temperature when it forms a clinker. It is then pulverized and a small amount of gypsum added to control the setting time. When it is mixed with water it sets (becomes firm) and then hardens. This is a chemical process called hydration. The sand, gravel and crushed stone make up the filler material of the concrete. The aggregate (gravel and crushed stone) must be clean and of a size which is acceptable for the job to be done. The maximum size is generally set at ¾ to 1½ inch. In heavy construction it may be 2 inches, depending on the engineer's specifications.

The ratio of the mix is very important because the workability, the setting properties and the strength are involved. A ratio of 1:2:4 means 1 part of cement, 2 parts of sand (or fine aggregate) and 4 parts of gravel (or course aggregate). Other typical formulas are 1:3.75:5 used for footings and heavy foundations and 1:2.5:3 used for the base of driveways.

Certain additives may be used to give the concrete special qualities.

Concrete which has air trapped in its structure (air-entrained) has a high resistance to freezing and thawing. In mild weather air-entrained concrete is more easily worked. This effect is achieved by using an air entraining cement or an additive in the water used in mixing the concrete.

It is often important that concrete set as fast as possible and reach a high degree of strength. To obtain high-early-strength concrete, admixtures such as calcium chloride are added to the water. The length of time that protection from freezing is required is an important factor. Concrete is not considered to have developed its designated compressive strength until 28 days after pouring. Some of the results of using high-early-strength concrete are: a saving of some of the cost of heating and protecting the concrete, an earlier use of the finished concrete, and a chance to reuse the forms sooner.

The person who is responsible for the concrete operation must be aware of the fact that loss of moisture is of great significance. The inside surface of wood board forms should be soaked with clean water and kept continuously wet for 12 hours before the concrete is placed. Forms should not be removed in less than four days, except for early-strength concrete when they may be removed in two days. All standard concrete shall be kept wet by sprinkling (or covering to prevent evaporation) for five days after pouring. This process of slow hydration is called curing.

Factors in Form Design

In building forms, some of the things to keep in mind are the weight of the concrete, the rate of pour, the temperature of the surrounding air and of the concrete, and the method of placement. The weight of the concrete is determined by the specification for the mix. It does not vary greatly unless light weight aggregate is used. The rate of pour may be slow enough so that the concrete will begin to set up, thus reducing the pressure on the lower part of the forms. It may also be so rapid that the forms may have to stand great pressure. A low rate of pour would be from 1 to 2 feet per hour. If ready-mixed concrete is delivered to the job, the rate of pour may increase to 3 or 4 feet per hour or more, with the result that forms must be made much stronger than otherwise. To provide for higher pressure, the number of ties must be increased per unit area, and more wales (horizontal stiffening members) and bracing installed.

Temperature is also an important factor in form design. The setting of concrete is somewhat delayed at lower atmospheric temperatures, and formwork must be made to take the additional strain caused by the fact that the concrete remains liquid for a longer time. Ordinarily concrete should have a temperature of between 50 and 70 degrees Fahrenheit when it is placed in the forms. In cold weather the temperature should be maintained at 50 degrees or higher for at least five days after pouring. The concrete should be covered to retain moisture and prevent freezing. Another factor that affects form design is the use of vibrators. Immersion vibrators are used to compact freshly poured concrete. The vibrators tend to keep the concrete in a fluid state for its full depth. The concrete therefore exerts greater pressure on the forms than if the vibrators were not used.

Basic Formwork

The broad surfaces of the forms are generally plywood sheets. These are held the desired distance apart and prevented from spreading further by devices known as ties. Vertical members serve to stiffen the sheathing and horizontal members known as wales (or walers) hold them in line. The ties generally are fastened through some form of holder which transfers the pressure to the wales. Generally the ties, walers and vertical members are spaced uniformly in both the horizontal and vertical direction because they are designed to take the maximum load at all levels in the form. It is important that the carpenter appreciate the fact that forms must stand a great deal of pressure, the ties do the work of retaining the concrete and spacing the forms to give the required wall thickness. The vertical members and the wales stiffen the forms. Bracing serves the main purpose of keeping the forms in correct position.

Concrete Foundation Forming Systems

Carpenters use several different types of forming systems, because they encounter a number of different problems, and because they also have individual preferences. One type of forming, which is still used today though it has been largely replaced, is called "built-up" or "built-in-place" forming. The materials used are 2 × 4 inch vertical members and 1 inch boards. It is assembled much as a frame wall is assembled. After the forms are stripped, the materials used to build the forms are utilized in the building of the house.

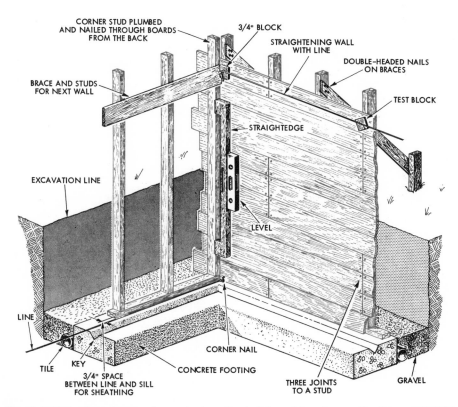

Fig. 3. Built-in-place forming is used when the builder wishes to use the form material in the structure of the house.

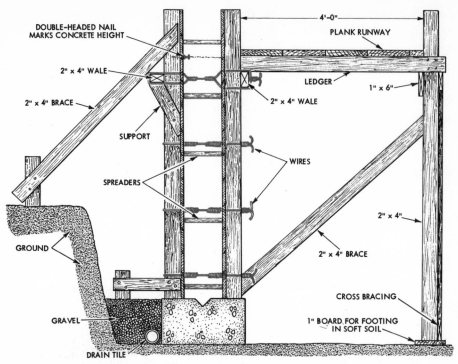

Fig. 4. A sectional view through formwork which is built-in-place. Notice the wire ties, wood spreaders, and bracing.

The 2 × 4s are used for studs and framing members, and 1 inch boards are used for rough flooring and sheathing. "Built-in-place" forming is used today on the farm, or where the carpenter builds one house and plans to re-use the material. This type of formwork is expensive because it takes much time to erect, brace, and strip. (See Figs. 3 and 4.)

Much of the concrete forming today is done using panel forms made by the carpenter. Some builders make the forms on the job site, while others build them elsewhere and transport them from job to job. They are made as large as can be conveniently carried and put in place. For low walls, the forms are made by nailing a number of 1 inch boards to evenly spaced 2 × 4 inch uprights. When the forms are stripped, the material may be re-used in building the house.

The forms used for houses with basements are modular 4 × 8 foot panels (or other convenient sizes) made with frames of 2 × 4 inch

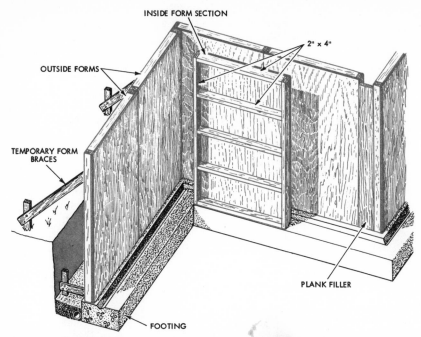

INSIDE FORM SECTION

2" x 4"

OUTSIDE FORMS

TEMPORARY FORM
BRACES

PLANK FILLER

FOOTING

Fig. 5. Panels with fillers of various sizes can be adapted to most forming problems. They may be reused many times. Forms of this type are generally made by the carpenter.

members having intermediate stiffeners, and faced with pieces of ¾ inch plywood. Several types of ties are used. Wire ties and band iron are still used but have been largely replaced by snap ties and various patented devices. See Fig. 5 for an example of this type of forming.

A number of manufacturers have developed several ingenious forming systems to replace, or to supplement, forms built by the carpenter. Some are quite simple, using sheets of plywood and special ties and clamps. Wood wales stiffen the plywood sheets and keep them in line. See

Fig. 6. Other forming systems use panel units with steel frames and plywood faces. They come in several sizes and require a variety of tying devices to meet special forming problems. See Fig. 7. The patented forms have several advantages, the most important of which are that they can be erected quickly by fewer men, and they can be re-used a great many times, and they are very durable. The companies that manufacture forms rent or sell them to builders. Some provide a service whereby they analyze the forming problems, prepare working drawings, and submit com-

57

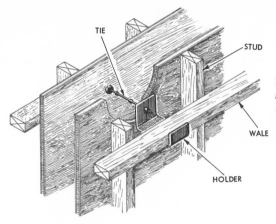

Fig. 6. Patented form ties and holders are used to hold wales against studs. (Allenform Corporation.)

Fig. 7. Some manufactured panels have steel frames and plywood faces. Patented corners and form ties are used to speed up assembly. (Universal Form Clamp Company.)

plete material lists. When a builder has much work that must be frequently repeated, it pays him to purchase a set of manufactured forms.

Form Ties

A form tie is a device that passes through both sides of a form, retaining them against the lateral pressure of the concrete. One type of tie that has been used for many years is the *wire tie*. It consists of a wire which is placed around a stud, with its two ends passed through both panels of the form, then around a stud on the other side, where the two ends are twisted together. A spreader, which is a stick cut to the exact dimensions of the wall thickness, is inserted between the faces of the forms. A piece of metal (or a stick) is placed between the wires and twisted until the forms are brought up tight against the spreader. (See Figs. 4 and 8.)

This method of tying forms together is not too satisfactory because of the time involved in installing the ties. The wires also tend to cut into the studs under the full pressure of the concrete, thus permitting the wall to become thicker than desired and irregular in places.

Snap ties are very popular and are used by many builders. They have several time-saving features. Most of them are self-spacing, which eliminates the need to insert spreaders. The forms are kept the proper distance apart by means of washers which are fixed to the tie. Two places about an inch inside of each washer are weakened by flattening. These are the points where the tie will be broken off after the forms are removed. Forms are installed quickly because snap ties are inserted through the forms and between the wales, and driven tight with a few

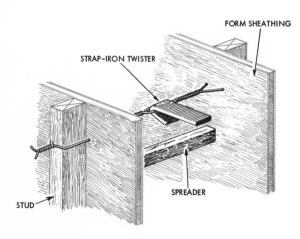

FORM SHEATHING

STRAP-IRON TWISTER

STUD

SPREADER

Fig. 8. Wire ties are twisted until the studs draw the sheathing tight against the spreaders.

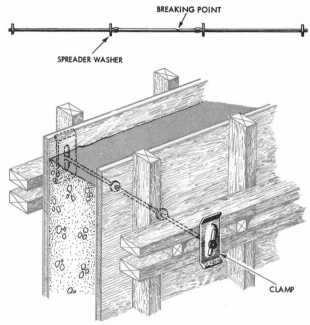

BREAKING POINT

SPREADER WASHER

CLAMP

Fig. 9. Snap ties provide a means of spacing the walls at the proper distance apart, and also clamping the whole assembly together.

blows on the snap tie clamps, which work on the wedge principle. See Fig. 9. When the forms are ready to be stripped, the clamps are struck a blow which releases the wales. The forms are then freed from the wall and slipped from the ties. When the end of the tie is twisted, it breaks off inside the wall at the "break back" point. This leaves a hole in the wall which is patched with grout. Some ties are equipped with wood or plastic cones which are removed by twisting with a special wrench, leaving a clean conical hole that may be patched neatly. See Fig. 10. Snap ties are made for different wall thicknesses and are designed to take different loads. They should be placed at proper intervals, depending on the problems, with wales arranged to keep the forms in line. Bracing can be kept to a minimum because the ties are effective in retaining the concrete in the forms.

Formed wire ties are used in the same manner as snap ties. A wedge and bearing plate provide the tightening device to hold the whole assembly together. Some forming systems are arranged so that the ties pass between adjacent forms instead

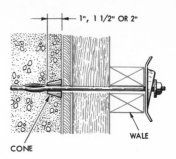

Fig. 10. Some ties are made with wood or plastic cones which are removed from the wall, leaving a smooth conical hole for patching. (Richmond Screw Anchor Co., Inc.)

of through holes in the plywood. It is easy to twist the tie ends to break them off by inserting a tool or bar in the loop. See Fig. 11.

Other types of form ties used with wood form panels have rods and clamp buttons. See Fig. 12. They are generally used on heavier construction, because the rods can be of larger diameter, ranging from $\frac{1}{4}$ to $\frac{5}{8}$ of an inch. A special tightening wrench is used to position the clamps, draw

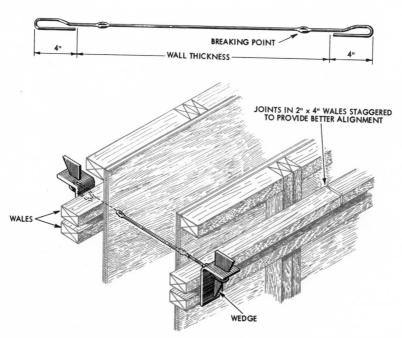

Fig. 11. Formed wire ties (twist ties) use a wedge to draw the forms up tight.

61

 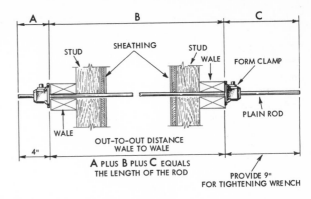

Fig. 12. A form clamp (left) which is used (right) for heavy work requiring rods of large diameter. (Universal Form Clamp Company.)

the forms into line, and tighten the assembly. See Fig. 13. After the wall is poured, and while the concrete is still green, the rods are pulled from the wall with a special rod puller. The rods can be used again.

Two types of ties use threaded devices to take up the pressure in the form. One of them uses a coil tie made to fit a lag screw or a bolt. A wrench is used to turn the lag screws up tight against flat washers. See

Fig. 13. When the tightening wrench is revolved around the rod, it drives the form clamp into position where it may be tightened. (Universal Form Clamp Company.)

Fig. 14. The other type uses a large nut or a handle washer. The handle washer is designed so that it slips over the threaded rod until it is very near the wale. Three turns are all that is required to bring it up tight. When the forms are to be stripped the nuts or handle washers are removed and the outer threaded rods are screwed out. The inside threaded rods remain in the wall. When cones have been used, they are removed and the holes repaired. See Fig. 15.

Form Material

Plywood is used almost universally for formwork except for low walls or where special problems are encountered. Where plywood is not used, 1 × 6 inch boards may be used. Boards are also used when the form is to be torn apart and the wood used in building the structure. Green lumber should be avoided because

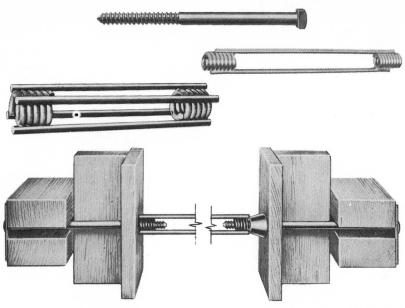

Fig. 14. Coil ties are designed to be used with lag screws and washers. (Richmond Screw Anchor Co., Inc.)

Fig. 15. Nut washers or tilt lock clamps are used in assemblies with threaded rods. (Richmond Screw Anchor Co., Inc.)

exposure to air and sun causes it to shrink. Shrinkage opens joints and allows part of the wet concrete to leak out leaving a concentration of the aggregate. On the other hand, if the wood is too dry it will soak up water from the concrete and swell. This may bring about distortion in the forms. It is good practice to hose down the forms the day before the concrete is to be poured and to continue hosing up to the time of the pour. Boards containing knots should not be used for forming, but if they must be used the knots should be covered with a piece of sheet metal. When making panel forms, of the types shown in Fig. 36, all joints in the sheathing should be broken so that they fall on different studs. While tongue and groove, and ship-lap boards will serve the purpose very well, square edge boards are most commonly used.

Forms for basement foundations are usually made of 4 × 8 foot plywood panels on frames made of 2 × 4s. Templates or jigs are not necessary for these forms, because the sheets of plywood have exact dimensions and have perfectly square corners. The frames are assembled to fit the plywood sheet. The plywood is made for this particular purpose in ⅝ and ¾ inch thicknesses. Plywood panels are by far the fastest and most economical panels to fabricate. They last longer and give a far better finish to the wall than sheathing, leaving a wall surface which is quite smooth. These panels may be obtained with a plastic surface that is waterproof, abrasion resistant, and easy to clean. Forms with plywood faces can be reused many times. Patented forms with metal frames provide edge protection for the plywood panels. The panels may be replaced when damaged or worn. (See Fig. 7.)

Ordinary plywood panels are given a coat of oil so that they will separate from the wall without difficulty. The oil coating also permits them to be cleaned easily. If the walls are to be painted or plastered, however, the oil in the concrete may prevent the finish from bonding. Some other agent may be used, such as a lacquer.

The HOUSE PLAN B

The plot plan for HOUSE PLAN B will serve to demonstrate how to stake out a house, and how to prepare the formwork required for footings and foundations. (See Fig. 16.)

The house is rectangular in shape, with an offset. Since there is a crawl space under the house, the foundation wall is comparatively low. The load is not great.

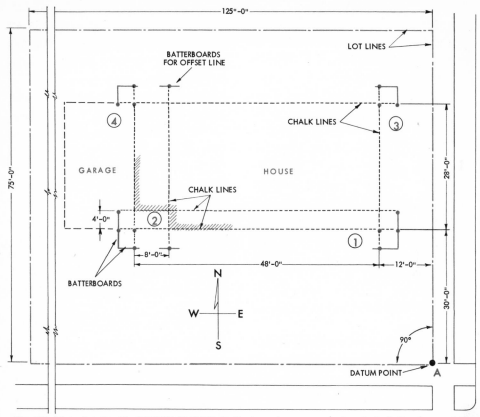

Fig. 16. Plot plan for the HOUSE PLAN B. Batterboards are erected and chalk lines stretched to indicate the location of building lines.

Staking Out the House Plan B

The lot is 75 feet by 125 feet, and fairly level. The garage and storage area will be laid out and poured later. The corner stakes for the lot have been located by the surveyor. Point *A* at the intersection of the sidewalks is considered as the datum point from which measurements and levels are taken. See Fig. 16.

Whenever possible the corners of the building should be located by a surveyor. When the carpenter has this responsibility, he should follow the architect's plot plan carefully, and he should find out about local building codes as they relate to set backs from property lines, side yard limitations, and so on.

PROCEDURE

1. Locate a point 30 feet from the south lot line and 12 feet from the east lot line and drive stake *1* at this point. It is important that lines be held approximately level when horizontal measurements are made. Drive a nail into the top of the stake to indicate the exact location of the point. (Ideal stakes can be made by cutting a 2 × 2 inch stick into pieces 2 feet in length.)

2. Set stake *2* 48 feet to the west of stake *1* and 30 feet from the south lot line.

3. The manner of making a right angle corner at stake *1* and establishing stake *3* can be done in several ways.

a. If a transit-level is available, set it up over stake *1* using a plumb bob to get the exact location over the stake. After the instrument has been leveled, release the lock-release lever so that it can move in a vertical plane. Depress the telescope and make a sight on point 2. Turn the telescope through 90°, measure 28 feet from stake *1*, drive stake *3* and locate point *3*.

b. If a builder's level is available, the same procedure is followed except that the telescope cannot be depressed to sight the stakes. It is necessary to use a rod instead which must be held in a vertical position above stake 2. Swing the telescope through a 90° arc and by using a rod again, set stake *3* and mark the point.

c. If there is no leveling instrument, use the following procedure: Along base line *1 — 2*, measure a distance of 6 feet from stake *1* and drive

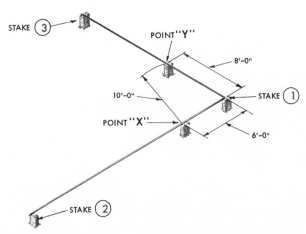

Fig. 17. The right angle at point 1 can be laid out using the 6-8-10 method.

a stake to mark point X accurately. See Fig. 17. Measure 8 feet from stake *1* and 10 feet from point X, drive another stake and establish point Y. Measure 28 feet from point *1*, passing the line over point Y to establish stake *3*.

4. Move the transit-level or the builder's level to a position directly over stake *2* and follow the same procedure as in steps 3*a*. or 3*b*. to locate stake *4*. If the 6-8-10 method is used, establish stake *4* by measuring from stakes *2* and *3*.

5. Check all of the building lines to make sure that they have the right measurements. Check the diagonals of the rectangle to see that they are equal. Measure the distance to the lot line to check that the building is located correctly.

6. The next operation is the erection of batterboards. Select three pieces of 2 × 4 for each corner of the building and sharpen the ends. Make them long enough so that when driven firmly in the ground they will extend to a convenient height above grade. Drive the stakes so that they will be parallel to, and about 4 feet away from, the building lines. See Fig. 18. Verify with the excavating contractor the clearance required to permit the excavating machinery to operate and set the batterboard stakes farther out if necessary.

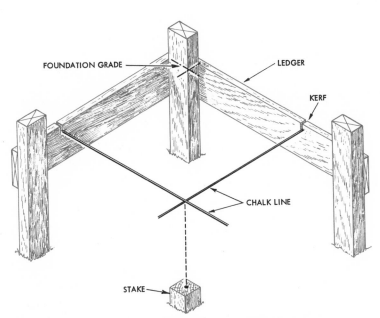

FOUNDATION GRADE — LEDGER KERF CHALK LINE STAKE

Fig. 18. Batterboards consist of stakes and horizontal ledgers. Chalk lines are fastened to the batterboards to locate the building lines.

7. Nail a ledger board to the stakes at a convenient working height. Make each board level as you nail it in place. The batterboards should be approximately level at the four corners of the building.

8. Using chalk lines and a plumb bob, stretch a line so that it passes directly over points marked on stakes *1* and *2*. Mark the top of the ledger where the lines cross. Make a shallow saw kerf in the ledger, pass the line through the kerf, and fasten the line to a nail. Repeat the operation for the other three building lines.

Note: Where an offset occurs as at corner *2*, batterboards are extended or new ones erected and additional lines are stretched. See Fig. 16.

Alternative Method of Staking Out the HOUSE PLAN B

There are two fundamental differences in the alternative method: (1) The level of the top of the foundation is marked on the batterboard stakes and the ledgers are established at that level or in relation to that level. (2) The building lines are established on the batterboards by measurement from the lot lines rather than from the temporary stakes placed at the house corners.

PROCEDURE

1. Locate a point 30 feet from the south lot line and 12 feet from the east lot line and drive stake *1* at this point.

2. Set stake *2* 48 feet to the west of stake *1* and 30 feet from the south lot line.

3. Set stake *3* 28 feet north of stake *1* and 12 feet from the east lot line.

4. Set stake *4* 48 feet west of stake *3* and 28 feet north of stake *2*. Check measurements and diagonals.

5. The next operation is the erection of batterboards. Make stakes of 2 × 4s, long enough to extend at least 6 inches above the foundation level. Drive the stakes so that the ledgers will be parallel to, and about 4 feet away from, the building lines. Verify with the excavating contractor the clearance required to permit the excavating machinery to operate and move the batterboard stakes back if more clearance is necessary.

6. Set the transit-level at a central point and shoot the exact foundation grade, marking it on the stakes at each corner. Check the section view of the working drawings to establish the grade level. See Fig. 19.

7. Nail 1 × 6 ledgers on the stakes with the top edge on the grade marks. Make sure that ledgers are level.

8. With the use of a tape and a plumb bob, tape the exact dimension from the lot lines and place marks on the top of the batterboards at corner *1*. See Fig. 20.

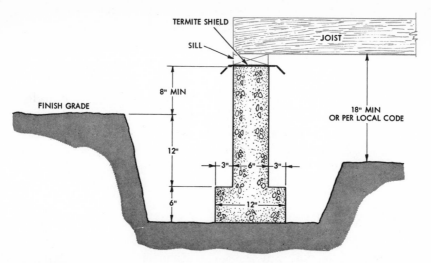

Fig. 19. This section view from the working drawings shows the relation between the grade and the top of the foundation as well as the bottom of the footing.

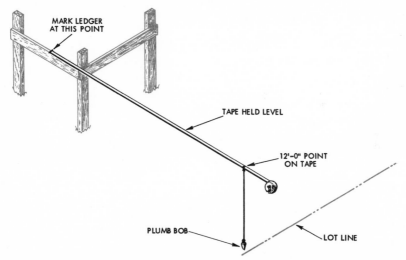

Fig. 20. Building lines are marked on batterboards by direct measurement from lot lines.

9. Make measurements in the same manner at corner 2.

10. Using a transit-level, a builder's level, or the 6-8-10 method, es-

tablish points on batterboards at corner 3 and corner 4.

11. When all batterboards have been marked, pull a chalk line across

69

each point. Check measurements between stakes to be sure that the dimensions are correct. Measure across the diagonals in both directions to see that the angles made by the lines are right angles.

12. Now make a pencil mark on each side of the chalk line. Pull the line to one side and make a kerf in the ledger about ¼ inch deep. Place the line in the kerf, tighten it and tie it to a nail.

13. The lines which have been established represent the outside lines of the foundation. Lay out the location of other working lines on the top of the ledgers from the building lines. See Fig. 21.

Note: Where an offset occurs as at corner 2, batterboards are extended or new ones erected and additional lines are stretched.

Excavation for Basement:
The HOUSE PLAN B

In firm soil, shallow excavations up to 5 feet in depth require a clearance of 18 inches outside the building lines for erecting and removing forms. For deeper excavations 2 feet or more must be allowed for working space between the building lines and the excavation.

To arrive at the depth of the excavation, the carpenter should study the vertical section view taken through the house and calculate the dimensions from the top of the foundation grade to the bottom of the footing. The distance the foundation will project above the finished grade will be marked on the section view. There must be a minimum exposure of concrete of 8 inches from grade to the lowest wood member as one

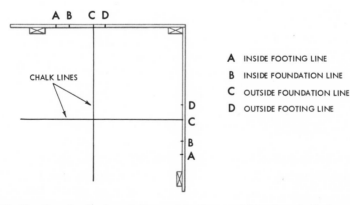

A   INSIDE FOOTING LINE
B   INSIDE FOUNDATION LINE
C   OUTSIDE FOUNDATION LINE
D   OUTSIDE FOOTING LINE

Fig. 21. Working lines for the foundation and footing are laid out on batterboards.

means of protection from termites. It is also important that surface water be drawn away from the house, and therefore it becomes necessary that the grade be sloped away in all directions. The foundation of the HOUSE PLAN B, according to Fig. 19, is 20 inches high with a 6 inch footing. There is an 8 inch distance from the top of the foundation to the finished grade. The excavation of the footings should be made 18 inches deep below finished grade. (It is assumed that the house is to be built in an area where there is no frost problem.) The excavation should be made so that the earth is not disturbed in the bottom of the areas where the footings are to be placed.

The work of excavating should not be done until all stakes have been checked to see that the building is located correctly from the lot lines and has correct dimensions.

Forms for Footing:
The HOUSE PLAN B

After all excavations have been made to the correct depths, forms for the footings should be laid out and erected. The footings must be straight and level and must rest on undisturbed earth so that the load of the building may be transferred to the ground in a uniform manner. There must be no settling later. The layout begins with driving stakes again at the building corners and establishing the level of the footing.

Note: When the banks of an excavated footing are compact and solid enough, footing forms are sometimes eliminated. See Fig. 19 for dimensions for the footing for the HOUSE PLAN B.

PROCEDURE

1. Fasten lines to the batterboards, running them through the saw kerfs previously made. See Fig. 22.

2. From the intersection of these lines at corner *1* drop a line and plumb bob to locate the position of the corner stake. Cut 2 × 2 stakes about 16 inches long. Drive a stake at the point indicated by the plumb bob.

3. Drive the stake to a height corresponding to the correct level for the top of the footing. The top of the stake should be 6 inches above the ground if the excavation is correct. Verify the level with the datum point by using a leveling instrument and a rod.

4. From each intersection of the lines at the other corners, drop a line and plumb bob and drive stakes.

5. Set up the transit-level or builder's level at a central point and sight the stake at corner *1*. Transfer the level to the other three stakes driving them to the same level and placing a nail at each building corner point.

6. Connect the corner stakes with

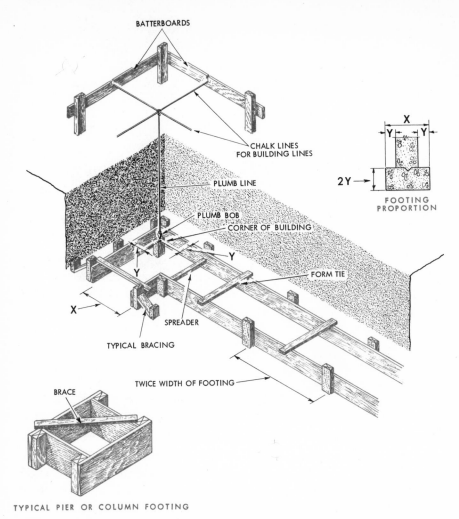

BATTERBOARDS

CHALK LINES FOR BUILDING LINES

PLUMB LINE

PLUMB BOB

CORNER OF BUILDING

Y

Y

FORM TIE

X

SPREADER

TYPICAL BRACING

TWICE WIDTH OF FOOTING

BRACE

TYPICAL PIER OR COLUMN FOOTING

X

Y Y

2Y

FOOTING PROPORTION

Fig. 22. A point is dropped from the intersection of the building lines and placed on a stake. Footings are located from this point.

lines tied to the nails. These are the building lines.

7. Erect outside footing forms so that the inside of the boards are 3 inches outside the building lines. The top of the forms must be level with the top of each corner stake. If 1 inch boards are used the stakes holding them should be set 2 or 3 feet apart. Stakes may be spaced farther apart if 2 inch material is used for form boards.

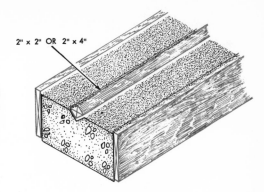

2" x 2" OR 2" x 4"

Fig. 23. A key is made by pressing a piece of wood into the footing before the concrete sets.

8. Erect inside forms just the reverse of the outside forms. Spreaders 12 inches long will help line up the inside forms so that the form boards and stakes are placed correctly. Brace footing forms at stakes. The spreaders are removed as the concrete fills the forms.

9. Place form ties at 4'-0" intervals or as required.

10. Check the footing forms in relation to the building lines. Check the level of the form boards all around so that the footing will be level when poured.

Note: On a low foundation wall the footing and foundations are often poured together, as shown in Fig. 19, making a monolithic foundation.

11. The next operation is the pouring of the concrete. Care should be taken not to disturb the corner stakes because they are of value in setting the foundation wall forms later.

12. Some builders in different parts of the country use keys. After the footing has been poured and the concrete has been struck off flush, a key made up of a piece of 2×4 with edges tapered or 2×2 is pressed into the top surface before it has set. The key serves as a tie between the footing and the foundation wall which will be poured later preventing lateral movement. See Fig. 23.

13. After the concrete of the footing has set, remove the form boards and stakes. Drain tile is often required (see Fig. 4). Lay it around the outside of the footing in a bed of gravel and connect it to the sewer or to a sump pump in the building. After the tile is laid it should be covered with gravel up to the level of the top of the footing.

Forms for Footing: Alternative Method

The alternative method is essentially the same except that the working lines on the batterboards locate the footings. No stakes are driven representing the corners of the foundation.

PROCEDURE

1. Locate the markings on the batterboards that indicate the outside footing lines. Secure the chalk lines in the kerfs and pull the lines taut. See Fig. 24. (Lines would be those from points marked *D* in Fig. 21.)

2. From line *1* near corner *1* drop a plumb bob to point *B*. Allow for the thickness of the form material and drive a marker stake at *C*. The stake should extend above the

ground more than the thickness of the footing so that cross ties or hangers can be nailed to them if required.

Note: If the footing and foundation are poured in one pour, the stakes must extend above the top of the foundation.

3. From line *1* near corner *2* drop a plumb bob and drive a marker stake in the same manner. Drive intermediate stakes. With a leveling instrument placed at a central point shoot the correct grade elevation of the footing on several of the stakes. (It should be 6 inches above the excavation.)

4. Place the form boards in position against the stakes and nail them

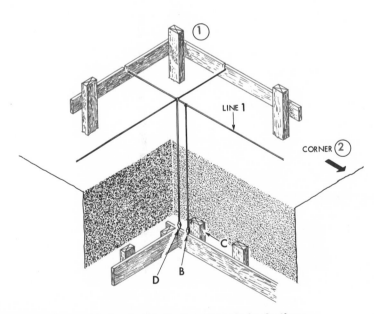

Fig. 24. Lines are dropped to locate outside form boards for footings.

in place at the height indicated by the grade levels. Be sure to let one of the boards run past the intersecting point at each corner.

5. Hang a plumb bob at the intersection of the lines and mark the point D on the form boards representing the intersection of the outside forms. Repeat necessary steps on all of the corners.

6. Nail and brace all of the forms securely. Cut a spacer equal to the width of the footing plus the thickness of the inside form material. Butt one end against the form and drive a stake against the other end. Repeat this operation around the entire area. See Fig. 25.

7. At various intervals use a hand level across the existing forms and

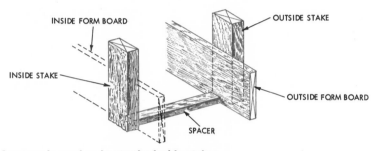

Fig. 25. A spacer is used to locate the inside stakes.

Fig. 26. A spreader is used to locate the end of the inside form board.

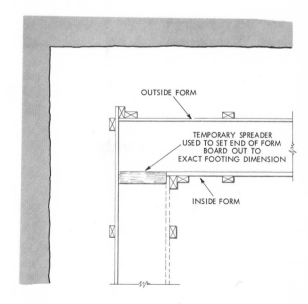

place a grade mark on the stakes.

8. Cut a spreader equal to the width of the footing. Place this spreader in line with the form that is going to be placed and let the end press against the outside form. With the inside form board against the other end of the spreader nail it in place holding the board at the proper elevation. See Fig. 26. Remove spreaders as the concrete fills the forms.

9. Place form ties as required throughout and brace forms securely at stakes.

Monolithic Forms for The HOUSE PLAN B

The fact that the foundation is very low for the HOUSE PLAN B suggests two procedures for the building of forms so that the footing and foundation can be poured together. (1) In areas where the earth is compact and firm it is common practice to cut a trench the size of the footing and dispense with footing forms. The foundation form for a very low wall may be suspended above the excavation. (2) Monolithic forms may be erected so that the footing and foundation forms are one unit.

PROCEDURE 1

It is assumed that the footing trench has been dug in the proper location and to the proper depth, and that chalk lines have been run from

points on the batterboards which give the building lines for the foundation.

1. Drive stakes at the intersections of the outside of the foundation walls, making allowance for the thickness of the form material. Stakes should project 1 or 2 inches above the grade level of the top of concrete. See Fig. 27.

2. Drive additional stakes in line around foundation at the desired spacing.

3. Set up the transit-level near the center of the foundation and establish the concrete grade point on all the stakes (A, Fig. 27).

4. Nail the first form board to line up with grade marks on stakes (B, Fig. 27). Nail boards below it to the level of the footing.

5. Install wales on stakes and line up wall by plumbing from chalk line stretched between batterboards (C, Fig. 27).

6. Cut a spacer which will be equal to the thickness of the wall plus the thickness of the sheathing.

7. Using the spacer to determine the correct distance, drive stakes for inside forms opposite the outside form stakes.

8. Place inside form boards in same manner as outside form boards. Check with level from outside boards.

9. Place wales on inside form stakes (E, Fig. 27).

10. Cut spreaders the exact thick-

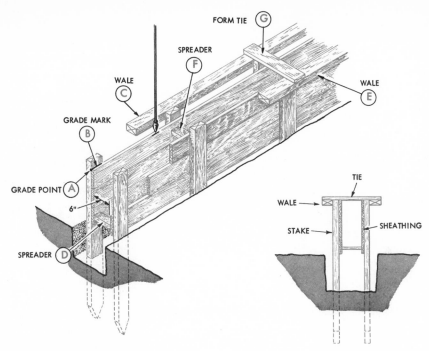

Fig. 27. Footing formed by earth trench and foundation wall supported by stakes provide for monolithic footing-foundation.

ness of the wall and place them near the top and bottom of the form (*D*, and *F*, Fig. 27). (When the concrete is poured the spreaders are knocked out as it reaches their level.)

11. Tie top of forms with form ties (*G*, Fig. 27).

12. Brace stakes as needed. The stakes are removed when the forms are stripped and the holes are filled with concrete.

PROCEDURE 2

1. The forms for the footings are set up as outlined under *Forms For Footings: Alternative Method*, with the exception that stakes must be long enough to extend 1 or 2 inches above the grade for the concrete wall.

2. Determine from the working drawings, or from the batterboards, the projection of footing beyond the foundation wall (in this case 3 inches). See Fig. 19.

3. Cut spacer blocks of 2 inch material with dimension *A* as one dimension and the height of the foundation wall as the other (3 inches by 20 inches in this case). If the foundation and footing form boards are not the same thickness, adjustments must be made. See Fig. 28.

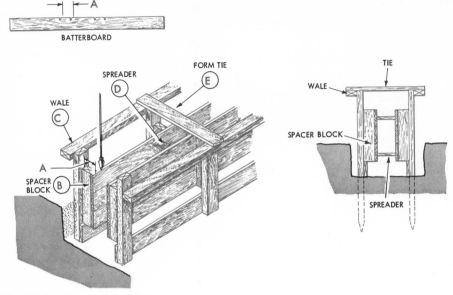

Fig. 28. Footings and foundation walls are poured in one piece.

4. Nail the sheathing to the spacer blocks on a bench, making the top of the sheathing flush with the top ends of the blocks. Rip off the bottom piece of sheathing even with the bottom end of the blocks.

5. Fasten assembled panels for outside walls to the stakes, resting them on the footing form boards.

6. Install wales at top of stakes and check to see that inside of the form is plumb with line stretched between batterboards.

7. Install inside forms in the same manner. Place spreaders cut to the wall thickness between forms. (When the concrete is poured the spreaders are knocked out as it reaches their level.)

8. Tie forms together with form ties. Brace stakes as needed.

"T" Type Footing

A "T" type footing such as shown in Fig. 29 provides a starter wall for the foundation and gives the forms a shoulder to rest on. It is used when the foundation is low, such as for HOUSE PLAN B. Several operations and much time is saved in forming the foundation wall later. The location and the thickness of the foundation wall will not have to be determined. There is no problem in pulling the forms together at the bottom and adjusting them for irregularities in the footing. The manner of making the "T" type footing is

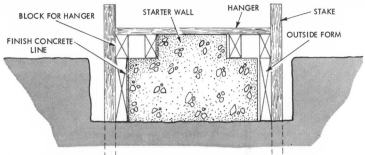

Fig. 29. "T" type forms are made by suspending wall form boards accurately above the footing forms.

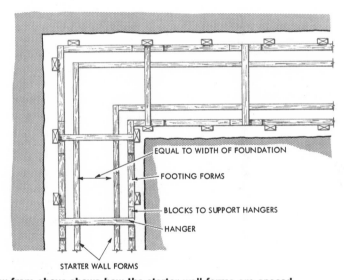

Fig. 30. View from above shows how the starter wall forms are spaced.

shown in Fig. 29 and Fig. 30. When the wall is low, stirrups may be used instead of the usual ties with a great saving of time. See Fig. 31.

PROCEDURE

1. Make the stakes for the footing long enough so that when they are driven into the ground they will ex-

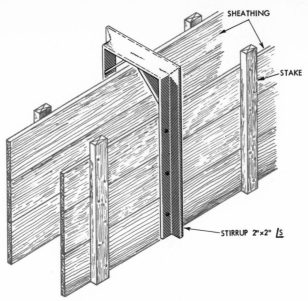

Fig. 31. Stirrups are used to space and brace forms for low walls.

tend above the top of the starter wall. Nail the footing forms into place.

2. Cut starter wall form material to a width equal to the height of the starter wall.

3. Cut hangers to fit between stakes.

4. Nail hangers and starter wall form material.

5. Use short lengths of starter wall form material as blocks for hangers; nail hangers to stakes.

6. Check with lines stretched from batterboards to see if starter wall is in the right location for the foundation wall.

Building Forms for Low Walls

Forms for low walls are generally made of 2 × 4 members and 1 × 6 sheathing. They can be made quickly on the job site, and may be taken apart and used for other building purposes. See Figs. 32 and 33. There will be more room to work on them if they are built away from the excavation area. See Fig. 34.

PROCEDURE

1. Determine the height of the foundation wall above the footing and secure studs which will enable you to build forms to that height. The studs do not have to be cut to the exact length, but may project

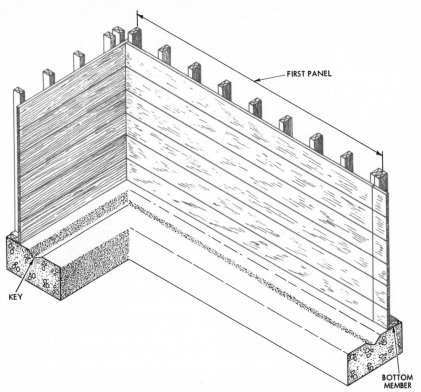

FIRST PANEL

KEY

BOTTOM
MEMBER

Fig. 32. Forms for low walls are made of 2 x 4 studs and sheathing. The material may be used later in the building of the house. The outside form is generally erected first.

above the form boards. The length of the forms is determined by the length of the material available for sheathing, and by the fact that they have to be carried some distance and put in place. Lay out the bottom plate for studs on 12 inch centers (center distance may vary). It is not necessary to have a top plate on the forms for a low wall. Start with a stud at the end of the plate and finish with a stud at the other end.

2. When sheathing is used, it is good practice to make a jig bench in order to make the panels uniform and square. See Fig. 34. One type of jig bench is made as follows: Lay two planks across two horses so that one will be in position for the bottom of the panel and the other for the top. Nail a 1 × 2 cleat on each side of the position for the first stud. Be sure that the cleats are square with the edge of the plank where the bot-

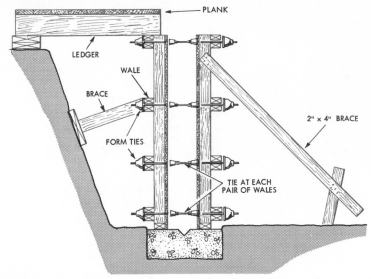

Fig. 33. Sectional view through a foundation form shows how the wall is held together and braced.

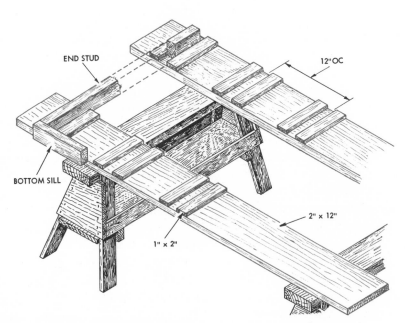

Fig. 34. A jig bench provides a handy platform on which to build form panels.

tom plate will go. Measure stud spaces and nail pairs of 1 × 2s to locate each stud.

3. Nail all studs to bottom plate with two 16*d* (sixteen penny) nails.

4. Begin laying the sheathing from the bottom and work upward. Nail each board with at least two 6*d* (six penny) nails or with two 8*d* (eight penny) nails if the forms are to be reused. Continue nailing the sheathing until you reach the mark for the top grade for concrete. The top full board will usually extend above the level of the top grade. When the forms are erected the top grade of concrete can be marked by a strip nailed in the form or by double-headed nails driven at the right height. When laying the sheathing, break all joints when sheathing

is pieced and cover all knots with pieces of sheet metal.

Make all the panels in this manner except the filler panel, which is the last one to fill out the wall at the corner. It is good practice to set all but the last panel and then measure the distance to the corner. Make allowance for the thickness of the sheathing at the corners so that the wall will have the correct length. The sheathing on one corner panel will extend beyond the last stud and will be nailed to the stud of the panel previously set. See Fig. 35.

5. Lay panels on the bank or in the excavation where they will be available when assembly begins.

6. Set the first outside panel at the corner of the starting wall and brace it with temporary braces.

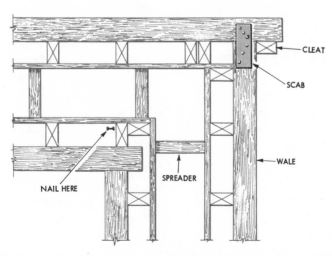

Fig. 35. This view shows how panels are tied together at corners. Cleats and scabs are short pieces of wood. Double-headed nails are used which are easily pulled when the forms are stripped.

Note: Usually the outside forms are erected first. However, if the forms are built outside the excavation area, the inside forms may be set first. The forms will not have to be lifted over the outside forms if this procedure is followed.

7. Erect all of the outer panels of the foundation, setting them in place and bracing them temporarily. Where panels join, nail them together with double headed nails.

8. Set the corner panel. Where corners meet nail the end of the sheathing to the last stud of the panel which was set previously. See Fig. 35.

9. Check the alignment by means of string and test blocks. See Fig. 3 for this procedure. Check walls so that they are plumb and located according to building lines.

10. Locate and install door and window bucks or frames. See Figs. 38 to 40.

11. The procedure for installing the inner wall is similar to that used for the outer wall except that it will vary with the ties used. If wire ties are used, start the panels so that the studs are opposite those on the outside wall. When snap ties are used the studs need not be opposite one another because the clamps bear against wales.

12. Leave a clean-out opening between two studs in the bottom piece of sheathing so that the space between the form walls can be cleaned

before the concrete is poured. Replace the cut out piece and fasten with cleats.

Alternative Procedure for Building Forms for Low Walls Using "T" Footing

The procedure for building forms for low walls, such as for HOUSE PLAN B, is essentially the same when "T" footings are used except as indicated in the following paragraphs. It is assumed that the forms are made on the site away from the excavation area and that the inner forms will be set first. See Fig. 36.

PROCEDURE

1. Determine the height of the foundation wall above the footing and build the panels according to the information under steps 1, 2, 3, and 4, under "Building Forms for Low Walls." When "T" footings are used and the forms are to be made level with the top of grade for concrete, the forms should be made ½ to 1 inch less in height to allow for wedges at the bottom. Generally forms extend above the foundation grade, and nails are driven into the form to indicate the top of concrete; or a strip of wood is fastened to the inside of the form to indicate the foundation grade.

2. Lay the panels on the bank and slide them into the excavation so that they are readily available.

3. Set the first inside panel at the

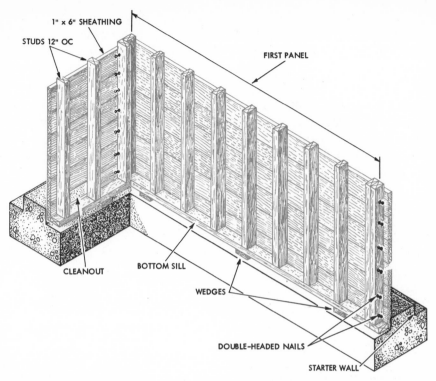

1" x 6" SHEATHING

STUDS 12" OC

FIRST PANEL

CLEANOUT

BOTTOM SILL

WEDGES

DOUBLE-HEADED NAILS

STARTER WALL

Fig. 36. Panel forms used with a "T" footing. Note the wedges used to level the forms. The inside panels are erected first.

corner of the starter wall and brace it temporarily. Place wedges under it and adjust the panel to a level position. See Fig. 36.

4. Erect all of the other panels and temporarily brace each one. Wherever panels join, nail the end studs together with double-headed nails. Adjust horizontal alignment by using wedges under the forms. Make allowance for the thickness of the sheathing material when making the last panel for each wall. Nail the last studs at corners so that forms may be removed easily.

5. Provide a clean-out opening between two studs in the lowest piece of sheathing so that the form space may be cleaned out before the pouring of the concrete. Replace the cut out piece and fasten with cleats.

6. Check the alignment of the forms by means of string and test blocks. (See Fig. 3 for this procedure.) Check walls so that they are plumb and located according to building lines.

7. Locate and install all door and window bucks or frames. See Figs. 38 to 40.

8. The procedure for installing the outer wall is similar to that used on the inner wall except that it will vary with the ties used. If wire ties are used, start the outside panels so that the studs are opposite those on the inside wall. Wire ties may also be used around wales. In this case the studs do not have to be opposite one another. See Fig. 37. When snap ties are used the studs need not be opposite one another either, because the clamps bear against wales.

Openings in Concrete Walls

The frames for windows and doors that are located in the foundations (for both HOUSE PLANS A and B) are installed in some instances before the pouring of concrete. In the case of some metal basement windows, the frames are put in place and wood forms are used to make the sill and sides of the window opening. For other windows a strip is nailed to the form, which makes a recess in the concrete when it is poured. When

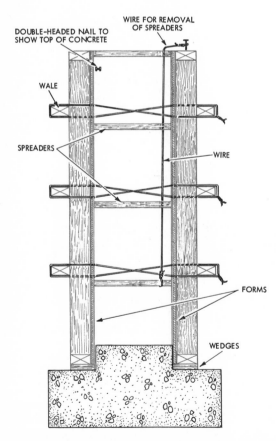

Fig. 37. Sectional view through foundation forms shows how forms are leveled by wedges and tied together by using wire ties over wales.

the form for the window is removed, a recess is left in the wall into which the metal sash is dropped. It is sealed with grout. See Fig. 38. Some finished frames are put in place in the forms and are held by a key strip. The concrete stops against the frame. See Fig. 39. Other openings are made by using a buck, which is removed after the concrete is poured, leaving blocks or strips in the wall to which the frame is later fastened. One important thing to remember is that the buck must be made so that

it can be removed without too much trouble. The corners of the window buck are mitered, and the bottom piece is cut through, so that it will slip out easily. See Fig. 40.

PROCEDURE

1. Study the working drawings carefully to find where the openings should be.

2. Mark the position of the opening on the inside of the form that was erected first. Make sure that the lines are level and plumb.

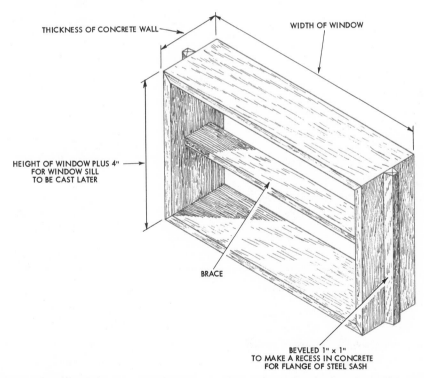

THICKNESS OF CONCRETE WALL

WIDTH OF WINDOW

HEIGHT OF WINDOW PLUS 4"
FOR WINDOW SILL
TO BE CAST LATER

BRACE

BEVELED 1" x 1"
TO MAKE A RECESS IN CONCRETE
FOR FLANGE OF STEEL SASH

Fig. 38. The rough form for steel basement windows is removed after the wall is poured, leaving a recess for the window frame.

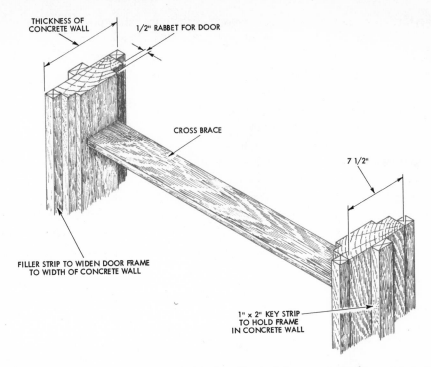

THICKNESS OF CONCRETE WALL

1/2" RABBET FOR DOOR

CROSS BRACE

7 1/2"

FILLER STRIP TO WIDEN DOOR FRAME TO WIDTH OF CONCRETE WALL

1" x 2" KEY STRIP TO HOLD FRAME IN CONCRETE WALL

Fig. 39. The door frame is often installed before the wall is poured. The key strip holds the frame in place.

3. Make the buck to suit the frame. See Figs. 38 and 40.

4. Cut template and nail the form so that it will be inside the buck and so that the buck can hang on.

5. Nail the buck in place through the sheathing, using double-headed nails.

6. Proceed to build the remaining wall of form, thus enclosing buck.

The HOUSE PLAN A

The HOUSE PLAN A will serve to demonstrate how to stake out a house and how to prepare footings and formwork where a basement is required. The working drawings will be found at the end of Chapter 1. The Plot Plan (Fig. 41) shows the location of the house on the lot and the elevations of floors above datum point. Regrading must be done to reach required grade and to provide for drainage of surface water.

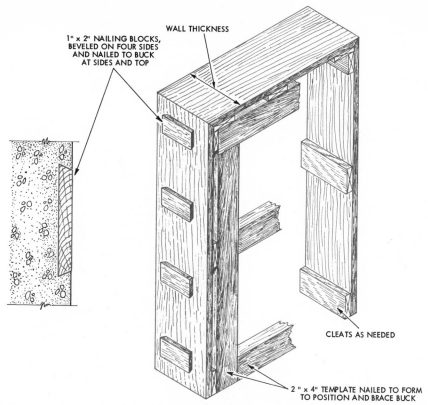

WALL THICKNESS

1" x 2" NAILING BLOCKS,
BEVELED ON FOUR SIDES
AND NAILED TO BUCK
AT SIDES AND TOP

CLEATS AS NEEDED

2 " x 4" TEMPLATE NAILED TO FORM
TO POSITION AND BRACE BUCK

Fig. 40. A rough buck is made so that nailing blocks are left in the wall. The template is fastened to the form sheathing on one side; it is made part of the buck on the other side.

Staking Out the HOUSE PLAN A

The manner of staking out the house will follow the same general procedure outlined for the HOUSE PLAN B on pages 66 to 68.

PROCEDURE

1. Fasten lines between stakes set up at lot corners $A, B, C,$ and D (Fig. 42).

2. Locate a point 10'-10" from the west lot line and 40'-6" from the south lot line and drive stake *1* at this point. Ideal stakes for this purpose can be made by cutting 2 × 2 sticks into 2 foot lengths. Drive a nail in the stake at the exact point.

3. Set stake *2* 37'-6" to the east of stake *1*, and 40'-6" from the south lot line.

4. The manner of making a right angle corner to locate point *3* is described in detail in step 3 of *Staking Out the* HOUSE PLAN B, page 66.

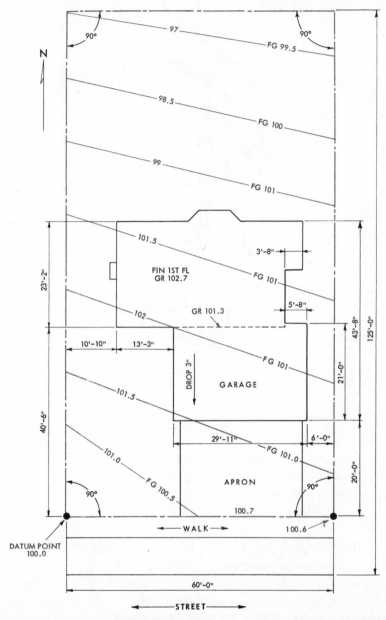

Fig. 41. Plot plan for the HOUSE PLAN A shows the contour of lot and grade levels for the floor of the garage and of the house. The location of the house is given to the lot lines.

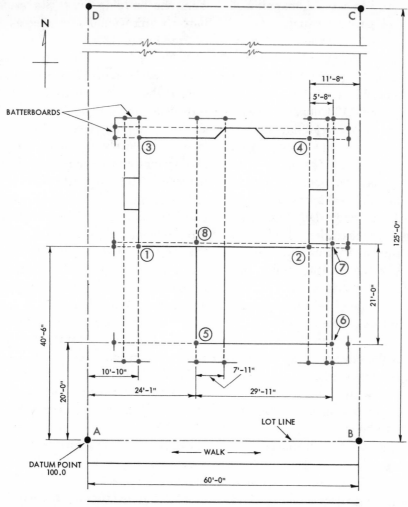

Fig. 42. After the corner stakes are located, batterboards are erected, and lines are stretched to indicate building lines.

Measure a distance of 23′-2″ from point *1* to establish point *3*.

5. Locate and drive a stake at point *4* by measuring distances 37′-6″ from point *3* and 23′-2″ from point *2*.

6. Stretch lines between points *1*, *2*, *3*, and *4*.

7. Check these measurements again: (a) from the lot lines to the building lines, (b) the four sides of the house, and (c) the diagonals

from points *1* to *4* and from points *2* to *3* to see if they are equal.

8. Stake out the garage and entry passage area as follows: Locate point *5* 24'-1" from the west lot line and 20'-0" from the south lot line. Locate point *6* 29'-11" from point *5* and 20'-0" from the south lot line. Locate point *7* by measuring 21'-0" from point *6* and 5'-8" from the line stretched between points *2* and *4* (this point will be 6 inches north of line *1—2* extended). Locate a stake at point *8* by measuring 21'-0" from point *5* and 24'-1" from the west lot line. Check the measurements and diagonals for points *5, 6, 7* and *8*. The main points of reference for the house and garage area have now been located. Some builders would locate stakes for the bay, stairway to basement, and chimney, but these can be determined with enough accuracy for the excavation after the batterboards have been erected.

9. Erect batterboards in each corner. Select pieces of 2 × 4 long enough to extend into the ground firmly and to project above ground 2 to 3 feet. The excavating contractor will tell you the clearance needed to operate the excavating machinery. The carpenter will decide how much space is required between the bank of earth and the outside form. Usually 18 to 24 inches is enough space for a man to work. If the ground is firm it would therefore be safe to set the batterboards back about 4 feet from the building lines. Stakes for batterboards should be erected as indicated in Fig. 18.

10. Nail ledger boards to the stakes making each board level. (The contour of the lot is such that the batterboards can be kept approximately at the same grade level, although it is not absolutely essential. Grades for footings and foundations will be determined by other means.)

11. Using a chalk line and a plumb bob, stretch a line so that it passes directly over points *1* and *2*. Mark the top of the ledger where the lines cross. Make a shallow saw kerf in the ledger, pass the line through the kerf, and fasten the line to a nail.

12. Measure two points 6 inches north of the line just established and make a second saw kerf on each batterboard. A line through these kerfs will locate the short wall at the back of the garage passing over point *7*.

13. Following the same procedure for plumbing lines and fastening them, stretch a line for the rear building line *3—4*.

14. The projection for the bay is 2 feet. Measure 2'-0" on the batterboards from line *3—4* and establish a line which will indicate the face of the bay.

15. Stretch a line to pass over points *5* and *6*.

16. Stretch a line to pass over points *1* and *3*.

17. The chimney projects 2'-1". Measure 2'-1" on the batterboards

from *1—3* and establish a line indicating the face of the chimney.

18. Stretch a line to pass over points *5* and *8*.

19. The west wall of the garage is 7'-11" east of line *5-8*. Measure this distance on the batterboards and stretch a line.

20. Stretch a line over points *2* and *4*.

21. Stretch a line over points *6* and *7*.

22. The wall for the exterior stairs to the basement is located 3'-8" from the building. Measure this distance on the batterboards from line *2—4* and stretch a line.

23. Check all measurements.

Excavation for Basement:
The HOUSE PLAN A

Temporary stakes are driven outlining the excavation. They are placed so that proper allowance is made for a man to work between the bank of earth and the outside forms (usually 18 to 24 inches).

To arrive at the depth of the excavation, study the Plot Plan (see Fig. 41) and the Working Drawings (see end of Chapter 1). The Plot Plan indicates that the finished first floor has an elevation of 102.7'. The typical wall section, Working Drawing, Sheet No. 8, shows that the bottom of the concrete floor is 8'-4" below the finished first floor grade level and the bottom of the footing is 9'-2" below the finished first floor

grade level. The finished first floor grade level should be established by using a transit-level or builder's level, using the datum point for reference. This point can be marked on the corner batterboard stakes for reference during the excavating.

The garage presents two problems. It has a sloped floor and there is a step footing where the garage foundation joins the house foundation. The garage floor has a 3 inch drop from back to front for drainage. The floor will be 1.8' below the finished first floor level at the south end. See Working Drawing Sheet No. 2 and Fig. 41. The top of the concrete is 1 inch above the finished grade at the front of the garage. The foundation wall for the garage is 8 inches above the general grade so that the siding may end well above the ground level. The top of this wall is to be made level so that the studs may all be cut the same length and the siding installed in a level position. It is cut down at the overhead door opening. Anchor bolts are installed at 4 foot intervals to hold down the plates. The excavations for the garage and entry passage foundation walls should be made with a minimum allowance to permit the forms to be put in place so that the earth will be disturbed as little as possible. The area under the concrete slab should be graded to permit the 6 inches of sand fill to be placed properly, giving the floor the required slope. The earth should be disturbed as little as possible where this slab is to be poured.

The manner of joining the garage to the house by means of walls supported by stepped footings is shown on Working Drawings, Sheets Nos. 1, 4, 5 and 6. This method is used because when the excavation for the house is made, the earth in a space of 2 feet or more outside of the foundation wall is disturbed. In order to give a firm base to the garage wall the footing is made in three steps.

When the contour of the lot is to be changed radically it is usually done before the work of laying out the building and erecting the batterboards is done so that the carpenter can work on a level area. In the case of the HOUSE PLAN A, the Plot Plan indicates that the part of the lot on which the house will stand is to be cut down and that the back of the lot is to be built up. When the top soil is removed, the necessary regrading can be accomplished with little additional expenditure of time. However, the change of contour is not radical enough in this case to require that it be done before the building is laid out.

Forms for Footings:
The HOUSE PLAN A

The procedure outlined under *Forms for Footings: the* HOUSE PLAN B, page 71, is to be followed in laying out footings for building proper.

The footing at the fireplace is located 4 inches out from the line stretched from the batterboards that indicates the face of the chimney. Measurements of 8'-3" should be made from points *1* and *3* to locate the position of the outside fireplace footing. A 4 inch offset is to be made at the inside of the footing also under the fireplace hearth. Sheets 1 and 2 at the end of Chapter 1 show the location of the fireplace.

The footing for the bay is located 4 inches outside a line established previously on the batterboards and according to measurements shown in Sheet No. 1 of the Working Drawings. (Notice that the measurements are given to the foundation wall and not to the footing. This necessitates drawing the outside line of the foundation, measuring 4 inches in front of the line, and 14 inches in back of the line.)

There is no footing under the wall which supports the platform at the kitchen door.

There is no footing for the foundation for the wall at the exterior stair to the basement. Care must be taken in excavating so that where there is to be no footing, earth is not disturbed.

The steps for the footing for the garage are built the same as other footings, with a board across each end to retain the concrete.

Drive stakes and mark the center location of the two columns which

support the girders. Build boxes 2'-6"
square and one foot high, and locate
them per basement plan so that the
column will be in the center of the
footings. See Fig. 22.

Foundation Framework:
the HOUSE PLAN A

Several types of forming could be
used for the foundation of the HOUSE
PLAN A. If a carpenter or builder had
only one house of this type to build
and did not anticipate building any
more for a long time he might use
"built-in-place" forms such as were
described on page 55. If the studs
were left 8 feet or more in length, and
the sheathing left in long lengths
also, they could be reused in the
house. (See Fig. 3 for this method.)

Many carpenters build panels or
sectional forms with the intention of
re-using them. The panels are made
of frames using 2 × 4 inch members
and 4 × 8 foot plywood sheets described earlier in this chapter. Although 4 × 8 foot sheets are generally used, some carpenters prefer 2
foot wide forms because they are
lighter to handle and they can use
certain patented snap ties. Many
carpenters use special patented
forming systems and a variety of ties.

It is assumed that the carpenter
doing the forming for the HOUSE
PLAN A will use 4 × 8 panels with
plywood faces, snap ties, and three
sets of wales. The following procedure is intended to give some general

principles. There are many variations.

PROCEDURE

1. Beginning at one corner of the
building set the first outside section.
See Fig. 43. It should be carefully
plumbed, braced and anchored at
both top and bottom. It is very essential that it be lined up carefully
with the building lines. Some carpenters use band iron underneath
the form, bending it up and nailing
it to the bottom member on each
side. See Fig. 44.

2. Bring the second section into
position and fasten it to the first section with 20d nails driven through
the frame of the section. Continue
to add sections until the outside wall
is enclosed. Use temporary bracing
wherever necessary.

3. Place fillers wherever needed.
(Only if a house was planned on a
modular scale would panels work out
without some sort of fillers and even
then adjustments would be required
for the inside panels.) Builders who
do much concrete work have 1 foot,
2 foot, and other size fillers available. If they do not have fillers they
must build them as needed or improvise with pieces of plywood. Narrow
strips, 2 × 4s and planks are used
to fill small spaces. The fillers can
be kept in line better if they are
placed in the wall at some location
away from the corners.

4. Special forming must often be
done at places such as the bay, chim-

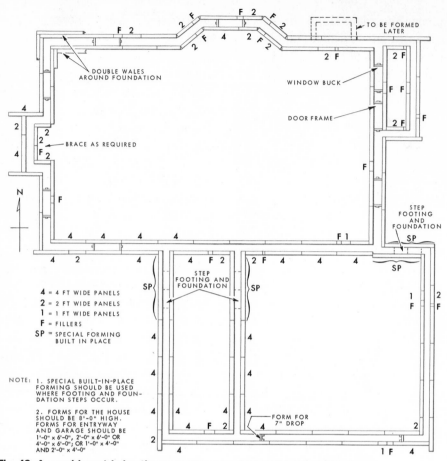

Fig. 43. A panel layout helps the carpenter save time as he erects the forms.

ney, and exterior stairs to the basement. The walls supporting the platform at the kitchen door will be formed later. Wherever possible, 4 × 8 foot panels, and 1 × 8 and 2 × 8 foot fillers are used. When a job is repeated many times, forms are built to meet the special problem, such as at the bays.

5. Install bucks for windows and doors.

6. Erect the inside panels in the same manner as the outside panels. Insert snap ties as the forms go into place. Drill holes in panels with an extension bit wherever holes are needed.

7. Install double 2 × 4 inch wales

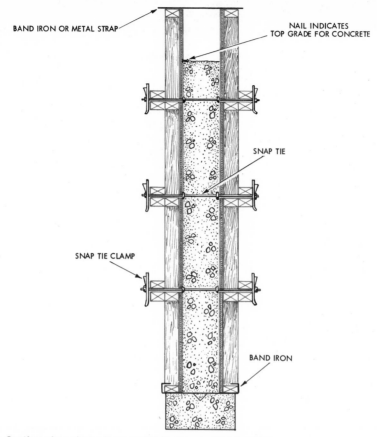

BAND IRON OR METAL STRAP

NAIL INDICATES
TOP GRADE FOR CONCRETE

SNAP TIE

SNAP TIE CLAMP

BAND IRON

Fig. 44. Section view shows how panel forms are tied together.

and place snap tie clamps in place. Line up forms carefully with the building lines and drive clamps tight. See Fig. 44. The wales serve to line up the forms and should be as straight and long as practical. They may extend beyond corners and are usually nailed together at corners.

8. Nail band iron or steel bars made for that purpose across the top of the forms, tying the wall together. Nail band iron around the panel studs at the corners.

9. Determine the grade for the top of concrete by referring to the Working Drawings, Sheet No. 8. Typical Wall Section, and the Plot Plan, Fig. 41. By use of a builder's level and a rod held at several points along the formwork, mark the grade for con-

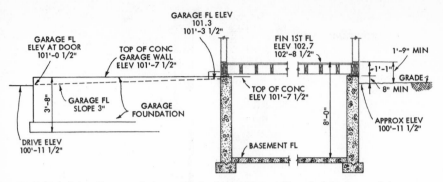

Fig. 45. Determining the top of the concrete foundation wall and slabs is crucial.

crete inside the foundation forms. Drive double headed nails at intervals to indicate the line.

Fig. 45 will illustrate how the grade level for the top of the concrete in the forms is derived. The elevation drawings indicate that the top of the concrete wall is level all around and at the same height for the house and the garage. The datum point has an elevation of 100.0'. Therefore, the top of the concrete foundation wall would be 1'-7½" higher than the datum level.

After the forms are stripped, trenches should be dug and forms erected for the walls for the platform at the kitchen door.

Removal of Forms: The House Plan B

Generally four days should elapse before the forms are removed if time will permit. The panels are usually removed in the reverse order from which they were placed. Form tie clamps are knocked off and the wales removed first. The forms are pried from the walls with care in order not to damage the concrete. The ties pull out of the forms and remain projecting from the wall. It is wise to wait a day or two longer before re-

moving the tie ends. This is done by twisting or pulling on the tie end so that it breaks at the "break back" point within the wall. The hole in the wall is then repaired with grout.

Minor Jobs. A few minor jobs remain. The foundation walls under the platform at the kitchen door could be formed with the foundation, but may be formed with greater ease after the main foundation has been poured and the forms stripped. In cases like this reinforcing rods are often placed so that they project from the foundation wall to provide a tie for the new wall. Care should be taken so that the earth is not disturbed any more than necessary because the wall has no footing. The large 4 × 8 foot panels used for the foundation will be awkward to use for this purpose because the wall is only 3'-6" high. The carpenter may have to build a simple box-like form, designed so that the inside part can be removed easily.

Metal areaways should be in-

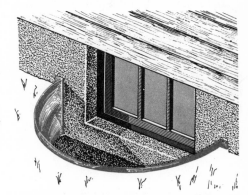

Fig. 46. A basement window protected by a steel areaway.

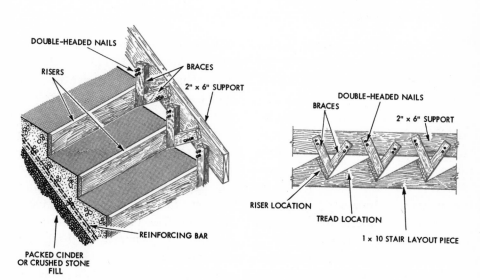

Fig. 47. Concrete stairs are formed by risers which are held in place by braces.

stalled before the earth is backfilled and graded. Areaways may be made with concrete walls similar to those under the platform described in the preceding paragraph. However, unless the windows are large, metal areaways are generally used. See Fig. 46. They are installed quickly and are adequate in most locations.

The stairs to the basement should be worked out with the same number of risers as called for on the Working Drawings, Sheet No. 2. The carpenter will find it to his advantage to mark out the profile of the stair on the walls where it is to be placed. Then 2 × 6 boards are nailed to the concrete walls near the line which

would connect the nosings of the finished stair. See Fig. 47.

The risers are cut to the exact height of finished stair risers and wide enough to fit snugly between the two walls. The lower edge is beveled so that the cement finisher can trowel the top of the tread smooth all the way to the back. The risers and braces are nailed together, placed in position and then nailed to the 2 × 6 boards. Crushed rock or cinder fill is placed before forming is done and tamped before placing concrete so that it is not disturbed by the carpenter. Reinforcing bars are suspended last. They will provide maximum strength to the concrete.

Foundations for Homes with Slab-At-Grade

An increasing number of homes are being built in all parts of the country in which a concrete floor is laid directly on the ground. See Fig. 48. Certain precautions must be made in order that the floor be satisfactory. The Small Homes Council suggests the following: The earth around the house must be graded so that water will drain away properly. The entire area where the floor will be laid should be covered with 4 inches of washed gravel or crushed rock in order to reduce the capillary rise of moisture. A membrane should be provided over the gravel strong

enough to resist puncturing when the concrete is placed. This membrane serves as a vapor barrier to keep moisture from entering the slab from the ground. Polyethylene film, asphaltum board ⅛ inch thick, or reinforced duplex paper with asphaltum center may be used. Overlap paper 4 inches. One additional problem to solve in cold climates is heat loss. The heat loss is primarily around the perimeter of the house, and to counteract the loss, and prevent condensation resulting from the cold floor, edge insulation is required. Two inch thick rigid waterproof in-

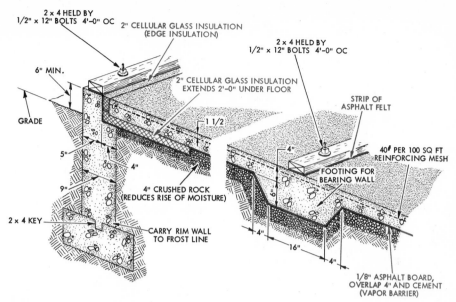

Fig. 48. A concrete floor laid on the ground requires a vapor barrier, and in cold climates must have edge insulation.

sulation extending 2 feet from the walls is suggested. Where panel heat is used in the floor the insulation should cover the entire floor area.

The footing and foundation wall will be formed in the manner used locally. Several methods have been outlined in detail in this chapter. In some areas the foundation wall is omitted entirely and a simple perimeter support is constructed instead by merely thickening the edge of the slab. See Fig. 49.

In some regions of the South, footings are laid both for the exterior wall and the bearing partition by making trenches in the firm earth. Reinforcing rods are used in the footings and

cement block is used for the foundation wall. A polyethylene film is spread over the earth where the slab is to be laid. The floor slab will be finished with terrazzo and in order to make it as rigid as possible, wire mesh is imbedded in the concrete. See Fig. 50.

In some areas where the soil is too unstable to permit the use of conventional footings and foundation walls, grade beams may be used. See Fig. 51. (Grade beams are continuous beams running around the house perimeter; they rest on piers.) Holes are dug at the perimeter of the building, a maximum of 8 feet apart, to a depth sufficient to bring them to solid

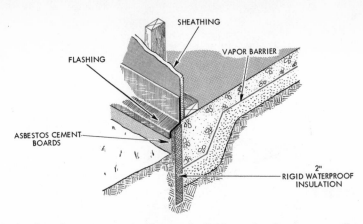

Fig. 49. A simple perimeter support will serve for light construction in warm climates.

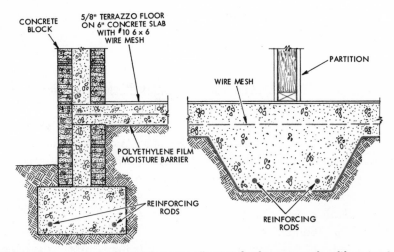

Fig. 50. Detail shows method used in warm climates for houses made with concrete block exterior walls and terrazzo floors.

soil well below the frost line. Concrete is poured into the holes, or into shells made for that purpose, to form piles. Forms are made to contain the grade beams which rest on the piles. A steel rod (a dowel) serves to posi-

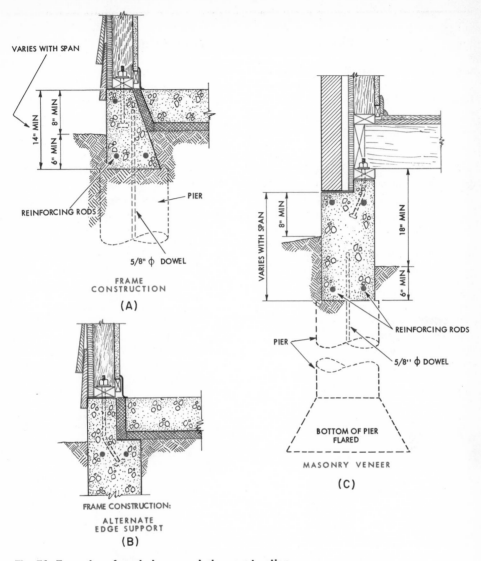

VARIES WITH SPAN

14" MIN

8" MIN

6" MIN

PIER

REINFORCING RODS

5/8" φ DOWEL

FRAME
CONSTRUCTION

(A)

VARIES WITH SPAN

8" MIN

18" MIN

6" MIN

REINFORCING RODS

PIER

5/8" φ DOWEL

BOTTOM OF PIER
FLARED

MASONRY VENEER

(C)

FRAME CONSTRUCTION:

ALTERNATE
EDGE SUPPORT

(B)

Fig. 51. Examples of grade beam and pier construction.

tion the grade beam. Horizontal reinforcing rods add strength to the grade beams. This construction may be used with slab-on-ground foundations and for houses with crawl spaces.

103

Checking On Your Knowledge

The following questions give you the opportunity to check up on yourself. If you have read the chapter carefully, you should be able to answer the questions. If you have any difficulty, read the chapter over once more so that you have the information well in mind before you go on with your reading.

DO YOU KNOW

1. Why is the rate at which the concrete is poured and the atmospheric temperature important factors in the building of forms?

2. Is there any advantage in using "built-in-place" forming?

3. What are the main reasons for the use of patent ties and forming systems?

4. How does the snap tie and clamp perform the following functions: (a) space the width of wall, (b) hold the wall together, (c) provide break back of tie ends?

5. What is the size and thickness of plywood sheets usually used for forms?

6. What is the purpose of the batterboards?

7. Where does the carpenter find information about the grade elevation for the first floor and the grade elevation for the excavation?

8. Why should footings rest on undisturbed earth?

9. When may footing forms be eliminated?

10. What is the function of wales?

11. When the carpenter erects forms, what factor must he keep in mind regarding stripping the forms?

12. How are bucks located?

13. How is a slab at grade protected from moisture and heat loss?

14. What is a grade beam?

15. Which parts of this chapter have particular application to local practice in your area?

Wall and Floor Framing

Each step in building a house is important. When a person examines a building which has been completed he must have a good background in the industry to know anything about its basic structure because most of it is covered up. Much of the responsibility for quality in framing rests with the carpenter who must make a great number of decisions as to how the various members should be put together as the work progresses.

The primary objectives are to build a building which is structurally sound and capable of withstanding forces such as high winds and floor loads. The stresses caused by the shrinkage of lumber must also be considered. Provisions for the comfort of the occupants requires that the framing permit the installation of heating, air conditioning, plumbing and electricity. An almost infinite variety of building plans, the result of the creativity of architects and the desires of owners, must be covered by adaptations or new departures in framing procedures.

Some of the things to be considered in framing a house are:

1. The carpenter has a part in choosing the type of framing to meet the problems of a particular building. In order to solve minor problems he often finds that he must improvise. Most of the buildings erected today follow one of three basic structural systems. Each one has special advantages.

2. He must know how to use his materials to their best structural advantage. This is where his "know-

105

how" comes in. Basic considerations include such things as framing the floor system to provide adequate support (particularly around stairwells and other openings), and building exterior walls and interior partitions which are strong and have openings which are framed correctly. The carpenter should have some knowledge of the various stresses placed on the structural members of a building. This chapter helps you understand why a joist or beam must be of a certain size.

3. The carpenter has the privilege of choosing between a constantly changing variety of new building products, new tools, and new techniques. Two questions come to mind in making decisions. Will they stand up under the test of time? Are they economical to use? The use of metal studs in framing partitions has been perfected; plywood and fiberboard have been adopted for many uses; and a variety of new tools for nailing, fastening, sawing and planing have been developed. The carpenter must be alert to changes which are constantly being made in the industry.

4. The general methods used in construction to bring about speed and economy as well as quality must be considered. Some builders find it quite satisfactory to build in the conventional manner. Other builders, particularly those who are erecting a number of similar buildings in the same vicinity, will build compo-

nent parts such as wall sections at a central location and then move them to the building site. Some have developed prefabricated units which are made in a factory and transported long distances. Small buildings are delivered in one piece to be placed on foundations already prepared for them. Other buildings are delivered in several sections which are then assembled on the job.

Along with these innovations in general building procedures is the introduction of new ways of making the components. New types of headers over openings and the extensive use of trusses for roofs are examples.

5. The matter of safety is always in the mind of the carpenter. How shall he erect the framework and apply the exterior finish so that workmen are protected from falling as they work? Correct scaffold procedures and other supporting devices is considered a part of rough framing.

The Figures. The figures in this chapter showing how the various members of a building are assembled will be useful wherever the same problem occurs in any frame house. In addition to the general information on framing, there is a detailed analysis of the structure of the HOUSE PLAN A, illustrated with isometric drawings. The working drawings in Chapter 1 for the HOUSE PLAN A are typical architects' drawings which give the necessary structural information and show what the building will look like when it is finished. The builder must draw on his experience, and information such as given in this chapter, for the details

of construction. The HOUSE PLAN C is introduced in order to present problems in framing peculiar to a tri-level house.

Rough Framework

The wall and floor framing, together with the roof, form the skeleton of a building. This chapter deals with all of the framing except the roof, which will be studied in detail in Chapter V. The sheathing, outside finish, inside wall finish, trim, and rough and finished floor are fastened to the rough framework. These areas will be covered in Chapters VI and VII. Since the strength and rigidity of a building depend upon good structural design and workmanship, it is advisable to give these two factors special consideration. When erecting the framework of a building, there is often a choice of methods that may be employed depending upon design, conditions peculiar to a certain locality, materials available, and the experience and preference of the builder. Before taking up the discussion of framing in detail, some of these methods will be considered.

Types of Wall Framing

During the early history of our country timber was abundant, but the means of making it into lumber were primitive. There were no power sawmills; timbers and planks were

cut by hand saws or were rough hewn. Because of the necessary handwork, it was cheaper to use large-sized members when framing a building than to cut the lumber into smaller sizes. Because nails were comparatively scarce and expensive and labor was cheap, it was the usual practice to use mortise-and-tenon joints where various pieces of the framework came together. The pieces were then held in place by wooden pins. These methods were used until about the middle of the nineteenth century.

However, during the subsequent years modern power sawmills have made it possible to produce lumber of small dimension at a relatively low cost so that framing could be designed strong enough to carry the required loads and yet not be wasteful of wood.

With new materials available, the methods of framing buildings gradually began to change. Two methods of framing that have come into general use are called platform framing (also called western framing) and balloon framing. Material which has a nominal 2 inch thickness is generally used throughout the structure in both systems. Occasionally a 4 × 4 inch post may be used, or a girder which may be a large dimension timber. Sometimes when larger pieces are needed, several 2 inch members are nailed together to serve that purpose. The many members of the house are now nailed together rather than joined as in former days. Metal devices such as joist hangers and anchors may be used to support and fasten members.

A return to the use of large dimension lumber has occurred in the last few years with plank and beam construction (also called post and beam), in which posts 4 × 4 inches square or larger support roof beams which are 4 × 8 inches or larger. The posts, floor beams, and roof beams are spaced at wide intervals when compared to conventional framing. The beams support 2 inch planks which serve as flooring or roof sheathing. Because of the great distance between supports, the planking serves a structural purpose.

1. Platform or Western Framing

When a builder chooses this type of framing, he can build the house rapidly with maximum safety for the workmen because a platform is laid before the walls are erected at each floor level. No attempt is made to eliminate shrinkage, but instead the exterior walls and interior partitions are framed so that the shrinkage is equal in both. Where steel beams are used instead of wood girders, wood of the same cross-section size as the sills on the foundation should be used on top of the beam to insure an equal amount of shrinkage. Each floor is framed separately, story-by-story. Note the balance of shrinkage materials on the outside walls and load-bearing partitions at points *A* and *B*, *C* and *D*, *E* and *F*, Fig. 1.

Platform framing automatically provides fire stops for the walls and partitions at each floor level. Diagonal planks or plywood sub-flooring may be laid easily for each story before partitions are made and tilted up into place, thereby providing a safe base on which the workmen may stand.

Platform framing is used mainly on one story buildings, but can be used on two-story buildings also. The exterior walls and interior partitions are assembled on the floor and tilted up into place. See Fig. 2. After the second floor joists are put in place the second floor rough flooring is installed to serve as a platform. Exterior walls and interior partitions are again made on the floor and tilted up into position. Platform framing has the great advantage of ease of assembly of the wall and partition units.

2. Balloon Framing

This modern type of framing, acceptable for the building of substantial houses in all parts of the country,

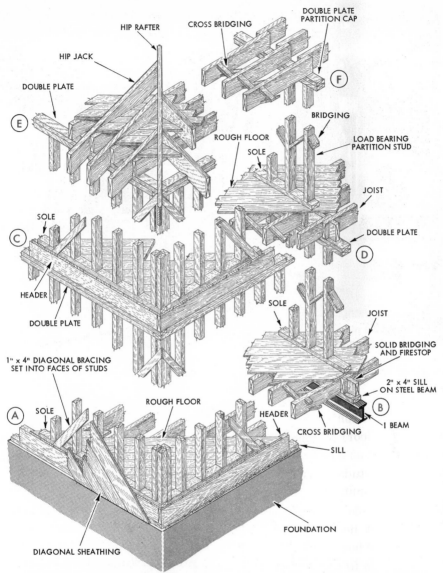

Fig. 1. Platform or western framing is popular because it compensates for shrinkage and can be erected quickly and easily. The rough floor provides a platform for the workmen.

is shown in Fig. 3. The distinguishing feature of this type of framing is the fact that studs (vertical members) are made to extend the full two stories from the foundation to the rafter plate. On the second floor level

109

Fig. 2. The rough members which make up the walls and partitions for platform framing are assembled on the floor and tilted up into place. (Western Pine Assoc.)

the joists (horizontal members supporting the floor) rest on a ribbon board, shown at *A*, Fig. 3, and are nailed to the studs. The ribbon used in balloon framing is cut into the supporting studs. The use of a ribbon makes it necessary to put in short pieces of board called *fire stops* between studs to prevent the circulation of air in the walls, See *B* and *C*, Fig. 3. Where plywood or structural insulation board is used for sheathing, the (1 × 4) diagonal brace which is shown at *D*, Fig. 3, may be eliminated unless high winds

or earthquake hazards are prevalent. The attic floor or ceiling joists rest on the doubled top plate, shown at *E*, Fig. 3.

The outside wall and load bearing partition studs extend from the foundation sill to the rafter plate. These continuous studs make possible easy installation of service pipes without the cutting of plates and consequent weakening of the structure. The balloon frame also possesses rigidity and reduces shrinkage by cutting down the amount of cross-section lumber to a minimum. Lumber shrinks

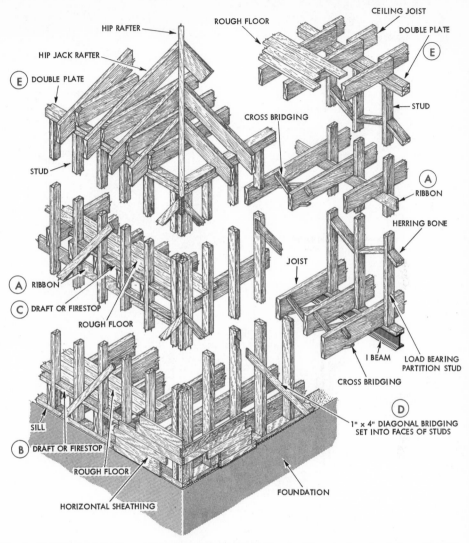

HIP RAFTER

ROUGH FLOOR

CEILING JOIST

DOUBLE PLATE

E

HIP JACK RAFTER

E DOUBLE PLATE

STUD

CROSS BRIDGING

STUD

A RIBBON

HERRING BONE

A RIBBON

C DRAFT OR FIRESTOP

JOIST

ROUGH FLOOR

I BEAM   LOAD BEARING
PARTITION STUD

CROSS BRIDGING

D

1" x 4" DIAGONAL BRIDGING
SET INTO FACES OF STUDS

SILL

B DRAFT OR FIRESTOP

ROUGH FLOOR

FOUNDATION

HORIZONTAL SHEATHING

Fig. 3. Balloon framing is used to frame a two-story house. The studs extend from the sill to the plate for the rafters.

across the width of the board. Shrinkage along the length dimension is negligible. See Fig. 4A and 4C. The manner of supporting floor joists at the first floor level and the second-floor level is exactly the same at the outside wall and at the bearing partition.

111

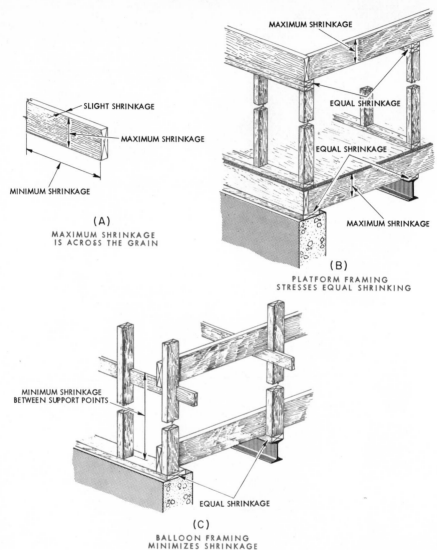

SLIGHT SHRINKAGE

MAXIMUM SHRINKAGE

MINIMUM SHRINKAGE

(A)

MAXIMUM SHRINKAGE
IS ACROSS THE GRAIN

MAXIMUM SHRINKAGE

EQUAL SHRINKAGE

EQUAL SHRINKAGE

MAXIMUM SHRINKAGE

(B)

PLATFORM FRAMING
STRESSES EQUAL SHRINKING

MINIMUM SHRINKAGE
BETWEEN SUPPORT POINTS

EQUAL SHRINKAGE

(C)

BALLOON FRAMING
MINIMIZES SHRINKAGE

Fig. 4. Shrinkage of lumber is important in house framing.

Balloon frame walls, even though two stories in height, are assembled in sections on the ground by many builders. All rough openings for windows and doors are framed before the wall is raised into place. Adequate temporary bracing must be used so that the walls remain square and the joints stay tight during and after erection. Other builders erect the structure stud by stud.

Balloon framing has its greatest use in two story buildings. It is an excellent means of preventing excessive shrinkage where masonry veneer or stucco is used for exterior wall covering. It is used on solid masonry buildings with ordinary construction at the bearing partitions, in order to reduce shrinkage to a minimum. (Ordinary construction is solid masonry exterior walls with wood joists and wood bearing partitions.) An excellent application of the use of balloon framing is in the bearing partition of a tri-level house. (Such as HOUSE PLAN C, page 221.)

Platform framing and balloon framing are often combined in two story frame buildings with the use of balloon framing for outside walls and platform framing for partitions. The differential in shrinkage may cause strain at wall and ceiling corners and at wall openings and may produce cracks in the wall finish.

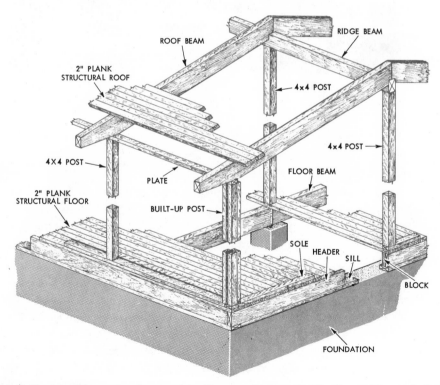

Fig. 5. Plank and beam framing requires the use of heavy structural members and planks for floors and roofs.

Fig. 6. Plank and beam framing gives a special effect of exposed heavy beams and high sloped wood ceiling. The supporting posts are uniformly spaced in the walls. (Weyerhaeuser Company.)

3. Plank and Beam Framing

Plank and beam framing has become popular because it provides a novel effect with heavy exposed roof beams and plank ceilings. There is some saving of labor because there are fewer members in the building and much less nailing. The characteristics of plank and beam framing (also known as post and beam framing) are (1) the large dimension floor and ceiling beams spaced far apart supported on piers, foundation walls, and posts, and (2) the 2 inch planks which span the distance between the beams to form the floors and roofs. The heavy plank material is necessary because it must have much more structural value than ordinary flooring or sheathing. This method of framing has distinct limitations because the posts, which are equally spaced in the wall, prevent flexibility in placing windows and doors. Interior posts limit the arrangement of rooms if the posts are to be concealed in the partitions. Greater care must be used in designing a building using this type of framing because the posts which support the structure must have a fixed location. See Figs. 5 and 6.

Frame Construction Details

The details of frame construction include such items as sill construction; erection of girders and beams, and columns and posts; framing of joists; application of rough flooring and bridging; construction of stud walls and partitions; rough framing for openings; wall sheathing; drywall application; etc.

Sill Construction

The sill (sometimes called mudsill) is the first part of the frame to be set in place. It rests on the foundation wall and extends all around the building wherever wood framing members are to be erected. It is made of one or two 2 × 4, 2 × 6, or 2 × 8 members depending on the construction used. It is embedded in mortar, carefully leveled and fastened in place with anchor bolts. The anchor bolts serve to fix the exact position of the exterior walls and to keep the building from shifting or raising under the pressure of high winds. The size, length, and spacing of the anchor bolts are usually specified in the local building code. Anchor bolts for the HOUSE PLAN A are ½ inch in diameter, 16 inches long and bent, and are spaced 4 feet on center.

The main feature of the sill for balloon framing is that it provides solid bearing for the studs and for the joists. 2 × 6 members are wide enough for this purpose if the joists run to the outside of the plate as shown in Fig. 7. Fire stops are cut so that they fit snugly between the joists. An alternative construction which is permitted in some areas is shown in Fig. 8. The fire stops are 2 × 4 pieces placed between studs.

The box sill is the best construction to use with platform framing. The ends of the joists are given adequate bearing and fire stopping is provided automatically by the flooring and the sole. When the subfloor is nailed in place it provides a platform on which to work on walls and partitions. See Fig. 9.

The double sill, which can be used in any kind of sill assembly, has the advantage of permitting the members to lap at the corners and at joints. However, single sills are generally adequate if they are well anchored every 4 or 6 feet.

Protection Against Termites

The wood-devouring termite or white ant is one of the enemies of wood construction. Of the many different species of termites the two

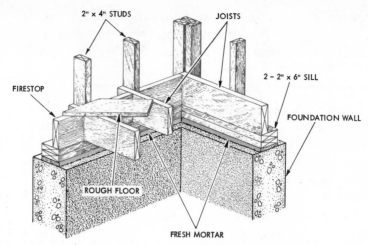

Fig. 7. The sill for balloon framing supports joists and studs. Firestops are cut to fit between joists.

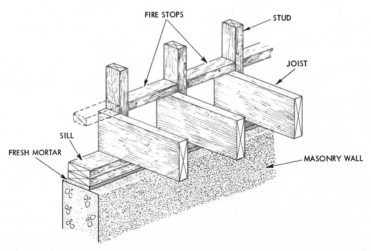

Fig. 8. An alternative method of sill construction for balloon framing provides for placing firestops between studs.

most common in the United States are the subterranean and the non-subterranean (or dry-wood) types. The subterranean termite is most ac-tive and can be found in almost every state in the Union. However, it is more prevalent in the southern part of the country. These destructive in-

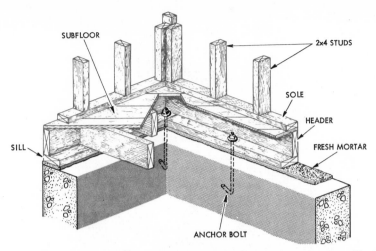

Fig. 9. The box sill provides adequate bearing for joists for platform framing. No firestops are needed.

sects live underground, coming out to feed on wood. After feeding, they return to the ground for moisture. If shut off from moisture they die. These termites will burrow through poor mortar in order to reach the wooden superstructure of a building. Sometimes they build earthlike shelter tubes over materials through which they cannot burrow. Then they travel back and forth through these tunnels between the ground and the wood on which they feed. See Fig. 10.

In localities where the attack of the subterranean termite is inevitable, preventive measures must be taken at the time of construction. A minimum of 18 inches is recommended between the joists and the soil in a crawl space and 12 inches between girders and soil. The lowest wood member on the exterior of a house should be placed 8 inches or more above the grade. Metal termite shields of 24 gage galvanized iron projecting on each side of the masonry wall should be provided. Concrete walls should be poured so that they do not develop cracks, and when masonry units are used they should be laid in mortar rich in cement. In the areas of the country where termite damage is great, all of the lumber should be pressure-treated with chemicals. In other areas, all of the wood used below the finished first floor should be given the same pressure treatment. All raw ends of pieces which have been cut must be treated

117

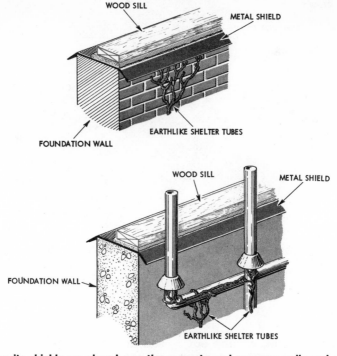

Fig. 10. Termite shields are placed over the concrete and masonry walls and also on pipes.

with the same chemical. Other precautions which may be used are: poisoning the soil inside and outside the foundation wall around the perimeter of the building; providing good ventilation for crawl spaces; suspending pipes from the floor above so that they do not come in contact with the earth; and inspecting foundations periodically for signs of termites.

Girders, and Beams

The joists rest on sills placed on top of the foundation walls around the outside of the building. However, the distance between the foundation walls (the span) is usually so great that additional support must be provided between the walls. When such support is necessary it may be in the form of a bearing wall, a wood girder, or a steel beam. The girders or beams are supported at the ends where they rest in girder pockets in the wall or on a pilaster of the foundation. See Figs. 11 and 12. An air space around the end of a wood girder will help prevent decay.

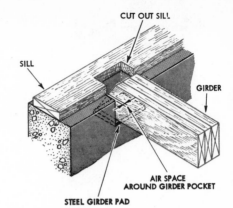

Fig. 11. A girder is supported by the foundation in a girder pocket.

CUT OUT SILL

SILL

GIRDER

AIR SPACE
AROUND GIRDER POCKET

STEEL GIRDER PAD

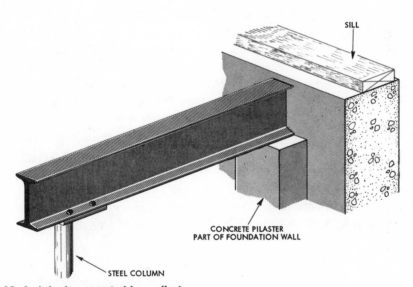

SILL

CONCRETE PILASTER
PART OF FOUNDATION WALL

STEEL COLUMN

Fig. 12. A girder is supported by a pilaster.

Columns and Posts

Usually, additional support is provided by the use of one or more posts or columns placed at intervals under the girder. Necessary footings must be constructed for them. When wood posts are used it is advisable to construct a concrete base with a 6 inch pier which will bring the bottom of the post safely above the moisture of the basement floor, as shown in Fig. 13. A ¾ inch iron dowel pin in concrete pier will hold post in place.

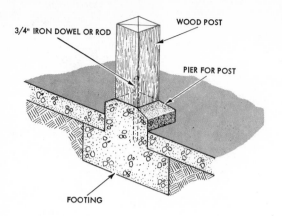

3/4" IRON DOWEL OR ROD

WOOD POST

PIER FOR POST

FOOTING

Fig. 13. A pier is provided to keep post above the basement floor.

Steel beams, either I or wide flange, usually are supported by *lally columns;* that is, iron pipes filled with concrete, set on plates on footings and bolted to the beams at the top. See Fig. 12.

Framing Joists at Girders or Beams

Methods of framing joists on foundation walls was explained in connection with the directions given for sill construction, and illustrated in

Figs. 7, 8 and 9. Several different methods may be used when framing joists at girders; the simplest method is to rest the joists on top of the girder as shown in Fig. 14. Another method which may be used successfully is to cut away a portion of the joists and frame them so that they rest on a ledger spiked to the girder, as shown in Fig. 15. When flush ceilings are required underneath the joists, the ends of the joists may be supported by joint hangers (also

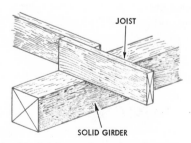

JOIST

SOLID GIRDER

Fig. 14. Joists are lapped and rest on the girder.

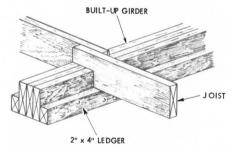

BUILT-UP GIRDER

JOIST

2" x 4" LEDGER

Fig. 15. Joists are cut to rest on a 2 × 4 ledger.

120

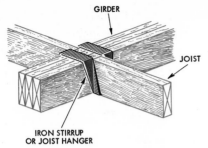

GIRDER

JOIST

IRON STIRRUP
OR JOIST HANGER

Fig. 16. When joists are hung using joist hangers, the maximum headroom is obtained below the girder.

called stirrups) as shown in Fig. 16. The method used for framing joists at girders depends upon the requirements for the ceiling below and the procedure necessary to equalize the shrinkage of the structural lumber used in the building.

Girders may be solid timbers, as shown in Figs. 14 and 16, be built up as illustrated in Fig. 15, or be made of several planks laminated by glueing. Girders are built up by placing two or more members side by side and fastening them together with nails or bolts. They usually consist of several planks held together with ⅝ inch bolts, which are staggered and spaced 20 inches apart. When the planks are not long enough to extend the whole distance, they may be spliced. Splices should be made to occur over posts and one or two of the planks should continue at each post. See Fig. 17. Built-up girders have the advantage of not developing checks and splits as easily as solid wood girders, and are less likely to contain decayed wood.

Framing joists at steel beams presents problems slightly different

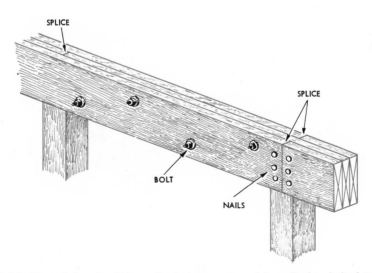

SPLICE

SPLICE

BOLT

NAILS

Fig. 17. A built-up girder should be spliced at supports and be spiked or bolted together.

from those involved in framing joists on wood girders. However, joists may be attached to steel beams with iron hangers the same way as to wood girders. The iron hangers, either double or single, can be bolted to the steel beams. When this method is used, the joists should always be set with a clearance of not less than ⅜ of an inch above the top flange of the steel girder to allow for shrinkage of the lumber.

If hangers are not used the construction is done as shown at *A* and *B*, Fig. 18. Fig. 18*A* shows two members bolted to the web of the I beam. The joists are cut to fit the I beam with at least ⅜ inch clearance over the top in the event that the joist should shrink. The joist would come to rest on the I beam and tend to split. A metal tie serves to hold the joists in line. Fig. 18*B* shows a more common procedure, provided that headroom in the basement is not important. A 2 × 4 inch piece is bolted or clinch nailed to the top of the I beam. The joists are then nailed to this member. The joists are lapped a minimum of 4 inches and spiked together. Resting the joist directly on the lower flange of an I beam is not recommended because the narrow, sloping surface of the beam does not provide sufficient bearing for the end of the joist.

When flush ceilings are required underneath the joists, metal plates can be bolted or welded to the bottom of the steel beam as shown in Fig. 19. Such a plate provides a wider resting surface for the ends of the

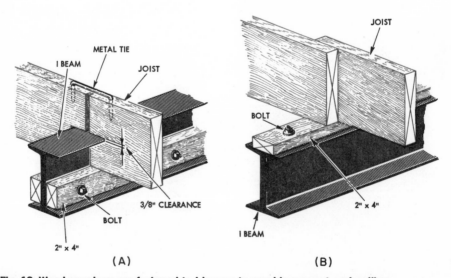

Fig. 18. Wood members are fastened to I beams to provide support and nailing.

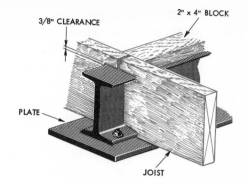

Fig. 19. An I beam and plate are used to support the joists so that the ceiling below can be made flush.

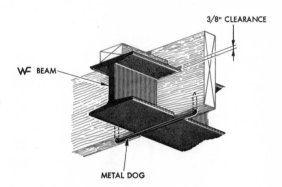

Fig. 20. Joists are cut to fit the shape of a wide flange beam.

joists. Another method of framing joists at steel beams is illustrated in Fig. 20. In this case a wide flange beam is used. The joists are framed into the beam and the ends of the joists held together with a metal dog, or strap, as shown in the illustration. See detail on Sheet No. 1, HOUSE PLAN A in Chapter 1.

When a part of a joist extends over the top of a steel beam, an allowance, or clear space, of at least ⅜ of an inch for a 2 × 10 joist must be pro-

vided above the top flange of the beam for shrinkage.

Doubling Joists

In the framing of floor joists, it becomes necessary to cut joists for openings in the floor for stairwells, or when framing around chimneys and fireplaces. When joists are cut, the strength thus lost must be replaced or compensated for in some way. The usual procedure is to frame them against double headers, as shown in

123

Fig. 21. (A single header may be used up to a maximum of 4'-0".) These headers, in turn, are supported by double or triple joists called trimmers. The framework around openings is tied together in this way, thus compensating for the strength which was lost through cutting the joists. When it becomes necessary to use headers more than 6 feet in length, they should be fastened to their supporting joists by means of joist hangers, shown in detail in Fig. 21. It is not necessary to double the joist which is nailed to the wall studs.

Sometimes a building is so constructed that the second story overhangs the first story; that is, the second story projects beyond the wall of the first story. If the second floor joists are parallel to the joists which overhang the wall of the first story, the framing is comparatively easy, and may be accomplished by merely using longer joists for the sec-

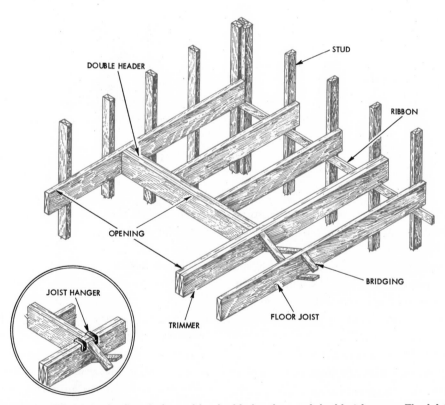

Fig. 21. An opening in the floor is framed by double headers and double trimmers. The joist along the outside wall need not be doubled.

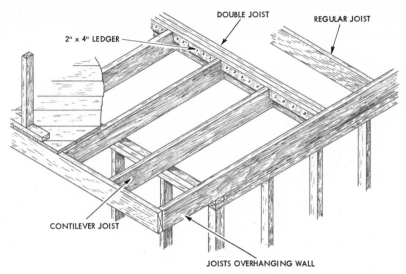

Fig. 22. Cantilever joists rest on the wall plate and are fastened to a double joist and ledger.

ond floor than for the first floor. However, if the second floor joists are at right angles to the joists which overhang the wall, then it becomes necessary to cantilever short joists as shown in Fig. 22.

The rooms of an upper story are not always planned so that every partition will come directly above a partition of the story below. When partitions do not line up and when a partition of an upper story runs parallel with the floor joists, the joists supporting the partition must be doubled to carry the additional load placed upon them. Frequently pipes or heating ducts are run in such partitions. This makes it necessary when doubling the joists to place a joist on each side of the partition to

leave room for ducts. The procedure for this type of framing is shown in Figs. 23 and 26. When a partition runs crosswise to a floor joist, additional support may be required by doubling up some of the joists.

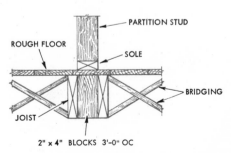

Fig. 23. Joists are doubled under partitions which run parallel to them. Pipes, conduit and ducts may pass between the two joists.

Rough Flooring

Material for rough flooring may be either plywood or boards. Plywood has been found to be very satisfactory and economical because of the large sheets, 4 × 8 feet or larger, which can be nailed or stapled in place rapidly. The thicknesses are generally ½, ⅝, ¾ or ⅞ of an inch depending on the joist spacing and the floor load requirements. The sheets are laid parallel to one wall with joints between sheets of plywood placed over joists. The second row is staggered so that joints fall on other joists. When an underlayment for tile or carpeting is used, the panels of underlayment are staggered so that the joints do not coincide with the joints of the subfloor. See Fig. 24. The underlayment is usually ¼ or ⅜ inch plywood or hardboard. A combined subfloor underlayment is available using ½, ⅝ or ¾ inch panels with tongue and groove edges. Special care must be used in framing the joists, using seasoned lumber. If square edge panels are used in this application, blocking must be placed between joists to support the joints between sheets. A 1⅛ inch tongue and groove panel has been developed for a floor system with 4 foot spacing between supports. See Fig. 25.

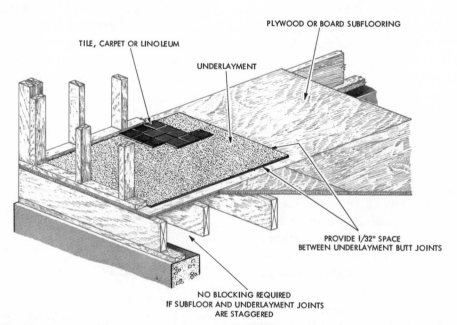

TILE, CARPET OR LINOLEUM

UNDERLAYMENT

PLYWOOD OR BOARD SUBFLOORING

PROVIDE 1/32" SPACE
BETWEEN UNDERLAYMENT BUTT JOINTS

NO BLOCKING REQUIRED
IF SUBFLOOR AND UNDERLAYMENT JOINTS
ARE STAGGERED

Fig. 24. Plywood subfloors are installed quickly because of the large panels. (Douglas Fir Plywood Assoc.)

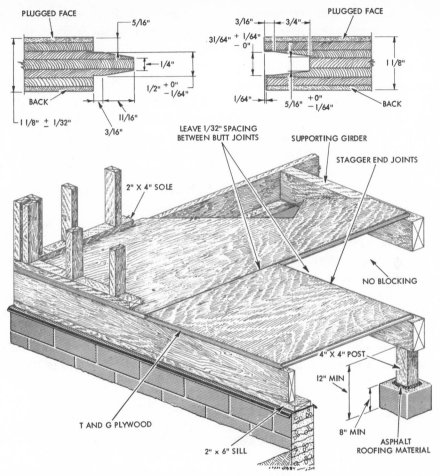

PLUGGED FACE

5/16"

1/4"

1/2" +0" −1/64"

BACK

1 1/8" ± 1/32"

11/16"

3/16"

3/16" 3/4"

31/64" +1/64" −0"

PLUGGED FACE

1 1/8"

1/64" 5/16" +0" −1/64"

BACK

LEAVE 1/32" SPACING BETWEEN BUTT JOINTS

SUPPORTING GIRDER

STAGGER END JOINTS

2" X 4" SOLE

NO BLOCKING

4" X 4" POST

12" MIN

8" MIN

T AND G PLYWOOD

2" x 6" SILL

ASPHALT ROOFING MATERIAL

Fig. 25. Plywood panels 1⅛ inch thick serve in a wide span support system (Douglas Fir Plywood Assoc.)

The boards commonly used for rough flooring are 1 × 6 and square edged, although sometimes 1 × 8 shiplap or 1 × 6 dressed-and-matched lumber is chosen. However, since dressed-and-matched material increases the cost of construction, and an underlayment or finished floor must be applied, the advantage of its use for rough flooring is questionable.

Rough flooring may be laid either straight or diagonally. The main reason for laying flooring diagonally is to brace the building. If the building has two floors, the second floor rough

127

flooring should be laid beginning in a corner adjacent to that used on the first floor so that the rough flooring on the upper floor is at right angles to that on the lower floor. Laying the rough flooring diagonally permits laying of the finish flooring either parallel or crosswise on the floor joists. Laying the rough flooring diagonally is also an advantage when the floor joists are not all framed in the same direction; that is, the floor joists of one section of a building are laid at right angles to the floor joists of an adjoining section. Unless the lumber used is end matched, the ends of the rough flooring boards should be joined at a joist and nailed to the joist.

It requires more time to lay rough flooring diagonally than to lay it at right angles to the floor joists. There is also more waste in cutting the boards for a diagonal floor than for one in which the joists and flooring are at right angles. When the work of other tradesmen, such as electricians and plumbers, makes it necessary to remove the rough flooring, it will be found that diagonal rough flooring is more difficult to replace than straight laid flooring. However, the added structural value of diagonal flooring is a valuable feature.

Bridging

The term *bridging* is used when referring to a system of bracing for floor joists. *Cross bridging* and *solid bridging* are illustrated in Figs. 26 and 27. Compression type metal bridging is illustrated in Fig. 28. The

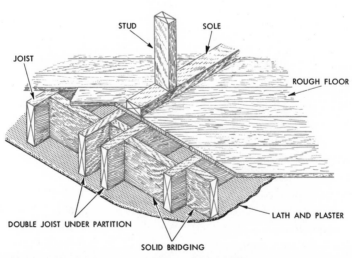

Fig. 26. Bridging adds rigidity to the joists; solid bridging may be used in narrow spaces.

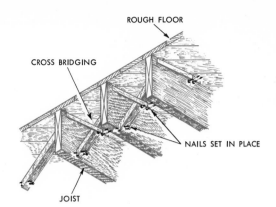

ROUGH FLOOR

CROSS BRIDGING

NAILS SET IN PLACE

JOIST

Fig. 27. The lower end of each piece
of bridging is fastened after the floor
joists have adjusted themselves.

advantage of bridging lies in its effectiveness in helping to distribute a concentrated floor load, such as a piano, over a large area of floor space. Bridging also distributes the force and vibration of live loads such as people walking. Bridging stiffens the joists, helps to hold them in alignment, and also helps to prevent them from warping.

Solid bridging consists of single pieces of boards, or blocks, set at right angles to the joists and fitted between them, as shown in Fig. 26. Cross bridging consists of transverse rows of small diagonal braces, or struts, set in pairs and crossing each other between joists, as shown in Fig. 27. It is customary to insert rows of cross bridging from 5 to 8 feet apart. To be most effective, the rows of bridging should be in straight lines extending continuously the entire length of the floor (offset enough to permit nailing for solid bridging).

Exceptionally long joist spans should be bridged at distances of every 6 feet. Cross bridging is considered to be superior to solid bridging because there is less careful fitting required. When the braces are nailed in place they are wedged tightly against the joists. Each bridging strut should be set in such a position that it will be directly opposite the corresponding strut of an adjacent pair, as shown in Fig. 27. Cross bridging is usually made of material size 1×3 or 1×4.

Metal bridging does not require cutting. See Figs. 28 and 29. The upper end is driven into place with hammer blows on the end of the strut. The lower end is forced into position and driven into place with a few hammer blows.

When wood bridging struts are placed in position, they are first nailed to the joists only at the top, with the lower end of each piece left free until after the rough flooring

129

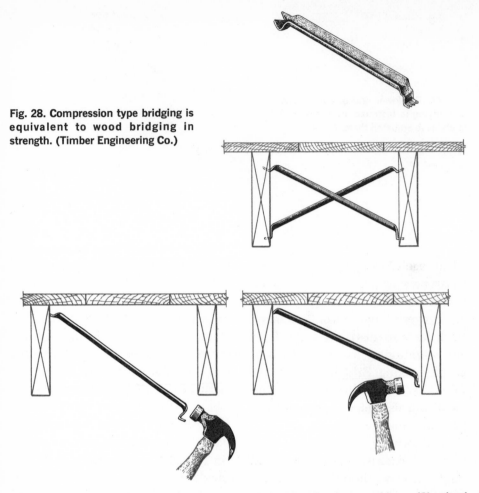

Fig. 28. Compression type bridging is equivalent to wood bridging in strength. (Timber Engineering Co.)

Fig. 29. Compression type metal bridging is installed with a few hammer blows. (Cleveland Steel Specialty Co.)

has been nailed to the joists, as shown in Fig. 27. When the floor joists have adjusted themselves to the rough flooring, the lower end of each bridging strut is nailed in place. In order to speed up the bridging operation, after the material has been cut for the bridging but before nailing begins, two nails are set on each end of each piece.

The angle of cut and the length of the bridging braces may be obtained by making a full-size layout on a piece of joist or plank. The width of

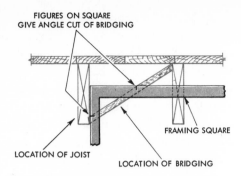

FIGURES ON SQUARE
GIVE ANGLE CUT OF BRIDGING

FRAMING SQUARE

LOCATION OF JOIST

LOCATION OF BRIDGING

Fig. 30. The framing square is useful in laying out bridging.

the plank must be the same as the width of the joists to be used. First lay out the position of two adjacent floor joists and draw two diagonal lines representing the bridging brace, as shown in Fig. 30. Then lay a framing square in position along the line representing the inner edge of the floor joist, as shown in the illustration. Select a figure on the tongue of the square somewhere near the middle point, for example 6, and

place this figure directly over the line representing the upper edge of the bridging brace. On the body of the square, take the figure at the point where the square crosses the same diagonal line. Transfer these two figures to the top edge of a simple miter box by nailing together a 2 × 6 and a 2 × 4, as shown in Fig. 31. Hold the square firmly in position at the correct figures and draw a line along the outer edge of the tongue. This gives the correct angle of cut for the bridging braces. Make a saw cut on this line through the side of the miter box guide for cutting the braces. At a distance equal to the length of the diagonal, place a stop, as shown in the illustration, for cutting the bridging braces to the correct length.

Note: The cutting lines for the top and bottom of the bridging braces must be parallel. After the first brace is cut, it should be fitted into position to make sure that it has the cor-

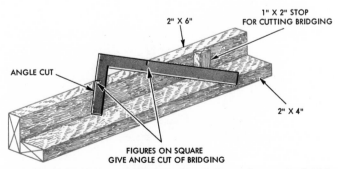

2" X 6"

1" X 2" STOP
FOR CUTTING BRIDGING

ANGLE CUT

2" X 4"

FIGURES ON SQUARE
GIVE ANGLE CUT OF BRIDGING

Fig. 31. The angle cut is made in a miter box. A stop is used to make bridging uniform in length.

131

rect dimensions and angle of cut. It is advisable to fit all braces into position soon after they are cut, as the distance between the joists may vary slightly and material may be wasted if too many braces are cut at one time. When finding the angle of cut for bridging braces, use the dimensions which fit your particular job.

Some carpenters prefer finding the required length of bridging braces by holding a strip of wood in place between the joist and cutting the braces while in this position. This procedure is not recommended when the spacing between the joists is to be uniform, since the joists can be brought into alignment and held in place more easily when all the bridging braces are of the same length. However, when the spacing between the joists is not uniform, cutting the bridging braces while holding them

in position is a simple and practical method to use.

Regardless of the method used, it requires a considerable amount of time to cut bridging braces, in addition to the time required for fitting and nailing them in place. Therefore, with a view to reducing labor cost, metal bridging has an advantage. This bridging can be installed in a fraction of the time required for cutting and installing wood braces. Steel bridging comes in various sizes designed to meet the needs of most jobs.

Corner Construction

The corners of the wall construction may be of either a solid or built-up type. In present day construction, wall corners are usually made of three studs. The studs for this kind of construction can be assembled in

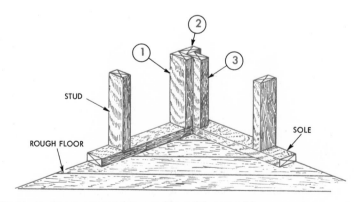

Fig. 32. Corner studs are arranged to provide quick assembly.

one of several ways. The method used depends upon the requirements for the application of wall sheathing and outside finish, as well as for the application of lath and plaster or other interior finish.

The studs for all corners should be of the best straight stock available, carefully selected and nailed together firmly. The type of corner requiring the least amount of material and also taking the least amount of time to construct is shown in Fig. 32. After the material has been cut to the correct length for three studs, stud *1* is nailed to stud *2*. Then stud *3* is nailed in place. If the corner construction is for a two-story building of a balloon type of frame with a ribbon, the housing for the ribbon

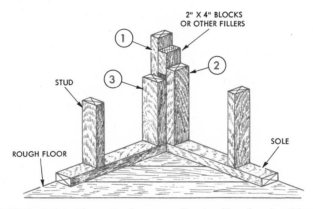

Fig. 33. 2 × 4 blocks help make a sturdy corner. Good nailing for sheathing is provided.

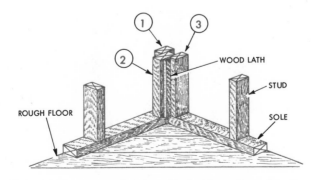

Fig. 34. A lath added to the corner studs brings the inside surfaces into line.

should be laid out and cut on stud *1* before the corner studs are assembled.

Another type of built-up corner assembly, shown in Fig. 33, requires the nailing of 2 × 4 blocks to stud *1*. These blocks should be spaced at regular intervals of about 3 or 4 feet apart. In this type of assembly, stud *2* is nailed to the blocks. Special attention must be given to nailing of the blocks and studs so the corner will remain square. Stud *3* must be nailed to both stud *1* and stud 2.

Still another method of assembly for built-up corners is shown in Fig. 34. This method requires the nailing of a piece of ⅜ inch stock such as wood lath on stud 2, to build the stud out to full-wall thickness. In this kind of construction the studs are assembled in the order indicated by the numbers.

Partition Corners

When constructing partition corners, and the intersection of partitions with exterior walls, provision must be made for tying the walls together firmly. Solid anchorage is essential where two walls meet. This is a construction detail that cannot be stressed too strongly, as careless treatment at corners may cause unsightly plaster cracks later. Also, improper or careless framing of partition corners may allow infiltration of cold air. One method of framing partition corners is by the use of three studs tied together with spikes, as shown in Fig. 35. Another method illustrated in Fig. 36 allows the studs in the main wall to follow their regular spacing of 16 inches on center (o.c.) with the corner stud of an adjoining partition wall placed between two main wall studs. As shown in the illustration, the corner stud of the partition is backed with a 1 × 6 or 1 × 8 to provide a nailing base for lath or wallboard. The partition stud is tied to the main wall with 2 × 4 cross blocks, and spiked to all three studs.

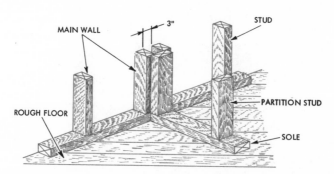

Fig. 35. Intersection of exterior wall and partition is framed by three studs spiked together.

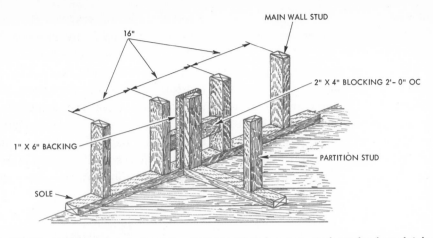

Fig. 36. The partition corner is framed so that the 16 inch c. to c. stud spacing is maintained. Notice the backing for lath.

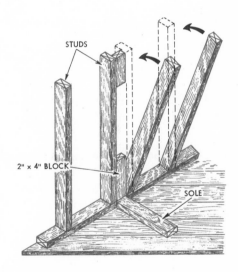

Fig. 37. A simple type of wall corner (channel) provides good nailing when walls or partitions are tilted up into place.

A third manner of framing the intersection of partition or wall corners (or channel), which is adaptable to platform framing, is shown in Fig. 37. Between the studs, blocks are placed to serve as spacer and nailing blocks. When the partition is raised into' place the last stud will be nailed to the blocks and the corner will be formed by 2 × 4 studs.

135

Wall Plates

Continuous wood members placed on top of a wall as supports for joists and rafters are called wall plates. The primary purpose of wall plates is threefold: (1) They tie the studding together at the top and insure stud alignment; (2) they provide support for the structural members above the plates, for example, attic joists and roof rafters; and (3) they provide a means to tie intersecting walls and partitions together.

Wall plates should be doubled at the top of walls and partitions. For walls which have the same plate height, the outside corners and partitions should be tied together by lapping the plates as illustrated in Fig. 38. In the balloon frame, the parti-

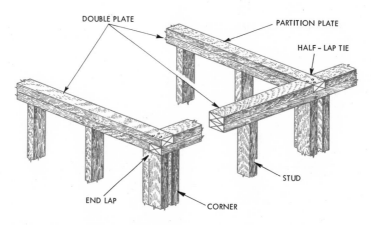

Fig. 38. Wall plates should be lapped at corners and partitions.

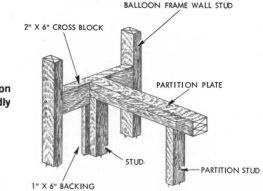

Fig. 39. A partition plate in a balloon framed house should be fastened solidly to a cross block placed between studs.

tions on the second-floor level are tied to the outside walls with 2×6 cross blocks fitted between the studs, then nailed to both the studs and the partition plate, as shown in Fig. 39.

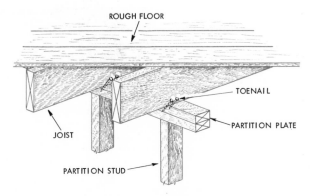

ROUGH FLOOR

TOENAIL

PARTITION PLATE

JOIST

PARTITION STUD

Fig. 40. When joists run at right angles to the partition, they are anchored to the plate by toenailing.

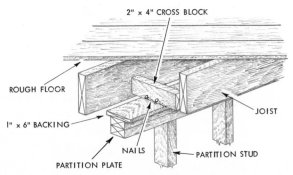

2" x 4" CROSS BLOCK

ROUGH FLOOR

JOIST

1" x 6" BACKING

NAILS

PARTITION STUD

PARTITION PLATE

Fig. 41. When joists are parallel to the partition, cross blocks are used to hold it in position. The 1×6 backing provides nailing for the ceiling lath.

Framing Top of Partition Walls

Proper framing of the top of partitions, tying them firmly to joists, and installing suitable backing is just as important as providing solid anchorage for wall corners. Where partitions run across the joists (at right angles to them), each joist is toenailed to the wall plates, as shown in Fig. 40. When partitions run par-

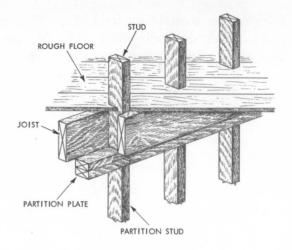

Fig. 42. When studs continue through floor, joists are nailed on each side.

STUD

ROUGH FLOOR

JOIST

PARTITION PLATE

PARTITION STUD

allel with the joists and come between two adjacent joists, as shown in Fig. 41, the top wall plates are backed with 1 inch material to provide a nailing base for interior-ceiling finish. The walls are anchored to the joists with 2 × 4 cross blocks at intervals of every 3 feet. When the partitions are parallel with the joist and the partition studs are continuous, or the second-floor studs extend down to the wall plates of the first-floor partition, a joist may be nailed to both sides of the studs, Fig. 42.

Framing Rough Openings for Windows and Doors

Any one of several methods may be used for framing openings in stud walls. One method is to erect all the studs first, spacing them 16 inches on center (o.c.), before laying out and cutting any openings. Another method is to lay out the openings on the sole of the wall in addition to the regular stud spacing, then erect only those full-length studs which come outside of the openings. Framing of the openings is completed later. A third method is to frame the wall, including all openings, on the floor or ground. When the framing is completed, the entire wall, or a section of it, is raised into position. See Fig. 2.

The rough openings may be framed as shown in Figs. 43 and 44, in which headers and subsills are cut between regular studs, and the rough opening framed with cripple studs. The header has been extended to fit between two regular studs spaced to fall on 16 inch intervals. Cripple studs support the ends of the header and transfer the load imposed on the header directly to the sole. Double

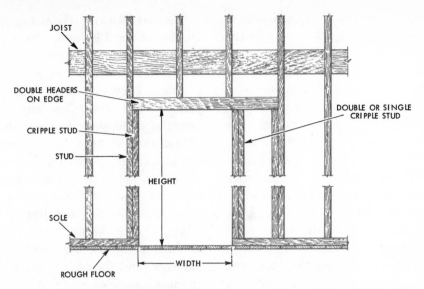

Fig. 43. The rough opening for a door in a balloon framed house is framed with the use of a long header.

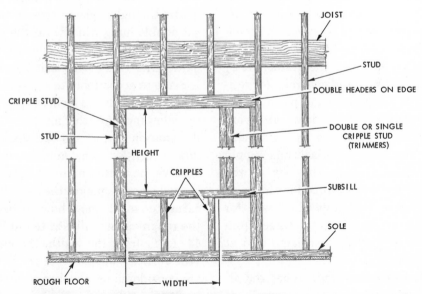

Fig. 44. The rough framing for a window provides adequate strength to support the wall above and nailing for the window frame and trim.

studs are preferred at each side of the opening to provide nailing for the window frame and trim.

An alternative method used by some carpenters is to introduce new full studs where the openings occur, as shown in Figs. 45 and 46. The regular stud space of 16 inches is continued, except for the short studs over the opening for a door and over and under the opening for a window. Again the load of the wall above the header and the structural members above is transferred to the sole through sturdy cripple members. This method is used frequently in platform framing because there is some saving in cutting and fitting members.

Calculating Rough Opening Sizes

Package doors and windows are manufactured to precision in standard sizes and are delivered ready to install, including the frame. They have been adopted generally for residential work. In some parts of the country metal windows are very popular, particularly in warm, dry climates. The manufacturers supply information as to the size of the rough opening required for each window type. Generally the space for fitting is very small and ranges from ¼ to ½ inch at each jamb and at the head.

The various window types and allowances will be discussed in Chapter VI, Exterior Finish.

Size of Rough Opening for Double Hung Windows. In northern sections of the country the double hung window remains very popular. They are dimensioned on plans in two ways. One way is to give the dimensions to the outside of the sash. A 36/48 inch window would measure 36 inches wide and 48 inches high to the outside of the sash, and this would also be the inside dimensions of the frame. By adding the thickness of the frame, and the allowance for patent sash balances, and for fitting, the rough opening may be determined.

Windows are also dimensioned as shown on sheets No. 4, No. 5, No. 6 and No. 7 of the elevation drawings of the HOUSE PLAN A in Chapter 1. The windows are dimensioned by giving the light (glass) size. A typical double hung window on the second floor (sheet No. 6) is designated 32/22 Div. This means that the sash is made to accommodate a glass area 32 inches wide by 22 inches high with no allowance for the muntin. The designation Div. means that the window is divided. The millman must observe how the muntins are arranged when he makes the sash. The carpenter must know how to figure the rough opening illustrated in Fig. 44. In figuring the width, the stiles (the vertical side pieces of the sash) are considered as 2 inches wide, the jamb (the side and top pieces of the window frame) ¾ of an inch thick,

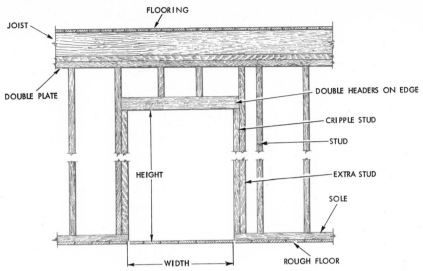

Fig. 45. An extra full stud is inserted at the side of the rough door opening. (Platform framing.)

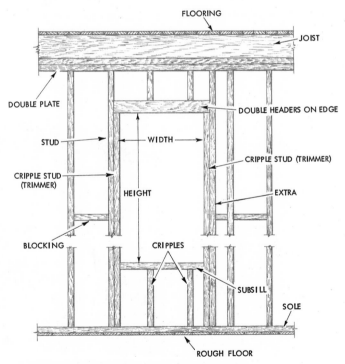

Fig. 46. Cripples (or trimmers) at each side of the rough opening give support to the header and provide nailing for trim. Full studs maintain 16 inch centers.

with ½ to ¾ inch allowed for fitting. The rough opening would then be made 6½ or 7 inches over glass size.

In figuring the vertical dimension of the rough opening, 2 inches are allowed for the top rail (rails are horizontal members of each sash), 1 inch for the meeting rail (check rail), 3 inches for the bottom rail, 2 inches for the sill including the bevel, ¾ of an inch for the top jamb, and ½ or 1 inch allowance for fitting. The dimension would work out to be approximately 9½ or 10 inches over glass size. The rough opening for a 32/22 double hung window using patent sash balances would be 32 + 7 = 39 inches wide maximum, and 22 + 22 + 10 = 54 inches high maximum.

Header Sizes. Header size and construction depends on the load to be supported. Headers are usually placed on edge in order to develop the maximum strength. Two 2 × 4s are used to bridge the opening unless it is very wide. The Federal Housing Authority suggests the following header sizes for rough openings for one story buildings under certain roof loads. Each type of load would have different requirements:

	Openings in Outside Walls
Two 2 × 4s on edge	3'-6" max.
Two 2 × 6s on edge	6'-6" max.
Two 2 × 8s on edge	8'-6" max.
Two 2 × 10s on edge	11'-0" max.
Two 2 × 12s on edge	13'-6" max.

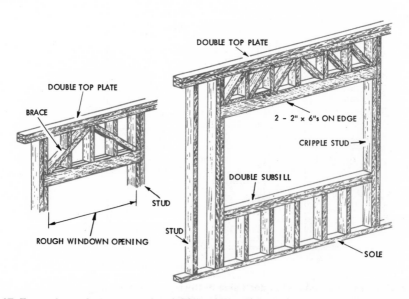

Fig. 47. Trussed openings are used to bridge wide spans.

Trussed openings are used occasionally to span wide spaces. They have the advantage of shrinking less than wide wood headers. Plaster cracks often develop when a header shrinks in 'a wall. There are several arrangements of members which may be used. Fig. 47 shows two of them.

Built-up box headers were also developed to bridge wide spans over openings; 2 × 4 inch members were used with plywood glued and nailed on one side or both sides. The header is light in weight and therefore easy to erect. The built-up header, because of its construction and its plywood face, overcomes the problem of shrinkage. See Fig. 48.

The carpenter should check the working drawings and specifications to see if the sizes of headers and their construction are specified, and also the local building code to find out what the required sizes are for various openings. The rule of thumb should never be the guide for headers which have special loads to carry. All such loads should be carefully figured by a competent architect or engineer, and the proper header designed for the load to be supported.

Wall Sheathing

After completing the framework of a new building, a covering known as sheathing is fastened to the frame. In addition to serving the purpose of covering the frame, sheathing also furnishes a base for exterior trim, such as siding or masonry veneer. The sheathing also helps to stiffen the building, making the structure

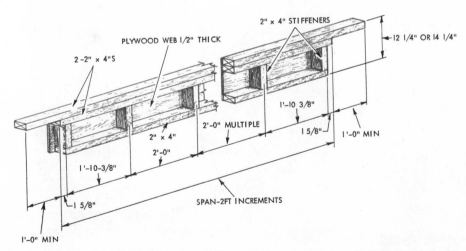

Fig. 48. A built-up box header bridges a wide span over an opening. Shrinkage is brought to a minimum.

more resistant to wind pressure, as well as providing some insulation against extreme weather conditions.

Four distinct types of material are generally used for sheathing. They are boards, plywood, fiberboard and gypsum board. They present different problems in application, vary in structural value, resistance to infiltration of air and moisture, and in cost.

Wood boards are still used although other types of sheathing have replaced them to a great extent. Those used are usually 1 × 8 inch square-edge boards, although tongue and groove or shiplap may be sub-

stituted for greater weather tightness. When nailed in place horizontally, two 8 *d* (8 penny) nails are required at each stud. The ends of the sheathing boards are cut so that the joints fall on studs. Joints on one row of boards must not fall in line with those directly below. Walls which are sheathed with horizontal boards require diagonal bracing. See Fig. 49. The bracing material is generally 1 × 4 inch boards let into the outside face of the studs and placed at as close to a 45° angle as conditions will permit. When window or door openings occur the bracing must be made ac-

Fig. 49. Let-in braces are arranged to accommodate an opening for a window. (U. S. Forest Products Laboratory)

Fig. 50. Boards when used as diagonal sheathing provide a strong skin for the wall. (Western Wood Products Assoc.)

cordingly. Fig. 49 shows how braces may be arranged at a window.

When wood boards are installed diagonally the wall is stronger and corner bracing is not required. Two 8 *d* nails are used at each stud. Joints are arranged so that they do not fall on the same stud in succeeding rows. See Fig. 50. The direction of the sheathing should be reversed at corners.

Fiberboard is made of several dif-

ferent substances, such as sugar cane, corn stalks and wood pulp, which are processed and pressed into boards generally ½ or 25/32 inch thick. They are asphalt impregnated to make them water resistant. They are cut to 2 × 8, 4 × 8 or 4 × 9 foot panels. The 2 × 8 foot panels are V type, tongue and groove on the long edges and square cut on the short edges. They are installed in a horizontal position. See Fig. 51. Roofing

145

Fig. 51. Insulation board sheathing is easily installed. The long edges are tongue and groove. (Armstrong Cork Co.)

nails (1½ inch) are spaced 4 inches on center on studs for ½ inch sheathing. For 25/32 inch sheathing 1¾ inch nails are used. Walls sheathed with 4 × 8 or 4 × 9 foot 25/32 inch panels placed vertically do not require corner bracing under ordinary circumstances.

Gypsum board is similar to fiberboard except that it is made of two layers of water repellent paper with a core of gypsum reinforced with fiberglass. The common sizes are 2 × 8, 4 × 8 and 4 × 9 foot by ½ inch thick. The 4 foot wide panels do not need corner bracing. The nailing procedure is similar to that of fiberboard.

Neither fiberboard or gypsum board may be used as nailing base for siding. Nails must penetrate the sheathing into the studs unless some form of furring is used. Both of these types of sheathing are easily cut and installed, are relatively inexpensive, and have excellent weather resistant properties.

Plywood has proved to be the strongest sheathing. The thicknesses used are $\frac{5}{16}$, $\frac{3}{8}$, ½ or ⅝ inch and the size is usually 4 × 8 foot panels. Larger sizes are available. The sheets are applied vertically with 6 d nails for the $\frac{5}{16}$ and ⅜ inch thicknesses, and 8 d nails for the ½ and ⅝ inch thicknesses. The nails are spaced on

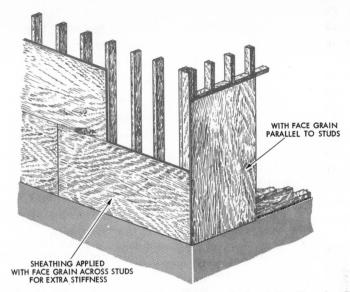

WITH FACE GRAIN
PARALLEL TO STUDS

SHEATHING APPLIED
WITH FACE GRAIN ACROSS STUDS
FOR EXTRA STIFFNESS

Fig. 52. Plywood sheathing may be applied vertically or horizontally. (Douglas Fir Plywood Assoc.)

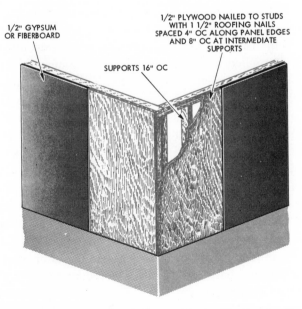

1/2" GYPSUM
OR FIBERBOARD

1/2" PLYWOOD NAILED TO STUDS
WITH 1 1/2" ROOFING NAILS
SPACED 4" OC ALONG PANEL EDGES
AND 8" OC AT INTERMEDIATE
SUPPORTS

SUPPORTS 16" OC

Fig. 53. Plywood and gypsum fiberboard are used in combination to eliminate the need for corner bracing. (American Plywood Assoc.)

6 inch centers on the edges of the sheet and on 12 inch centers on the two studs which fall inside of the sheet. No corner bracing is necessary. See Fig. 52. Plywood may be used in combination with fiberboard or gypsum board sheathing as shown in Fig. 53. The plywood serves to stiffen the corner thus making bracing unnecessary. In this case, fiberboard or gypsum board is used for the rest of the wall to save cost. Plywood is manufactured with one grooved surface so that one sheet may serve the purpose of sheathing and exterior wall finish at the same time. It will be discussed in Chapter VI, Exterior Finish.

Plaster Grounds

Although much of the interior wall finish is done using drywall, plastered walls are still used in many areas. Before lath is applied, strips of wood called grounds are nailed to the inside walls of buildings to serve as guides for the plasterer. Grounds insure a straight and true plaster surface against which the finished woodwork is nailed. In most cases the grounds should be placed so they will come near the edge of trim members where such members meet the plaster. Grounds vary depending on the kind of interior trim used for door jambs, baseboards, chair rails, wood cornice against the ceiling, special picture moldings, and wainscoting.

The thickness required for the grounds is determined by the combined thickness of the lath and plaster, which in common practice is $25/32$ of an inch. This thickness has been increased to $7/8$ of an inch in certain areas. The width of the grounds is usually 1 or 2 inches. Roughly speaking, grounds are made of 1×1 or 1×2 strips. Around inside door openings a 1×1 may be used. The strength of a 1×1 is sufficient here, because it has a solid backing. Where grounds are run across studs, as for base and waiscoting, 1×2s are commonly used. Occasionally even wider materials may be used to advantage to meet the needs of a particular situation. Window frames and outside rabbeted door frames are usually made wide enough to meet the lath and plaster requirements and, therefore, grounds are not always necessary for such openings.

The last of the rough interior work to be done is the placing of the grounds which are usually nailed on after the roof is finished, and all other tradesmen have completed roughing in their work. The location for the grounds must be determined carefully so they will be covered by the wood trim. This is especially important because of the work which must be done later, such as adding dadoes, wainscoting, chair rails, and baseboards. For the inside doors, the grounds are nailed against the studs next to the opening side, as shown in

Fig. 54. When frames are put in place before the plastering operation, the jambs may serve as grounds. The grounds around the doorway in Fig. 54 would then be omitted. For the base the best practice is to use a 1 × 2, nailed so that the bottom of the ground is slightly above the level of the finished floor.

In some parts of the country a flush type base is used. This is generally a piece of 1 × 4 tongue-and-groove. The plasterer finishes the wall down to the top of the piece. The groove serves as a key. The wood remains exposed as part of the trim.

Since the purpose of plaster grounds is to provide a guide for the plasterer to follow, it is essential that the carpenter exercise special care in placing the grounds, using a straightedge and a level, so that the position of the grounds will be absolutely correct and true. Any extra time consumed in setting the grounds accurately will be compensated for later when nailing on the trim. It will take much less time and patience to fit the trim to the plaster if the grounds are in the right place.

Grounds play an important role in masonry construction. Here they not only serve as a straightedge and guide for the plasterer to follow, but also provide a firm base on which trim members are nailed or otherwise

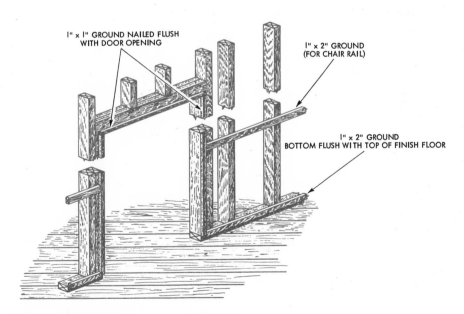

1" x 1" GROUND NAILED FLUSH WITH DOOR OPENING

1" x 2" GROUND (FOR CHAIR RAIL)

1" x 2" GROUND BOTTOM FLUSH WITH TOP OF FINISH FLOOR

Fig. 54. Grounds are fastened to rough members to provide a stop for the plaster and a nailing base for trim.

149

fastened. Grounds are not required on wood frame construction when walls are finished with materials other than plaster, such as drywall, plywood, or decorative fiberboard.

Stud Walls for Drywall Application

Manufacturers of gypsum products have expended great sums of money for research and experimentation to perfect drywall systems which would be practical and economical. Not only must the walls provide excellent surfaces for decorating but they must meet fire rating standards and also not exceed limits for sound transmission. As is true in all phases of building, a concept of good workmanship is a primary requisite and a certain amount of "know how" is essential for those

craftsmen who do the work. Partitions for drywall application and for plaster veneer ($\frac{1}{16}$ to $\frac{3}{32}$ inch thickness of plaster over gypsum board) may be made using conventional wood studs, metal studs, or several thicknesses of gypsum board in what is known as a solid partition. See Figs. 55, 56, and 57. Several methods of fastening may be used: coated nails, annular ring nails, drywall screws or a glued-nailed technique. See Fig. 58. (The manner of applying the wallboard, the finishing of joints and applying trim at openings and corners will be covered in Chapter VII, Interior Finish.)

Two considerations of utmost importance are fire rating and sound transmission. Fire ratings are established to comply with underwriter's tests. One layer of $\frac{5}{8}$ inch gypsum

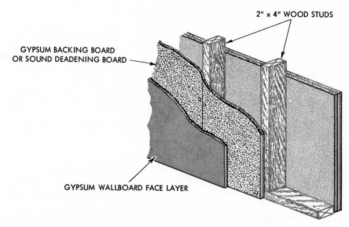

Fig. 55. Drywall is applied to a wood stud wall. (U. S. Gypsum Co.)

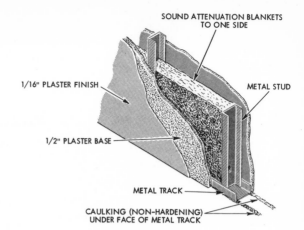

SOUND ATTENUATION BLANKETS TO ONE SIDE

1/16" PLASTER FINISH

METAL STUD

1/2" PLASTER BASE

METAL TRACK

CAULKING (NON-HARDENING) UNDER FACE OF METAL TRACK

Fig. 56. A metal stud wall serves for drywall or veneer plaster finish. (U.S. Gypsum Co.)

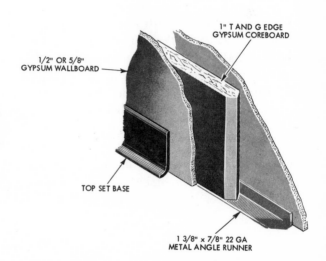

1" T AND G EDGE GYPSUM COREBOARD

1/2" OR 5/8" GYPSUM WALLBOARD

TOP SET BASE

1 3/8" x 7/8" 22 GA METAL ANGLE RUNNER

Fig. 57. Two inch solid gypsum drywall has a high fire resistance rating. (U. S. Gypsum Co.)

wallboard with fire resistant qualities on each side of a wood stud partition will provide a one hour fire rating. The fire resistance may be enhanced by using two layers on each side of the studs. Sound transmission is cut down by the manner in which the wall is built, by the use of insulation, and by using special devices to hang the gypsum board. Much of the sound is transmitted through the framing members and the wall covering itself. Resilient mountings permit the gypsum wall surface to "float", thus cutting down noise transmission.

1-1/4″ USG drywall screw—type W—bugle head

Fig. 58. Three types of nails are used to fasten drywall. (U. S. Gypsum Co.)

1-1/4″ GWB-54 annular ring nail

1-7/8″ 6d gypsum wallboard nail cement coated

Using Wood Studs with Drywall. Wood studs on 16 inch centers using conventional framing techniques form the usual base for drywall in residential construction. When the partitions are bearing partitions wood studs are used rather than steel studs. When it is important to lower sound transmission several expedients are used. (1) The inner layer of a two layer application may be made of sound deadening gypsum board. See Fig. 55. (2) An insulating wool blanket or batts may be installed in the stud space. See Fig. 56. (3) A staggered stud partition may be erected. See Fig. 59. (4) A double stud partition may be used. See Fig. 60. (5) Or resilient channels may be applied horizontally. See Fig. 61.

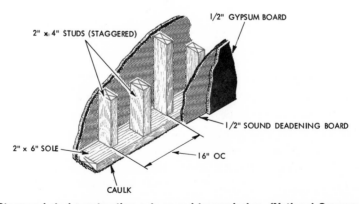

Fig. 59. Staggered stud construction cuts sound transmission. (National Gypsum Co.)

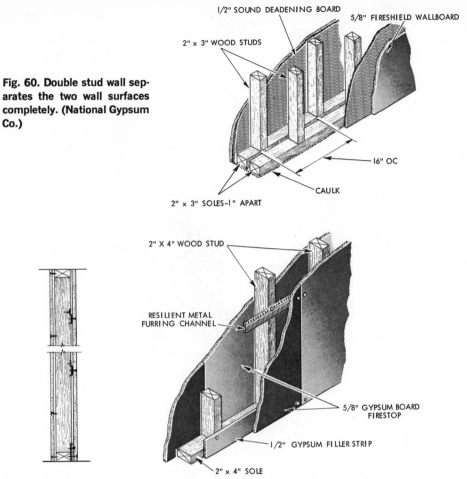

Fig. 60. Double stud wall separates the two wall surfaces completely. (National Gypsum Co.)

1/2" SOUND DEADENING BOARD

5/8" FIRESHIELD WALLBOARD

2" x 3" WOOD STUDS

16" OC

CAULK

2" x 3" SOLES-1" APART

2" X 4" WOOD STUD

RESILIENT METAL FURRING CHANNEL

5/8" GYPSUM BOARD FIRESTOP

1/2" GYPSUM FILLER STRIP

2" x 4" SOLE

Fig. 61. A resilient channel is fastened to the studs to permit the gypsum board to "float." (Georgia-Pacific Corp.)

Two or more of these methods are often used in combination to further decrease the noise level.

Using Metal Studs with Drywall. Metal studs have been developed to be used with ingenious devices for assembling the components, for fastening the members to the floor and ceiling, and for trimming around openings. Generally the partitions are non-load bearing and the studs are on 24 inch centers. A channel runner or track is fastened to the floor with nails, screws or powder

153

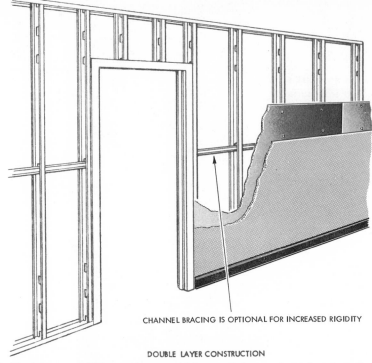

CHANNEL BRACING IS OPTIONAL FOR INCREASED RIGIDITY

DOUBLE LAYER CONSTRUCTION

Fig. 62A. Steel frame partition systems provide a satisfactory base for drywall. (National Gypsum Co.)

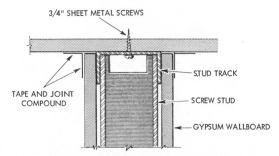

3/4" SHEET METAL SCREWS

STUD TRACK

TAPE AND JOINT COMPOUND

SCREW STUD

GYPSUM WALLBOARD

Fig. 62B. Joining to gypsum board ceiling. (National Gypsum Co.)

actuated fasteners. The studs, which are channels also, snap into place and are fastened to the floor track with a crimping tool or with screws. Another track is fastened to the ceiling to receive the upper end of the

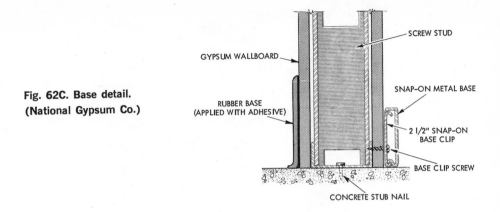

Fig. 62C. Base detail.
(National Gypsum Co.)

SCREW STUD

GYPSUM WALLBOARD

SNAP-ON METAL BASE

RUBBER BASE
(APPLIED WITH ADHESIVE)

2 1/2" SNAP-ON
BASE CLIP

BASE CLIP SCREW

CONCRETE STUB NAIL

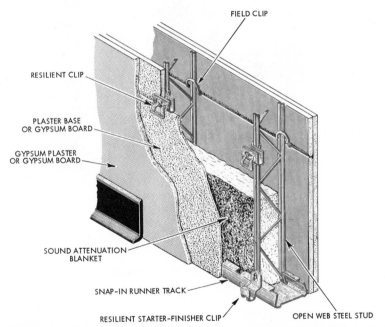

FIELD CLIP

RESILIENT CLIP

PLASTER BASE
OR GYPSUM BOARD

GYPSUM PLASTER
OR GYPSUM BOARD

SOUND ATTENUATION
BLANKET

SNAP-IN RUNNER TRACK

RESILIENT STARTER-FINISHER CLIP

OPEN WEB STEEL STUD

Fig. 63. Open web stud system uses clips to hold gypsum board. (U. S. Gypsum Co.)

studs. Holes or knockouts are provided 12 inches from the bottom and 12 inches from the top of the studs for conduit or piping. Some studs have other hole patterns. See Fig. 62. The details at doors and openings require the use of additional studs to frame the opening and jamb an-

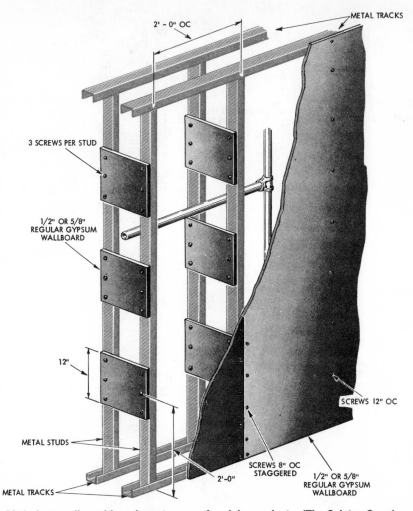

METAL TRACKS

2' - 0" OC

3 SCREWS PER STUD

1/2" OR 5/8"
REGULAR GYPSUM
WALLBOARD

12"

METAL STUDS

METAL TRACKS

2'-0"

SCREWS 8" OC
STAGGERED

SCREWS 12" OC

1/2" OR 5/8"
REGULAR GYPSUM
WALLBOARD

Fig. 64. A chase wall provides adequate space for piping or ducts. (The Celotex Corp.)

chors which tie the jambs securely to the studs. Open web steel studs provide greater flexibility for the passage of utilities. A base layer of ⅜ inch gypsum backer board is clipped in place to be followed by a second layer of ⅜ or ½ inch gypsum wall board. See Fig. 63.

When there is need for a thicker wall because of large diameter pipe a chase wall may be used. Two metal stud walls are erected and tied together at intervals with rectangular pieces of gypsum wall board fastened to the studs with screws. See Fig. 64.

Special Framing Problems

The building of a modern frame house involves the labor of many tradesmen other than carpenters. These tradesmen include plumbers, pipe fitters, sheet metal workers, electricians, tile setters, brick and stone masons, and others. The contractor for each trade is responsible only for his own work, but all trades-men must cooperate in every respect, since all of them share in the task of giving the owner the best house obtainable. With the proper co-operation on the part of all tradesmen, the completed house will conform to the specifications and agreements signed by the owner and contractors for the various trades represented.

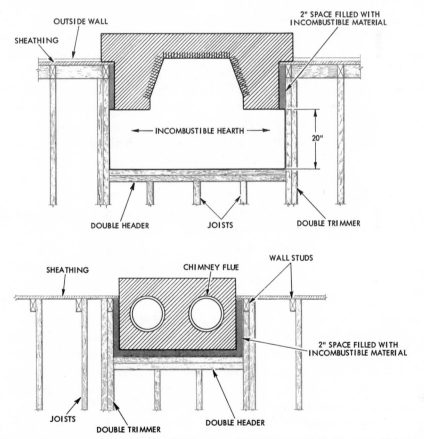

Fig. 65. A 2 inch open space is left in the framing of the floor around chimneys. This space is filled with incombustible material.

The carpenter is looked upon as the key man in construction since he provides the framework of the building into which other tradesmen must fit their work. The carpenter must have a working knowledge of the requirements of all other trades concerned with the erection of a modern house. The building must retain its structural strength, and be free from hazards common to frame and masonry buildings, after the tradesmen who install the pipes, heat ducts, electric wiring and fixtures and other special features have completed their work.

Fire Hazards. Many fires have started in the basement of a family residence and spread to the attic and roof before the occupants were aware of the danger. Such a catastrophe could be due to the neglect of the carpenter who failed to cut off drafts with fire stops at joist levels in the walls, as shown in Fig. 3 of this chapter. A fire could also result from the failure of the builder to pack incombustible material around pipes or heat ducts in wall spaces which connect with the basement. If left open at the top and bottom, the stud spaces in a frame wall are similar to the flues of chimneys. Such open spaces tend to create drafts in the walls, and are definite fire hazards.

The carpenter must know the size to which any brickwork will lay-up, in order to frame around chimneys and fireplaces so that a 2 inch open

space will be left between the framework and the masonry, as shown in Fig. 65. This 2 inch space must be packed with incombustible material to prevent the spread of fire if the flue or masonry become faulty. Cracks may develop in chimneys when the building settles. Any combustible materials or open space near such cracks constitute potential fire hazards.

Plumbing Pipes. The proper framing of walls for installing plumbing pipes and making provision for heating ducts presents the carpenter with two of his most difficult framing problems. The installing of pipe and heating ducts often require an unobstructed wall space extending from the basement to the second floor, and perhaps to the attic.

The soil stack, with a hub that measures about $6\frac{1}{4}$ inches, requires a wall with studs larger than 2 × 4 inch and free of plates or horizontal blocking, as shown in Fig. 66. In making provision for soil stacks, the wall must be designed so that any necessary cutting of the studs will not weaken the structure. Here 2 × 6 studs with 1 × 2s added, or 2 × 8 studs will be necessary. Then, too, in bathrooms or lavatories, the walls against which plumbing fixtures are set or fastened should have studs of no less than 2 × 6 in order to leave sufficient strength in the studs after the plumber has installed the 2 inch pipes for reventing the traps on the

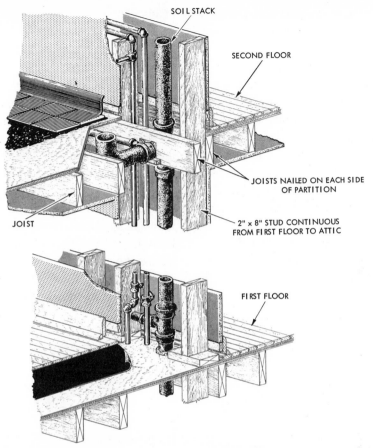

SOIL STACK

SECOND FLOOR

JOISTS NAILED ON EACH SIDE
OF PARTITION

JOIST

2" x 8" STUD CONTINUOUS
FROM FIRST FLOOR TO ATTIC

FIRST FLOOR

Fig. 66. A thicker wall is required for a plumbing partition. Joists at wall may be cut for soil pipe. Other joists must follow close restrictions regarding holes and notches.

fixtures. If the toilet is placed against the stack wall, the minimum joist clearance from the stack wall must be 16 inches. If the toilet is away from the stack wall the joist should be fitted with headers, or trimmers, which will not require cutting when installing the soil pipes. (Great care must be used in cutting holes or notches in joists. When holes are cut they should not exceed 2½ inches in diameter and a minimum of 2 inches from the top or bottom edges of the joist. When the top and bottom portions are cut the joist is weakened considerably. Joists should not be notched in the center one half of the span. Notches shall not exceed ⅙th of the depth of the joist.) The rough flooring in bathrooms should also be

159

cut at the wall line and nailed lightly so that it can be taken up easily and relaid by the plumber.

Heating Ducts. The sheetmetal worker will call on the carpenter to provide openings in the floors and walls for heating ducts. He should be provided with a heating duct layout showing the size and location of registers, ducts, and other equipment before he begins the framework. The layout will enable him to make holes in floors for such work as he proceeds with the framing of the house.

Where heat stacks run continuously from one floor to the next, it becomes necessary to line up the studs of the walls for the two floors so as to accommodate them. In the basement ample space must be left between the floor under partition walls and the beams or girders. This is especially important, since there must be room enough so pipe connections can be made with wall stacks. When registers in the walls fail to come within stud spaces, the studs must be cut and headers and cripple studs nailed in position. In many cases heat stacks in walls are brought up to the next floor level, where they are run horizontally to a new position in a second-story partition wall; in such cases the floor joist

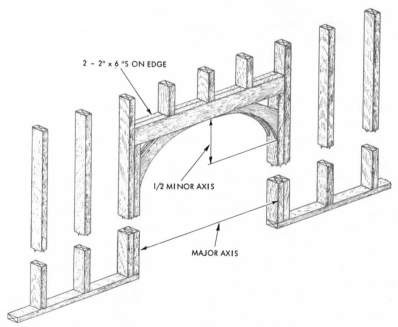

Fig. 67. Arches are formed by several pieces cut to the proper shape.

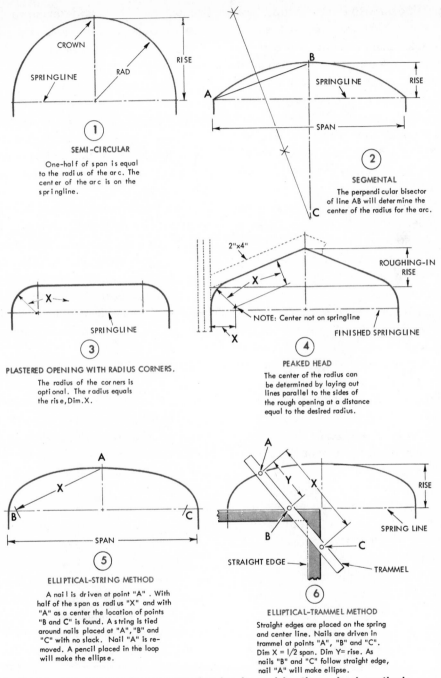

1

SEMI-CIRCULAR

One-half of span is equal to the radius of the arc. The center of the arc is on the springline.

2

SEGMENTAL

The perpendicular bisector of line AB will determine the center of the radius for the arc.

3

PLASTERED OPENING WITH RADIUS CORNERS.

The radius of the corners is optional. The radius equals the rise, Dim. X.

4

PEAKED HEAD

The center of the radius can be determined by laying out lines parallel to the sides of the rough opening at a distance equal to the desired radius.

5

ELLIPTICAL-STRING METHOD

A nail is driven at point "A". With half of the span as radius "X" and with "A" as a center the location of points "B and C" is found. A string is tied around nails placed at "A", "B" and "C" with no slack. Nail "A" is removed. A pencil placed in the loop will make the ellipse.

6

ELLIPTICAL-TRAMMEL METHOD

Straight edges are placed on the spring and center line. Nails are driven in trammel at points "A", "B" and "C". Dim X = 1/2 span. Dim Y= rise. As nails "B" and "C" follow straight edge, nail "A" will make ellipse.

Fig. 68. The carpenter can lay out several arches by applying these simple methods.

must line up with the wall studs. The foregoing instances are just a few examples showing how the carpenter can save himself a great deal of work and time later by planning the framework of a house so as to accommodate the heating ductwork.

Elliptical and Circular Arches. Plastered arches must have a rough frame, which follows the exact shape of the finished opening, and to which the lath and corner bead can be fastened by the lathers. Since it is not economical to cut the top of this rough frame out of one wide piece of lumber, it is usually made of four pieces of lumber either 1 inch or 2 inches thick. These four pieces are then nailed flush with the face of the studs, as shown in Fig. 67. The semicircular arch can be laid out rather simply by the use of a set of trammel points, or with a stick having a lead pencil attached to one end and a nail in the other end to serve as a center. Another simple method of laying out an ellipse or semicircular arch is by the use of a piece of inelastic string and a pencil. Several arches are shown in Fig. 68. The layout can be made on a wide board or a large piece of paper. After the shape is determined, it can be transferred to one or more boards which will form arch.

Plank and Beam Framing

Modern design trends have been toward the use of large areas which are open to each other with few partitions, the use of wide expanse of glass on outside walls, and the use of wood as a finish material for walls and ceilings. Plank and beam framing is admirably adapted to provide these effects. See Fig. 69. Posts are set at regular intervals to support roof beams and the ridge beam. These members are usually large dimension timbers or laminated members such as 3 × 8, 4 × 8, 4 × 10, etc. The roof beams support 2 inch decking. The floor may be made in 2 inch planking supported by floor beams. This structural system is dependent on the 2 inch planking serving a structural function. The spacing between beams may be 6 feet, 8 feet, or greater depending on the load requirements. See Fig. 5.

Houses which use this framing method must be carefully designed, because there are limitations caused by the regular intervals at which the posts are located. Partitions and openings must fall into this pattern. The carpentry work must be done with great care, because the fitting of every member in the walls and roof is exposed to view from inside the house.

Two adaptations of material have been developed for particular use in plank and beam framing. They are laminated decking and laminated beams. Laminated decking is made up of several pieces of plank which are glued together with an electronic gluing process which joins

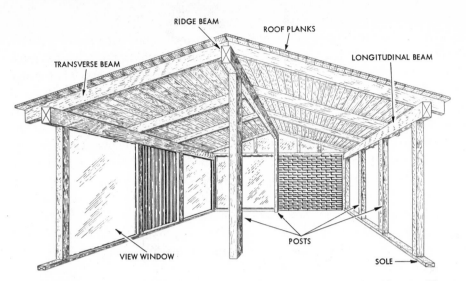

Fig. 69. Plank and beam framing requires careful placement of posts and beams. The roof planks must be strong enough to span the distance between beams.

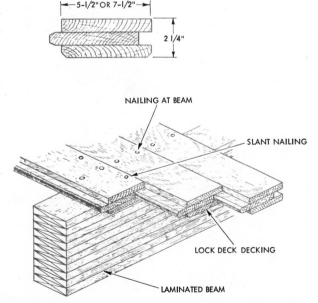

Fig. 70. Laminated decking and beams permit spanning wide spaces between supports. (Potlatch Forests, Inc.)

the pieces with great strength. The decking comes in 5½ or 7½ inch widths and 2¼, 2⅝ inch, or greater thicknesses. It is provided in lengths from six to sixteen feet long (at one foot intervals) and is end matched. See Fig. 70.

Laminated beams and trusses have been used for many years in heavy construction but are usually made to order for specific jobs. However, laminated beams are now available in a number of sizes for use in light construction. They are made up of a number of planks glued to-gether to make up the desired dimensions. Laminated members have structural qualities which far surpass those of solid members. They range in size from approximately 3 × 3 inches to approximately 11 × 21 inches. The moisture content of the laminating lumber is carefully controlled so that the members resist shrinkage when put to use. The material is selected so that it has an excellent appearance. Posts ranging from approximately 3 × 3 to 5 × 8 inches are made in the same way. See Fig. 71.

Fig. 71. Laminated beams, decking and posts provide great strength. (Potlatch Forests, Inc.)

Wood Framing for a Masonry Building

The use of wood members for the internal structure of a masonry building is fundamentally the same as for a frame building. However, when a brick house or one using other masonry units is built, an element of timing is added, because the carpenter must be ready to set joists, lay rough flooring, and set window and door frames when the walls rise to the proper height.

Joists are installed resting on the masonry and on a steel beam or wood girder in the same manner as in a frame building. The ends of the joists are cut on an angle for what is called a fire cut. See Fig. 72. In the case of a very severe fire, the joists would burn through or fail, and would fall into the building without destroying the wall. If they were not provided with a fire cut, the upper corner of the joist would act as a lever forcing the wall to fall outward, endangering the lives of anyone in the vicinity. Anchors are provided on every fourth joist. These are metal straps which should be fastened a little above the bottom of the joist so that in case of fire they will do as little damage as possible as they pull out of the wall. A short bar passes through the anchor and is embedded in the wall.

The matter of shrinkage in lumber is always a primary concern of the carpenter. It is particularly impor-tant here, because the masonry wall, once the mortar has set, is subject to practically no shrinkage. On the other hand, the structure at the center of the building, where bearing partitions are placed, may vary enough to create plaster cracks and open up joints in trim members. Fig. 73 shows a typical sectional view of ordinary brick construction. The first floor joist rests on a row of brick on a 12 inch wall and on the I beam. The rough floor is laid as soon as the joists are in position in order to provide a platform to work on. When the masonry reaches the height for the installation of second floor joists, bearing partitions are made and put in place in the same manner as de-scribed for the HOUSE PLAN A. Joists are then put in place resting on the masonry and the double plate of the bearing partition. (*Note:* shrinkage in lumber is mainly across the grain —in other words, across the width of a board. Lumber shrinks very little in length.) If shrinkage in each floor

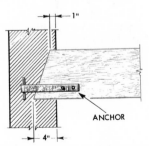

Fig. 72. The fire cut on joists permits the joists to fall without destroying the wall.

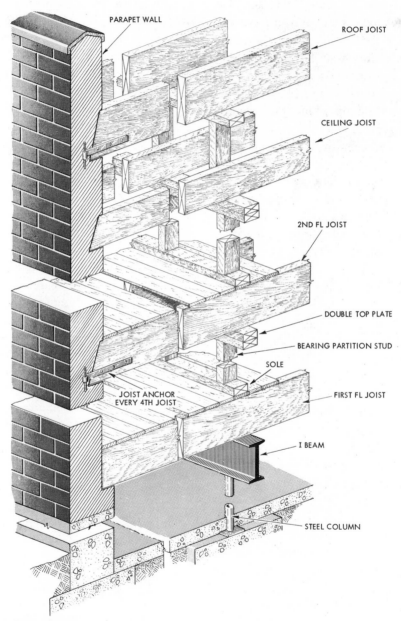

PARAPET WALL

ROOF JOIST

CEILING JOIST

2ND FL JOIST

DOUBLE TOP PLATE

BEARING PARTITION STUD

SOLE

JOIST ANCHOR
EVERY 4TH JOIST

FIRST FL JOIST

I BEAM

STEEL COLUMN

Fig. 73. Typical ordinary construction for a masonry building consists of wood joists and wood bearing partitions.

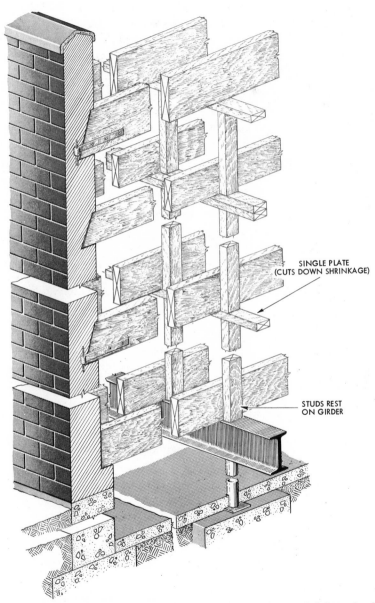

SINGLE PLATE
(CUTS DOWN SHRINKAGE)

STUDS REST
ON GIRDER

Fig. 74. Ordinary construction can be built so as to minimize shrinkage by having the studs go down to the beam or plate.

joist were ⅜ of an inch, the second floor would be ¾ of an inch lower at the bearing partition than at the outside wall, because the shrinkage of the first floor joist must be added to that of the second floor joist. Shrinkage will not be noticed until some time after the building is completed.

An idea which is related to the balloon framing principle in a frame house may be used to minimize shrinkage. See Fig. 74. It would be impractical to extend studs from the I beam to the top of the second floor and to support joists on ribbons. See Fig. 3. However, shrinkage can be cut greatly if the studs extend to the girder and then to a plate at each floor level, which serves a function similar to that of a ribbon. The rough flooring at the location of the bearing partition must be laid so that it can be removed when the partition is to be installed.

The ceiling joists at the roof are

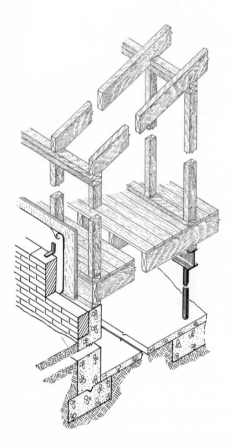

Fig. 75. A brick veneer house can use platform (western) framing.

generally of smaller dimension than those of the floors because their main function is to carry the weight of the ceiling and attic insulation. Short struts rise from the bearing wall plate to support the roof joists. These struts vary in length to provide a slope to the roof for drainage.

Wood Framing for a Masonry Veneer Building

Masonry veneer construction does not present any great problem for the carpenter who knows good con-

struction. Basically, a veneered house is a frame house with a skin of brick or stone. A few problems which should be given careful consideration involve the shrinkage of lumber, tying the masonry wall to the frame wall, and providing for the control of condensation within the wall.

The foundation is usually made with a top wide enough to support the sill of the wood framework, and a shelf to support the brick wall. Platform (western) framing may be used for single story houses. See

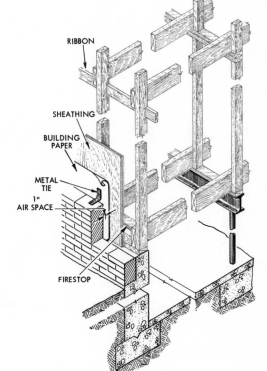

Fig. 76. Shrinkage will be less on a brick veneer house if balloon framing is used.

RIBBON

SHEATHING

BUILDING PAPER

METAL TIE

1" AIR SPACE

FIRESTOP

Fig. 75. Balloon framing is preferred, however, because the shrinkage in the wood wall is kept to a minimum with this construction. See Fig. 76. A ¾ inch or 1 inch space is provided between the wood wall and the masonry wall, and corrugated galvanized ties are placed in the mortar joists and fastened to the wall to tie or anchor the parts together. They are made so as to permit a slight amount of vertical adjustment when the lumber shrinks. F.H.A. requires that the ties be placed so that the brick wall is anchored to studs. Suggested tie spacings are given in Table I.

The space between the walls provides a means for ventilating the wall in order to prevent the accumulation of moisture. Sheathing paper and flashing protect the wood and weep holes permit the condensed moisture to escape. See Fig. 77.

Table I Tie Spacings

HORIZONTAL	VERTICAL (3" BRICK)	VERTICAL (OTHER)
32" O.C.	12" O.C.	16" O.C.
24" O.C.	16" O.C.	20" O.C.
16" O.C.	24" O.C.	24" O.C.

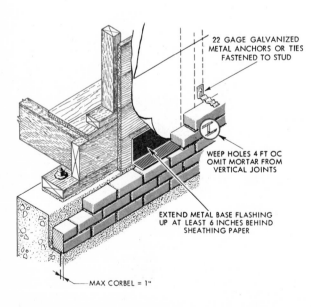

22 GAGE GALVANIZED METAL ANCHORS OR TIES FASTENED TO STUD

WEEP HOLES 4 FT OC OMIT MORTAR FROM VERTICAL JOINTS

EXTEND METAL BASE FLASHING UP AT LEAST 6 INCHES BEHIND SHEATHING PAPER

MAX CORBEL = 1"

Fig. 77. Special precautions must be used in a brick veneer wall to provide for condensation.

Scaffold Building

As the construction work of the building rises above the reach of workmen standing on the ground, scaffolds must be built. Although they are only temporary structures, they must be designed to carry the load of men, material, and tools and to provide maximum safety. Several types of scaffolds may be used, depending on the job at hand. It is essential that the carpenters who erect scaffolding be familiar with the requirements of the safety codes or statutes of his own state as well as the national standards. The *USA Standard Safety Code for Building Construction* gives detailed requirements for the materials to be used, and the manner of erection of scaffolds.

Metal Scaffolds

Metal scaffolds have been adopted by many contractors because they are portable and are easily and quickly assembled. The type usually used for low heights is made up of prefabricated frames and cross braces, see Fig. 78. A factor of safety of not less than four times the load is required. Care must be used in the erection of the scaffold so that it

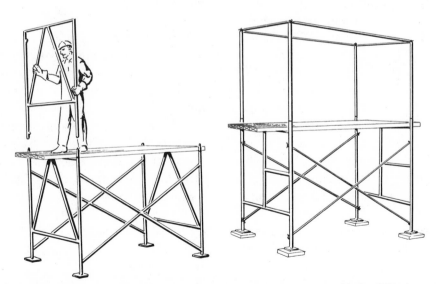

Fig. 78. Prefabricated metal frames and diagonal braces are assembled quickly to provide safe scaffolds.

171

rests on a firm base and is kept plumb and level as it is assembled. It must be inspected daily. Care must be taken to keep the frames from injury or from rusting so that they do not lose part of their design strength. Safety rules for metal scaffolding, recommended by the Steel Scaffolding and Shoring Institute, are shown in Data Sheet I, page 173.

Wood Scaffolds

Scaffolds are generally classified as *light trade pole scaffolds*, used by carpenters, painters, sheet metal workers and others; and *heavy trade scaffolds*, used by craftsmen who require the use of heavy loads or material, such as brick and masonry units which must be stored on the scaffold. Light trade scaffolds must be designed to carry a working load of 25 pounds per square foot, whereas heavy trade scaffolds must be designed to carry a working load of 75 pounds per square foot. The construction requirements are generally the same for both types except that the members used in a heavy trade scaffold must be of greater dimensions. Special rules apply when the scaffolding is over 24 feet in height (32 feet in some states).

Sometimes there is an advantage in having a scaffold stand on one set of poles or uprights with the other end of the bearers securely fastened to a block which in turn is fastened to the frame structure. If the wall is of brick the bearers are securely wedged into place where bricks have been left out for this purpose. This type is called a single pole scaffold. See Fig. 79. A double pole scaffold is built with double uprights and is free standing except that it is anchored to the wall. See Fig. 80. (Fig. 80 corresponds to Plate B-18, Data Sheet II.) Data Sheet II, page 174, illustrates the requirements of a particular state code for double pole scaffolds. It is chosen because it is typical of state code requirements. It is important that the carpenter be familiar with the code requirements of *his own* state. (See page 177 for further information.)

Carpenter's Bracket Scaffolds

Bracket scaffolds are easy to erect and are useful for light work in certain places. Metal brackets are generally used. They must be anchored through the wall with a bolt at least $5/8$ inch in diameter. See Fig. 81.

Some of the requirements stated in the *USA Standard Safety Code for Building Construction* follow:[1]

10.4 In erecting a bracket, a two by six (2×6) inch block shall be laid horizontally across the inside of two

---

1. Extracted from *USA Standard Safety Code for Building Construction,* A10.2-1944, Part 9, Section 10, with the permission of the publisher, The United States of America Standards Institute, 10 East 40th Street, New York, New York 10016.

DATA SHEET I

STEEL SCAFFOLDING SAFETY RULES

as Recommended by

STEEL SCAFFOLDING AND SHORING INSTITUTE

(SEE SEPARATE SHORING SAFETY RULES)

Following are some common sense rules designed to promote safety in the use of steel scaffolding. These rules are illustrative and suggestive only, and are intended to deal only with some of the many practices and conditions encountered in the use of scaffolding. The rules do not purport to be all-inclusive or to supplant or replace other additional safety and precautionary measures to cover usual or unusual conditions.

I. **POST THESE SCAFFOLDING SAFETY RULES** in a conspicuous place and be sure that all persons who erect, dismantle or use scaffolding are aware of them.

II. **FOLLOW LOCAL CODES, ORDINANCES** and regulations pertaining to scaffolding.

III. **INSPECT ALL EQUIPMENT BEFORE USING** — Never use any equipment that is damaged or deteriorated in any way.

IV. **KEEP ALL EQUIPMENT IN GOOD REPAIR.** Avoid using rusted equipment — the strength of rusted equipment is not known.

V. **INSPECT ERECTED SCAFFOLDS REGULARLY** to be sure that they are maintained in safe condition.

VI. **CONSULT YOUR SCAFFOLDING SUPPLIER WHEN IN DOUBT**—scaffolding is his business, **NEVER TAKE CHANCES.**

A. **PROVIDE ADEQUATE SILLS** for scaffold posts and use base plates.

B. **USE ADJUSTING SCREWS** instead of blocking to adjust to uneven grade conditions.

C. **PLUMB AND LEVEL ALL SCAFFOLDS** as the erection proceeds. Do not force braces to fit — level the scaffold until proper fit can be made easily.

D. **FASTEN ALL BRACES SECURELY.**

E. **DO NOT CLIMB CROSS BRACES.**

F. **ON WALL SCAFFOLDS PLACE AND MAINTAIN ANCHORS** securely between structure and scaffold at least every 30′ of length and 25′ of height.

G. **FREE STANDING SCAFFOLD TOWERS MUST BE RESTRAINED FROM TIPPING** by guying or other means.

H. **EQUIP ALL PLANKED OR STAGED AREAS** with proper guard rails, and add toeboards when required.

I. **POWER LINES NEAR SCAFFOLDS** are dangerous—use caution and consult the power service company for advice.

J. **DO NOT USE** ladders or makeshift devices on top of scaffolds to increase the height.

K. **DO NOT OVERLOAD SCAFFOLDS.**

L. **PLANKING:**

1. Use only lumber that is properly inspected and graded as scaffold plank.

2. Planking shall have at least 12″ of overlap and extend 6″ beyond center of support, or be cleated at both ends to prevent sliding off supports.

3. Do not allow unsupported ends of plank to extend an unsafe distance beyond supports.

4. Secure plank to scaffold when necessary.

M. **FOR ROLLING SCAFFOLD THE FOLLOWING ADDITIONAL RULES APPLY:**

1. **DO NOT RIDE ROLLING SCAFFOLDS.**

2. **REMOVE ALL MATERIAL AND EQUIPMENT** from platform before moving scaffold.

3. **CASTER BRAKES MUST BE APPLIED** at all times when scaffolds are not being moved.

4. **DO NOT ATTEMPT TO MOVE A ROLLING SCAFFOLD WITHOUT SUFFICIENT HELP** — watch out for holes in floor and overhead obstructions.

5. **DO NOT EXTEND ADJUSTING SCREWS ON ROLLING SCAFFOLDS MORE THAN 12″.**

6. **USE HORIZONTAL DIAGONAL BRACING** near the bottom, top and at intermediate levels of 30′.

7. **DO NOT USE BRACKETS ON ROLLING SCAFFOLDS** without consideration of overturning effect.

8. **THE WORKING PLATFORM HEIGHT OF A ROLLING SCAFFOLD** must not exceed four times the smallest base dimension unless guyed or otherwise stabilized.

N. For **"PUTLOGS"** and **"TRUSSES"** the following additional rules apply:

1. **DO NOT CANTILEVER OR EXTEND PUTLOGS/TRUSSES** as side brackets without thorough consideration for loads to be applied.

2. **PUTLOGS/TRUSSES SHOULD EXTEND AT LEAST 6″** beyond point of support.

3. **PLACE PROPER BRACING BETWEEN PUTLOGS/TRUSSES** when the span of putlog/truss is more than 12′.

DATA SHEET II

State of California Department of Industrial Relations *Construction Safety Orders* effective Aug. 8, 1965. Article 22 — Scaffolds — Various Types, Section 1640. [Plate B-18. Appendix: See Fig. 80, page 176.]

1640. Light-Trade Pole Scaffolds Built of Lumber. (See Plate B-18, Appendix.) Pole scaffolds to be used by carpenters, lathers, shinglers, painters, plasterers, sheet metal workers, or other trades not using heavy tools or storing heavy materials on the scaffold, shall be constructed as follows:

(a) **Uprights.** For heights not to exceed 32 feet, the uprights shall be 2-inch by 4-inch lumber or heavier, spaced about 3 feet between uprights at right angles to the wall and not more than 10 feet center to center, parallel to the walls. Scaffolds may be wider than 3 feet if the platform is wider, but the horizontal distance between the outer edge of the platform and the guardrailing shall not exceed 8 inches unless the guardrail is improved by the addition of a midrail, in which case the distance may be as much as 16 inches. The inside uprights may be omitted and ledgers attached to the permanent structure, provided that the method of attaching the ledgers to the permanent structure will make the connection as secure as though the ledger were nailed to the upright with 5 8-penny nails. (A suggested method is to spike a 24-inch piece of 2-inch by 4-inch material to the stud with 5 16-penny nails and properly nail the ledgers to the sides of these blocks.) The splices of uprights shall be made with square butt joints, and scabs of 1-inch by 4-inch or heavier material at least 30 inches long shall be nailed on 2 sides of each upright with 6 nails in each ½ of each scab. If the uprights of the scaffold rest on a surface that might cause slipping, a continuous sill or other means shall be provided to hold the uprights in place. When placed on the ground, the uprights shall be secured to sills adequate to sustain the load.

(b) **Ledgers and Ribbons.** The platforms of the scaffold shall be supported by ledgers. For ledgers spanning not more than 3 feet 6 inches between uprights, use either 1 piece of 1-inch by 8-inch board or 2 pieces of 1-inch by 6-inch board, 1 being on each side of the uprights and fastened securely at each point of support. Single 2-inch by 4-inch ledgers are not permitted. Vertical spacing of ribbons and ledgers shall not exceed 7 feet 6 inches. The ribbons shall be 1-inch by 6-inch or heavier material, placed on the outer uprights, directly under, and in contact with, the ledgers.

(c) **Ties and Braces.** The scaffold shall be securely tied to the building by means of double-wrapped No. 12 iron wire or equivalent or 1-inch by 6-inch boards with at least 2 nails at each connection. Ties shall connect to the inside uprights and shall not be more than 20 feet apart horizontally and vertically.

(d) **Railing.** Open sides and ends of working levels 7½ feet or more above grade shall be guarded by 1-inch by 6-inch or a 2-inch by 4-inch railing nailed to the uprights so that the top edge is between 42 inches and 45 inches above the platform. Midrails are required under certain circumstances. See following item on platforms.

(e) **Platforms.** (1) Platform planks shall be of 2-inch by 10-inch or larger material and of such length that they overlap the ledgers at each end by at least 6 inches. A plank shall not overlap an unsupported end of another plank. The working platform shall cover the entire space between scaffold uprights, except for the open area under the backrailing, which shall not be more than 8 inches wide, unless the railing is improved by the addition of a 1-inch by 6-inch or equivalent midrail, in which case the open space may be as much as 16 inches wide. Platforms shall be at least 20 inches wide and within 14 inches of the structure wall. A single 2-inch by 10-inch plank may be used for light-trades work up to a height of 4 feet.

(2) Working platforms for light-trades work may be made of ¾-inch Douglas fir plywood instead of 2-inch plank if the platform is at least 2 feet wide, nailed in place and supported on cross members at 4-foot or closer intervals along its length.

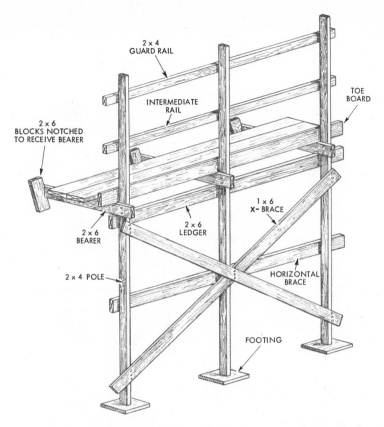

Fig. 79. A single pole scaffold must be securely fastened to the wall and adequately braced. (Terminology is taken from the "American Standard Safety Code for Building Construction.")

(2) studs, with the bolt passing through the block and screwed up tight.

10.7 The brackets shall be of sufficient strength to carry a load of four hundred (400) pounds located at the extreme outer end of the bracket.

10.9 The platform shall be formed of plank, not less than two (2) inches thick, laid tight together, and not less than two (2) planks wide, the

ends overlapping the bracket not less than six (6) inches nor more than twelve (12) inches, and the bracket shall be spaced not more than twelve (12) feet apart.

10.11 When bracket scaffolds are used at heights exceeding twelve (12) feet, guardrails shall be installed, formed by spiking vertical uprights to the horizontal members, and braced back by spiking a brace

175

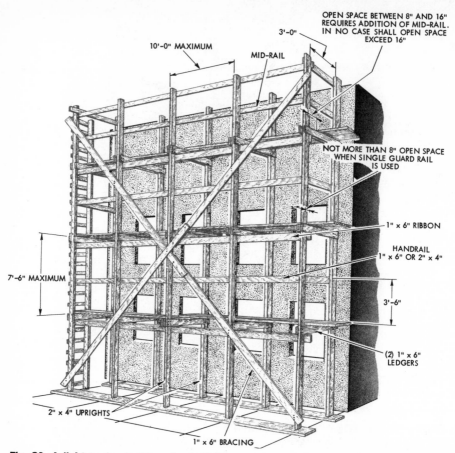

OPEN SPACE BETWEEN 8" AND 16"
REQUIRES ADDITION OF MID-RAIL.
IN NO CASE SHALL OPEN SPACE
EXCEED 16"

10'-0" MAXIMUM

3'-0"

MID-RAIL

NOT MORE THAN 8" OPEN SPACE
WHEN SINGLE GUARD RAIL
IS USED

1" x 6" RIBBON

HANDRAIL
1" x 6" OR 2" x 4"

7'-6" MAXIMUM

3'-6"

(2) 1" x 6"
LEDGERS

2" x 4" UPRIGHTS

1" x 6" BRACING

Fig. 80. A light trade, double pole scaffold must meet state code requirements. (State of California, "Construction Safety Orders.")

Fig. 81. Brackets provide economical and safe supports for scaffold planks. Planks are cut away to show bracket.

to the side of the uprights and the bracket, and a guardrail spiked along the top of the uprights.

Information on Scaffolding. The following sources will provide further information on scaffolding.

USA Standard Safety Code for Building Construction A10.2 - 1944
The United States of America Standards Institute
10 East 40th Street
New York, New York 10016

Specific safety requirements related to building and construction work: Department of Industrial Relations in each state.

National Safety Council
425 North Michigan Avenue
Chicago, Illinois 60611

Handbook of Rigging in Construction and Industrial Operations, by W. E. Rossnagel.
McGraw-Hill Book Co., Inc.
330 West 42nd Street
New York, New York 10036

Modular Planning

The general trend in building today is toward pre-built panels which are made either on the site or elsewhere and which are assembled to make the walls and partitions of the house. A whole new concept of planning buildings and manufacturing materials to fit the needs of modular design was necessary to make the idea possible. It was necessary first of all to decide on a common unit of measure which is called a module. As far back as 1938, the American Institute of Architects and the Producers Council sponsored a project to be carried out by the American Standards Association called "Coordination of Building Materials and

Equipment." A number of other organizations have participated in promoting the idea through the years. The primary aim is to bring about cooperation between architects, builders, and manufacturers so that plans are worked out on modular principles, and materials are manufactured to meet the size requirements.

This idea is based on the use of a standard grid which is divided into 4 inch squares.[2] The grid is three dimensional so that the module—the unit of measurement—is actually a 4 inch cube. See Fig. 82. All dimensions are based on multiples of 4; for example, 16" × 32" × 8'-0".

---

2. The HOUSE PLAN B lends itself to modular planning (see Fig. 82). Notice the 4 foot grid lines on the plan. In making a set of working drawings for this house, a grid using 4 inch as well as 4 foot modules would be used.

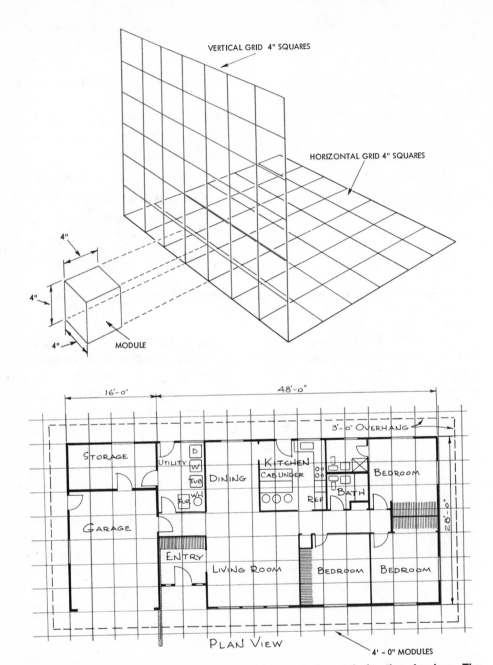

Fig. 82. A grid using 4-inch squares is used to lay out plan and elevation drawings. The module itself is a 4-inch cube. A preliminary plan is laid out on 4-foot modules, as shown by the plan view of the HOUSE PLAN B.

The first step in achieving modular coordination is accomplished by the architect. He lays out his plan over a sheet which is divided into squares representing 4 inch units (modules).

Modular coordination, however, still could not be attained unless the manufacturer produced materials of appropriate dimensions. Lumber, sheathing, panels, windows, doors, etc., are produced by many manufacturers to be adaptable to modular construction. Bricks, concrete blocks, and other masonry materials, however, must be made to allow room for the bonding material.

The modular idea, when applied to the construction of building components, uses multiples of 16, 24 and 48 inches wherever possible. These are all multiples of the 4 inch module. Modular layout demands careful work on the part of the designer of the building in order that the elements may fit properly within the grid and be in correct relation to the adjoining building elements.

Experiments In Framing

Builders, manufacturers and associations representing trade groups are continually experimenting to find new ways to build substantial houses at a lower cost. Some of their discoveries have been accepted quickly. However, many of the new ideas have been accepted slowly because the men in the building business have been reluctant to depart from present ways of doing things until they are convinced that other ways are better.

Among the most far-reaching experiments were those begun in 1953 by the Lumber Dealers Research Council (LuReCo) working with the University of Illinois. A whole new concept of building a small home was developed. Wall panels and other building parts were assembled and put through a series of rigorous structural tests. They were designed on a modular scale and made to fit together quickly. Wherever standard modular door and window frames were available they were used for the openings in wall and partition panels. See Fig. 83. Panels were used in floor construction, and lightweight wood beams which could be installed by carpenters were designed using 2 × 4 members and plywood. Light weight built-up headers were designed. Another feature was the development of light weight trusses to support the roof sheathing and the ceiling finish. The use of trusses simplified the roof framing problem greatly and also eliminated the need for bearing partitions. (Trusses will be discussed in Chapter V.)

Fig. 83. Windows and doors are made using modular dimensions. Platform framing permits the assembly of walls in a horizontal position. (Douglas Fir Plywood Assoc.)

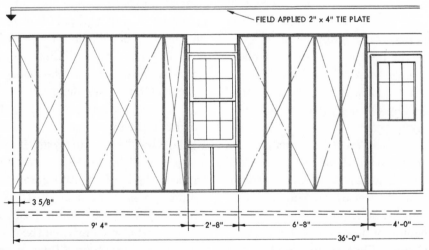

Fig. 84. "Unicom" panels are made in units which are multiples of 16 and 24 inches in width. (Professional Builder)

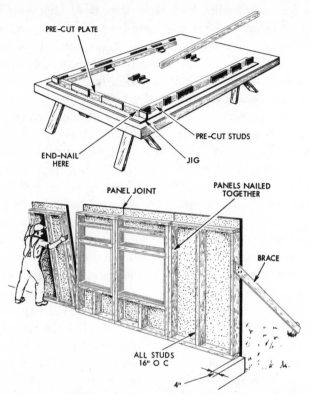

PRE-CUT PLATE

END-NAIL HERE

PRE-CUT STUDS

JIG

PANEL JOINT

PANELS NAILED TOGETHER

BRACE

ALL STUDS 16" O C

4"

Fig. 85. A jig bench is used to hold the pieces of a panel in position until they are nailed. Panels are made so that they may be handled and fastened in place with ease.

Another new construction system was introduced by the National Lumber Manufacturers Association (now called the National Forest Products Association) in 1962, called the *Unicom Method of House Construction* (Uniform Component). This system is a refinement of the modular concept of planning adapted for all types of homes and meets practically every problem a carpenter faces with the use of panels. Panels may vary in width but should be made in multiples of 16 and 24 inches if possible. See Fig. 84. They are made on the job site by some builders, although they can be made in a shop more economically. Jigs may be used to hold the framing members in place until they are nailed fast. Much labor is saved by precutting similar members such as studs and plates before assembly begins. See Fig. 85. Builders who are doing the construction work in large developments, where there are many

181

houses that are somewhat alike, find that they save on labor and materials costs when they use components. Others who build on a smaller scale find the savings negligible.

Wall Panels and Other Components. With Unicom system, exterior wall panels are made in multiples of 16 or 24 inches in width and 8 feet 1½ inches in height, which includes the sole at the bottom and the two plates at the top, the second of which extends over several panels. The corners are made so that the module line is also the line of the face of studs. See Fig. 86. Lintels over openings are made of doubled 2 × 4, 2 × 6 or 2 × 8 members on edge. The size is dependent on the width of the opening. Windows are limited to those which fit into the modular scale. Glass heights of 24, 36, 48, and 60 inches are generally used. The window frame is chosen so that it fits between the outside studs of the panel, and yet the outside dimensions of the panel remain multiples of 16 inches. See Fig. 84.

Box beams were designed in the LuReCo studies and used effectively to support floors made of 4 × 8 foot plywood panels. The box beams used 2 × 4 inch members and stiffeners with ¾ inch plywood webs glued and nailed on each side. An experiment, such as shown in Fig. 87, gives an idea how they could be used in floor systems. A common application is to have a box beam replace a girder in supporting flooring or roof decking or joists. It must be designed to support the load requirements. Box beams are light in weight, have practically no shrinkage and develop sufficient strength for wide spans. See Fig. 88. Built-up box headers were also developed to bridge wide spans over openings. See Fig. 48.

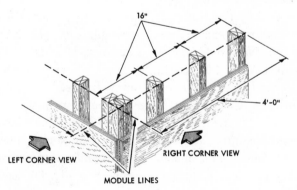

Fig. 86. Panels are made so that dimensions measure to the face of studs. (National Forest Products Assoc.)

Fig. 87. Box beams made of 2 × 4 frames with plywood webs are used in an experimental house. (Douglas Fir Plywood Assoc.)

Fig. 88. Box beams are designed for wide spans. They are light in weight and have practically no shrinkage. These beams have a 40 foot span over the entrance to a small plane hangar. (Douglas Fir Plywood Assoc.)

Fig. 89. An experimental floor system uses box beams and 4 × 8 foot plywood panels with 2 × 4 inch stiffeners. (Douglas Fir Plywood Assoc.)

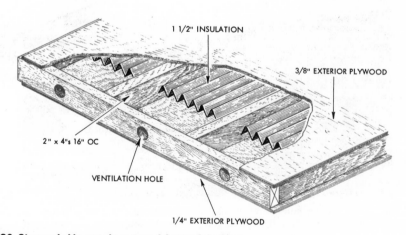

1 1/2" INSULATION

3/8" EXTERIOR PLYWOOD

2" x 4"s 16" OC

VENTILATION HOLE

1/4" EXTERIOR PLYWOOD

Fig. 90. Stressed skin panels are used for roof decking.

Fig. 91. Stressed skin panels provide both roof decking and ceiling. These panels span 12 feet between supports. (Plywood Fabricator Service, Inc.)

A floor system used with box beams or solid members requires a subfloor of 4 × 8 foot panels of plywood with 2 × 4 inch stiffeners nailed at regular intervals. See Fig. 89.

Stressed skin panels have been used for roof decking in many applications. See Figs. 90 and 91. They are made of a 2 × 4 inch frame with cross members and plywood faces glued and nailed on both sides. Insulation is installed in the panels as they are made. They are usually built away from the job and delivered ready to install. Because of their large size and light weight, the roof areas are covered quickly. They can be designed to bridge over wide spans.

Structural Design

Every carpenter should have some knowledge of structural design because:

1. Architects' drawings of residences and other small buildings do not usually show the arrangement of structural members in floors, walls, and roofs.

2. Much remodeling work is done without the services of architects. The carpenter in many instances must decide on the size and placement of members.

185

3. Almost all temporary construction (such as, scaffolding, barricades, sidewalk sheds, form bracing, shoring, etc.) is built by the carpenter and should follow good design principles in order to function properly using a minimum of material and labor to accomplish its purpose and yet provide maximum safety.

However, the design of the building, the size and spacing of columns, girders, posts, joists, and other supporting members is strictly the job of the architect because it is his responsibility to plan a safe and sound structure. Furthermore, the carpenter and builder cannot be expected to be able to make necessary calculations to determine the correct information. It is sufficient if he knows how wood members react under certain loads and has some understanding of how to read tables of maximum allowable spans for wood floor joists, ceiling joists and rafters.

Types of Stresses

Four types of stress act upon or within structural members. They are: tension, compression, shear, and bending.

1. *Tension* is a stress in a structural member which is caused by a load which tends to stretch the member or make it longer. *Example:* A vertical support for a suspended ceiling.

2. *Compression* is a stress in a structural member which is caused by a load which tends to compress a structural member or make it shorter. *Example:* A wood post supporting a girder is in compression.

3A. *Shear* results when two forces act on a body in opposite directions in parallel adjacent planes (like a pair of shears) tending to make the fibers of the two portions slide past one another. *Example:* The end of a joist resting on a brick wall is under stress which tends to cut the end of the joist off. The weight on the joist is one force and resistance of the wall to change is the other force.

3B. *Shearing stress parallel to the grain* results when the strain is such to tend to make the member split lengthwise. *Example:* When horizontal headers are notched into the vertical posts of a porch a shear effect is produced in the post tending to split the post.

4. *Bending* results when external and internal forces act on a horizontal member tending to cause it to deflect. *Example:* Girders and joists are subject to bending of their own weight

as well as the loads imposed by people, furniture, etc.

Working Stress

Powerful testing machines have been used to determine the point of failure of different materials. By studying the characteristics of materials under stress and making proper allowances for safety and variations in the material itself, tables are derived giving unit working stresses. Table II is a typical stress table taken from the building code of a large city. It gives maximum allowable unit stresses in pounds per square inch for the most common eight varieties of wood, of plywood, and laminated timber used in that area. Fig. 92 illustrates the stresses in a beam.

Extreme fiber stress is the resistance to the shortening and lengthening of the fibers when a member is placed in a position where it tends to bend under a load.

Horizontal shear is the resistance to the tendency of the fibers to slide past one another lengthwise in a member placed in a position where it tends to bend under a load.

Compression across grain is the resistance to compression at right angles to the axis of the member.

Compression parallel to grain is the resistance to compression parallel to the axis of the member.

Table II   Maximum Allowable Unit Stresses
(Pounds per Square Inch)

SPECIES AND COMMERCIAL GRADE	EXTREME FIBER STRESS AND TENSION PARALLEL TO GRAIN	HORIZONTAL SHEAR	COMPRESSION ACROSS GRAIN	COMPRESSION PARALLEL TO GRAIN	MODULUS OF ELASTICITY
CYPRESS	1300	120	300	900	1,200,000
DOUGLAS FIR	1300	100	325	1200	1,600,000
PLYWOOD (FIR) BUILT UP SECTION	1500	100	400	1500	1,600,000
LAMINATED TIMBER	1100	75	400	1500	1,600,000
HEMLOCK	1000	90	350	1100	1,400,000
OAK	1300	120	600	1000	1,500,000
REDWOOD	1100	75	300	1000	1,200,000
SOUTHERN PINE LONGLEAF	1300	120	450	1000	1,600,000
SHORTLEAF	1100	120	400	900	1,600,000
SPRUCE SITKA OR EASTERN	1000	75	300	800	1,200,000

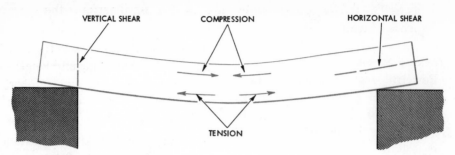

VERTICAL SHEAR COMPRESSION HORIZONTAL SHEAR

TENSION

Fig. 92. Stresses in a simple beam.

Modulus of elasticity is the relation of the unit stress to unit elongation. When a member is placed under stress it will elongate at a uniform rate until it reaches its limits of elasticity after which it will no longer return to its original length.

Allowable Spans

A carpenter should be able to read a table which gives minimum allowable spans for framing members. Each type of lumber and each grade has a different requirement.

A typical table taken from the Federal Housing Authority *Minimum Property Standards for One and Two Living Units* is given in Table III.

The lumber grades are based on strength and are classified by extreme fiber stress. For instance, Standard Structural J & P (Joist and Plank) has an extreme fiber stress of 1200 pounds per square inch and Construction J & P has 1450 pounds per square inch.

The *live load* requirements are set by the local building code according to the type of building. Residential buildings are usually rated for 40 pounds live load per square foot of floor area. Live load refers to people, furniture, etc.

The *size* of planks in Table III is for S4S lumber (surfaced four sides).

The *ceiling joist* table division for "no attic storage" is for roofs of 3 in 12 inch slope or less and the division "limited attic storage" is for roofs with more than a 3 in 12 inch slope.

For example, if the carpenter had to span a distance of 14'-0" with a floor joist of Douglas fir, coast region, construction J & P grade on 16 inch centers with a 40 pound live load, he could determine the size to use by referring to Table III. In this case he should use 2 × 10 inch members.

Table III   Maximum Allowable Spans: Douglas Fir, Coast Region

Nominal size (inches)	Spacing (inches o. c.)	Select Structural J & P 1950 f	Dense Construction J & P 1700 f	Construction J & P 1450 f	Standard J & P 1200 f	Utility J & P (¹)	Select Structural J & P 1950 f	Dense Construction J & P 1700 f	Construction J & P 1450 f	Standard J & P 1200 f	Utility J & P (¹)
		FLOOR JOISTS									
		30 LB. LIVE LOAD					**40 LB. LIVE LOAD**				
		Ft. In.	Ft. In.	Ft. In.	Ft. In.	Ft. In.	Ft. In.	Ft. In.	Ft. In.	Ft. In.	Ft. In.
2 x 6	12	11 4	11 4	11 4	11 4	8 4	10 6	10 6	10 6	10 6	7 4
	16	10 4	10 4	10 4	10 4	7 2	9 8	9 8	9 8	9 8	6 4
	24	9 0	9 0	9 0	9 0	5 10	8 4	8 4	8 4	8 2	5 2
2 x 8	12	15 4	15 4	15 4	15 4	12 4	14 4	14 4	14 4	14 4	11 0
	16	14 0	14 0	14 0	14 0	10 8	13 0	13 0	13 0	13 0	9 6
	24	12 4	12 4	12 4	12 4	8 8	11 6	11 6	11 6	11 0	7 10
2 x 10	12	18 4	18 4	18 4	18 4	16 10	17 4	17 4	17 4	17 4	15 2
	16	17 0	17 0	17 0	17 0	14 8	16 2	16 2	16 2	16 2	13 0
	24	15 6	15 6	15 6	15 6	12 0	14 6	14 6	14 6	14 0	10 8
2 x 12	12	21 2	21 2	21 2	21 2	19 8	20 0	20 0	20 0	20 0	17 8
	16	19 8	19 8	19 8	19 8	17 0	18 8	18 8	18 8	18 8	15 4
	24	17 10	17 10	17 10	17 10	14 0	16 10	16 10	16 10	16 10	12 6
		CEILING JOISTS									
		NO ATTIC STORAGE					**LIMITED ATTIC STORAGE**				
2 x 4²	12	11 10	-- --	11 8	8 10	-- --	9 6	-- --	8 2	6 4	-- --
	16	10 10	-- --	10 0	7 8	-- --	8 6	-- --	7 2	5 6	-- --
	24	9 6	-- --	8 2	6 4	-- --	7 6	-- --	5 10	4 6	-- --
2 x 6	12	17 2	17 2	17 2	17 2	13 6	14 4	14 4	14 4	14 4	9 6
	16	16 0	16 0	16 0	16 0	11 8	13 0	13 0	13 0	12 10	8 4
	24	14 4	14 4	14 4	14 4	9 6	11 4	11 4	11 4	10 6	6 8
2 x 8	12	21 8	21 8	21 8	21 8	20 2	18 4	18 4	18 4	18 4	14 4
	16	20 2	20 2	20 2	20 2	17 6	17 0	17 0	17 0	17 0	12 4
	24	18 4	18 4	18 4	18 4	14 4	15 4	15 4	15 4	14 4	10 0
2 x 10	12	24 0	24 0	24 0	24 0	24 0	21 10	21 10	21 10	21 10	19 6
	16	24 0	24 0	24 0	24 0	22 6	20 4	20 4	20 4	20 4	16 10
	24	21 10	21 10	21 10	21 10	19 6	18 4	18 4	18 4	18 0	13 10

¹ Denotes grade is not a stress grade.
² Denotes light framing grade. (Not Industrial Light Framing)
Notes:
(a) Spans may be increased 5 percent from those shown for rough lumber or lumber surfaced two edges (S2E).

(b) Spans shall be decreased 5 percent from those shown for lumber more than 2 percent but not more than 5 percent scant from American Lumber Standards sizes measured at a moisture content of 19 percent or less. Lumber scant more than 5 percent will not be acceptable.

If he had 2 × 6 inch construction grade Douglas fir, coast region material to be used for attic joists, with no attic storage, on 16 inch centers, he should limit the span to 16'-0" between supports. See Table III. If the roof were more steep so that the attic could be used for storage, a 2 × 8 inch ceiling joist, construction grade, would permit a maximum span of 17'-0" if the joists were on 16 inch centers, and 15'-4" if they were on 24 inch centers.

189

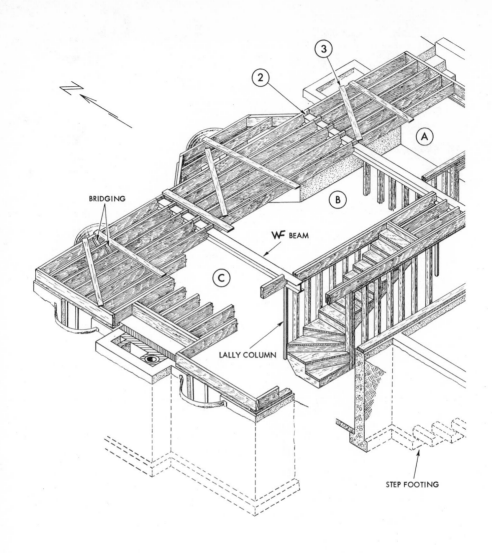

BRIDGING

WF BEAM

LALLY COLUMN

STEP FOOTING

Framing of the HOUSE
PLAN A: Platform Framing

Rough framing of a house has been covered up to this point but has been given a general treatment. Platform and balloon framing have been covered and specific instances as to how the members would be arranged and

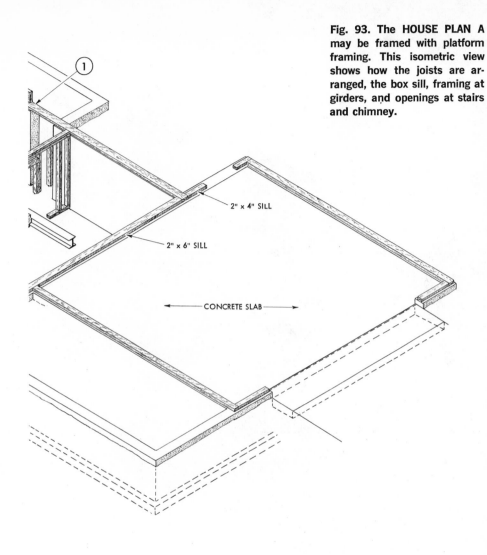

Fig. 93. The HOUSE PLAN A may be framed with platform framing. This isometric view shows how the joists are arranged, the box sill, framing at girders, and openings at stairs and chimney.

2" x 4" SILL

2" x 6" SILL

CONCRETE SLAB

fastened have been described. In this portion of the chapter, the HOUSE PLAN A, which is shown on the work-

ing drawings in Chapter 1, will be discussed as a framing problem. Study the plans carefully in order to

191

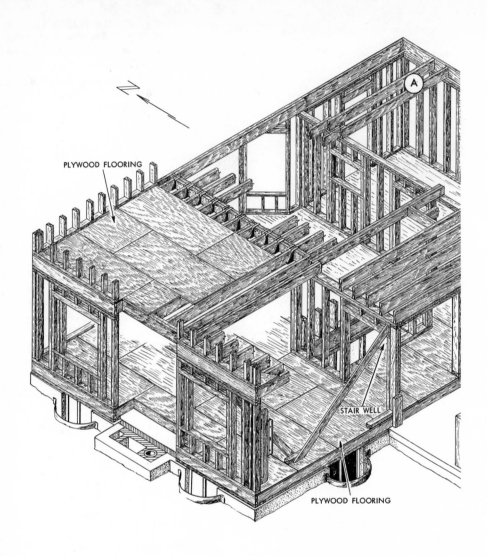

PLYWOOD FLOORING

A

STAIR WELL

PLYWOOD FLOORING

determine the size of joists, studs and other members, and the special problems which arise in framing a particular house. Also study the specifications in Chapter 1 to find information about framing which is covered in written form.

The section views on Sheet No. 8 (Chapter 1) show how the HOUSE PLAN A can be built using either plat-

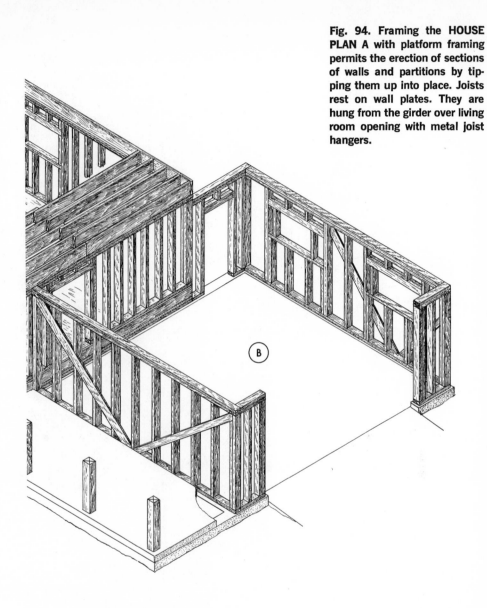

Fig. 94. Framing the HOUSE PLAN A with platform framing permits the erection of sections of walls and partitions by tipping them up into place. Joists rest on wall plates. They are hung from the girder over living room opening with metal joist hangers.

form framing or balloon framing. Most builders would prefer to use platform framing. See Figs. 93, 94 and 95. Some might prefer to use a combination of balloon and platform framing which will be discussed later in the chapter. (See Figs. 103, 104 and 105.)

When all concrete foundations have been completed, and the out-

193

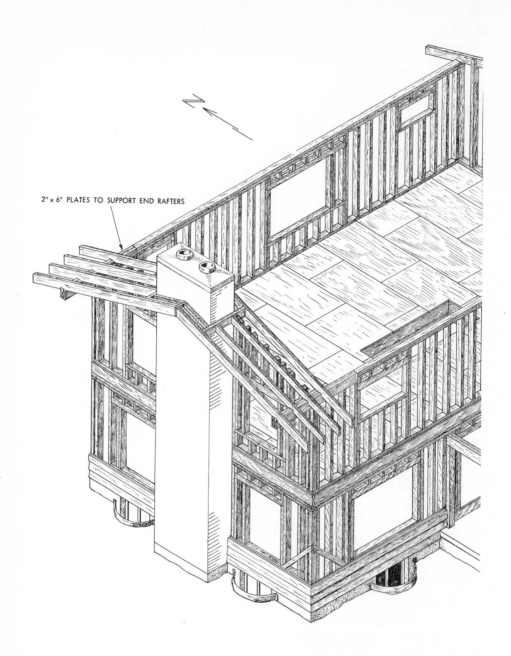

2" x 6" PLATES TO SUPPORT END RAFTERS

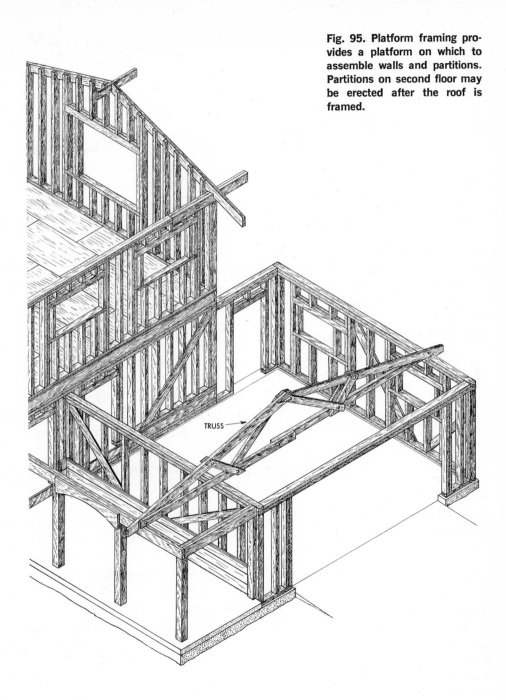

TRUSS

Fig. 95. Platform framing provides a platform on which to assemble walls and partitions. Partitions on second floor may be erected after the roof is framed.

side wall foundations backfilled with dirt to rough grade level, we can begin framing the floors and walls of the HOUSE PLAN A.

First Floor Framing

Sill Framing. Let us begin by setting the sills on the outside walls at the northeast corner, shown at *1*, Fig. 93. Proceed with the work by fitting and placing the sills on the east wall first, then following around the south and west sides, leaving the placing of the sills on the north side until the last. The sill construction used is shown in Fig. 9. A single 2 × 6 member will be used around the foundation. The sill pieces must be carefully lined up and measured because they establish the faces of the building.

PROCEDURE

Since the east foundation wall is 23'-2" long, select two 12 foot pieces of 2 × 6 for the sills and fit into place as follows:

1. Square both ends of the first 2 × 6. Remove the nuts from the anchor bolts in the concrete foundation wall. Lay the 2 × 6 on the wall against the bolts, as shown in Fig. 96. The end of the 2 × 6 should be set back ¾ inch from the outside of the north wall to allow room for the sheathing.

2. Square lines across the 2 × 6 from the center of each anchor bolt.

3. Measure the distance from the center of the bolt to the face of the concrete wall. Then subtract ¾ inch to allow for the sheathing. This will give the distance the bolt holes should be bored from the outside edge of the 2 × 6.

Note: Separate measurements must be taken for each bolt since it is difficult to set the bolts in the concrete the same distance from the outside of the wall when it is poured.

4. Locate all bolt holes, then remove the sill to a pair of sawhorses and bore the holes with an auger bit ⅛ inch larger than the bolt, to allow for slight adjustment in setting the sill.

5. Place the 2 × 6 in its proper position over the bolts. Take the next section of the sill to complete the east wall, saw one end square and lay it against the bolts with one end against the first sill section. Lay out bolt holes as before and mark the length by measuring in ¾ inch from the outside of the south foundation wall.

6. Remove the sill. Place it on two sawhorses and cut it to the exact length required. Bore the holes and place the sill in position on the wall.

7. Continue the same procedure around the entire building.

8. After all sill sections have been carefully fitted, each section should be removed and a good cement mortar placed on the wall. The sills are then replaced, leveled with a transit, straightened with a line, and fas-

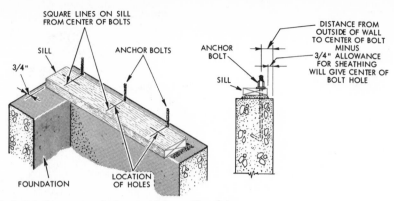

Fig. 96. Bolt holes are marked accurately on the plate.

tened down into place with washers and nuts over the ends of the bolts. Wedges driven under the sill where needed will hold it up in place and keep it level until the mortar sets.

ALTERNATIVE PROCEDURE

Some builders retain the batterboards in position until after the sills are located.

1. Pull a chalk line through the saw kerfs which locate the building lines on the batterboards.

2. Lay the sill in position as shown in Fig. 97 against the bolts. Using a combination square mark a line on the sill at each side of each bolt. Measure from the string to the center of the bolt and then measure the same distance from the center of the bolt to a point on the board. Allow ¾ inch for the sheathing. This point will be the location of the bolt hole.

3. Proceed to finish all sills and fasten them as described under Step 8 above.

Framing of the Joists. The joists which are 2 inch members (1½ inch actual dimension) are designed to take the load of the flooring, of partitions, plumbing fixtures and the live load of furniture and people.

The joist framing on the steel wide flange beam presents a special problem because the beam is not to project down below the bottom of the joists. If the recreation room ceiling were to be plastered it would be a flat ceiling. See detail on working drawing Sheet No. 1, Chapter I. The joists are to be cut out to rest on the lower flange of the beam and are to be fastened together in pairs by means of a metal dog running under the beam. See Fig. 20.

The outside joists on the north and south walls are put in place to

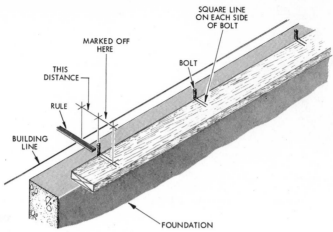

Fig. 97. An alternative method of laying out bolt holes uses the building line for reference.

line up with the outer edge of the sill and are toe-nailed in place. See Fig. 9 for detail of box sill. A header which is a piece of the same dimensions as the joists is placed along the east and west walls lining up with the outer edge of the sill and toenailed in place. The header serves to line up and fasten the joists, and serves later as nailing base for sheathing. The framing of headers and an outside joist at the bay is the last operation for the perimeter of the building.

PROCEDURE

1. Lay out the joist pattern for area *A*, Fig. 93. To find the length of the joists measure from the inside of the header to the middle of the wide flange beam and deduct one half of the thickness of the web of the beam. Make a template so that the joist will fit properly into the beam as shown in the detail on working drawing Sheet No. 1, Chapter I. Cut as many joists as are required for area *A*, Fig. 93.

2. The spacing from the corner will depend on whether plywood sheets are to be used for rough flooring or not. If plywood is to be used the sheets should join at the center of a joist 4 feet or 8 feet away from the face of the outside joist. See Fig. 98. In this case the center of the second joist should be placed 16 inches from the outside of the first joists. All other joists are placed on 16 inch centers across the building. Measure joist spaces and mark them on the sill for the east wall. Transfer the

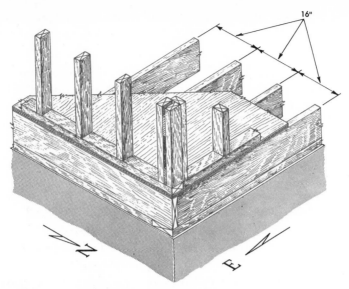

Fig. 98. The corner of a building with platform framing is arranged so that the walls can be tilted up into place. Joist spacing in this case depends on the rough flooring dimensions.

markings to the two sets of beams and to the sill on the west wall.

3. Line the joists up with the marks on the sill and beam beginning at *1* and *2* Fig. 93, and plumb the ends. When in a perfectly plumb position drive nails through the header into the ends of the joists. Also toenail the joists into the sill. Use a diagonal strip and a straight strip as shown at *3*, Fig. 93, tacking them to the joists to keep them in line until rough flooring is laid.

4. Lay out a pattern joist for area *B* with cutouts to fit the beams. Cut the joists and place them in position lining them up with the marks on the beams. Again fasten them in place with the use of temporary strips. Nail

metal ties or dogs between the joists in area *A* and area *B*. See Fig. 20.

5. Study the plans to find the location of the stairwell. Frame double trimmers on each side of the stairwell and a double header at the head of the stair. Frame short joists to fill in this space. See Fig. 21. Hold the joists back ¾ inch to allow for lath and plaster or drywall finish.

6. Cut the joists for area *C* and install them in the same manner as for area *A*. Study the plans to determine the header arrangement required at the hearth. See first floor plan Sheet 2, Chapter I. Fig. 65 'shows a typical application (not for the HOUSE PLAN A.) Install metal ties where the joists in areas *B* and

C join to keep them in line and to tie them together.

Subflooring and Bridging. Before starting to lay the subflooring, or rough flooring, check all joists carefully to make sure that each joist is plumb, straight, and braced. Also make sure that every joist is nailed securely in position. This final check will help to insure straight outside walls and full joist strength. When laying the subfloor, begin on the east side and proceed toward the west. The specifications (see Chapter I) call for 1 × 6 inch square edge boards for subflooring. Select a straight 1 × 6 inch piece and square one end. Mark and cut the other end so that when the board is placed flush with the outside of the joist of the north wall this other end will be on the center of a joist. After lining the board up flush with the outside of the joist and the outside of the header for the east wall, nail it in place with two 8*d* nails at every joist. Continue to cut and nail boards in place staggering the ends so that two adjacent pieces do not come together on the same joist. Cut and lightly tack the subflooring at the lavatory so that the plumber can remove it when he proceeds with his work. Continue fitting and nailing the rough flooring to every joist until the middle of area *A* is reached where bridging is to be placed.

Plywood, as shown in Fig. 94 and Fig. 98, would be the choice of many builders. In general it should be ½, ⅝, ¾ or ⅞ inch thick, 4 × 8 foot sheets and of interior or exterior grade. It should be laid so that the face grain of the sheets is at right angles to the joists.

Lay out and cut bridging according to instructions given previously. Set two nails on each end of the bridging pieces, and nail the bridging in place, as shown in Figs. 26 and 27. Remove the diagonal braces which hold the joists in line, then proceed with the laying of the rough flooring, placing the bridging at the middle of each span until the entire floor has been covered.

Exterior Wall Framing. The first step in framing walls and partitions is to study the plans to see what the floor-to-ceiling height is and the height of various openings above the subfloor. Choose a straight piece of 2 × 4 inch material to use for a master stud pattern or story pole. Lay out the various vertical dimensions carefully on it so that they may be transferred to other studs conveniently. If there are several different heights to mark off, it may be wise to use two or more master stud patterns.

The section drawing Sheet No. 8, Chapter I, shows the distance from finished first floor to finished second floor to be 9'-0". The finished flooring is ¾ inch thick and the furring strips under the finished flooring are ¾ inch also. The ceiling joists over the first floor are specified as 2×10 inches (actual dimensions $1\frac{1}{2} \times 9\frac{1}{2}$) as shown on the first floor plan Sheet No. 2. The lath and plaster ceiling thickness is $\frac{3}{4}$ inch. To lay out the master stud pattern lay the piece over two sawhorses, square one end, and cut it on the line. See Fig. 99A. Mark off $1\frac{1}{2}$ inches from the end to show the thickness of the sole. This is also the mark for the finished floor level ($\frac{3}{4}$ inch for furring and $\frac{3}{4}$ inch for finished flooring equals $1\frac{1}{2}$ inches). From the top of sole measure 9'-0" and mark the finished second floor line. Mark off the thickness of the finished floor ($\frac{3}{4}$ inch), the thickness of the furring strip ($\frac{3}{4}$ inch), the thickness of the rough floor ($\frac{3}{4}$ inch) the thickness of the joist ($9\frac{1}{2}$ inches), and the thickness of the double plate (3 inches). Make crosses and designate the lines for ready reference. See Fig. 99A. (Short-cuts can be used but beginning carpenters should proceed in this methodical way in order to avoid errors.)

The bottom of head jambs for windows is shown as 6'-8" above the finished floor on the section view Sheet No. 8. This dimension should be marked on the master stud pattern. See Fig. 99B. The head jamb is $\frac{3}{4}$ inch thick and the fitting space requires another $\frac{3}{4}$ inch. Mark these

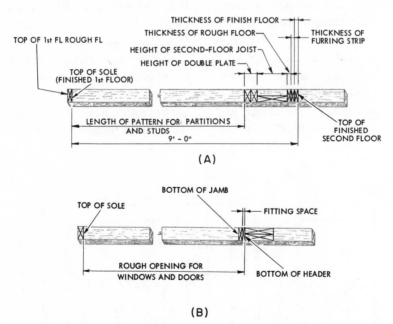

Fig. 99. (A) The Master stud pattern indicates various heights. These measurements are transferred to the studs. (B) Information for window and door headers is also marked on the master stud pattern.

spaces and draw lines. This last line would be the bottom of the header. Interior doors are 6'-8" with equivalent jamb and fitting space to that of windows. The first floor headers for openings would all be at the same height.

Study the elevation drawing Sheet No. 7 and the first floor plan Sheet No. 2 of the working drawings in Chapter I to gain information needed for the east wall which will be erected first. See Fig. 100. Cut the soles for the wall first and mark them for the location of studs and openings. See Fig. 101 for the procedure. (Fig. 101 shows how to lay out the sole and plate for the bearing partition at the kitchen.) Cut the required number of studs and arrange them on the floor to line up with the markings on the sole and plate. Cut crippled studs, headers and sills under windows and assemble the wall. Information on framing for doors and windows is shown on Figs. 45 and 46.

The east wall is not too long to be built in one piece. The south wall will have to be made in two or three assemblies. The north and west walls are broken up into small sections because of the fireplace and bay. True up the east wall which has been assembled on the floor by measuring diagonally across the corners and tack temporary braces in place to keep it from racking. If it is sheathed before it is tipped into place the temporary bracing is unnecessary. Several men must help to tip it up in position, to brace it with diagonals nailed to blocks on the floor, and to toenail the sole which must be done in a sequence of operations. See Fig. 102. The wall must line up with the outside of the header and rough floor edge below.

The carpenter may choose the order of building and erecting the other sections. If parts of the north and south walls were built next they would help brace the east wall. The

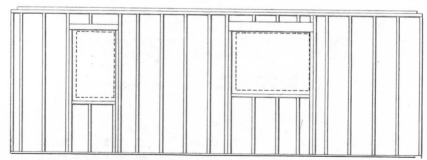

Fig. 100. The exterior wall is framed on the floor and tilted up into place.

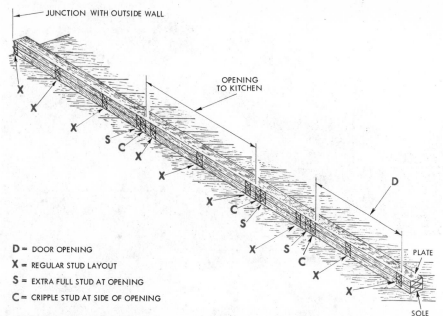

JUNCTION WITH OUTSIDE WALL

OPENING
TO KITCHEN

D

PLATE

D = DOOR OPENING

X = REGULAR STUD LAYOUT

S = EXTRA FULL STUD AT OPENING

C = CRIPPLE STUD AT SIDE OF OPENING

SOLE

Fig. 101. Openings in partitions and location of studs are marked on sole and plate. Note: Studs are marked at openings to locate cripple studs over opening and to maintain the stud spacing in the partition.

exterior walls should be checked to see that they are plumb and corner bracing installed unless structural sheathing is used.

Assembling and Erecting Partitions. Snap lines on the floor showing the location of all partitions and mark the openings in partitions. Tack all partition soles in place. Cut top plates and tack them temporarily on top of the soles. See Fig. 101. Where interior partitions intersect it is important that a decision be made as to which one will be installed first, because the plates lap as they tie into each other. After the plates have been tacked to the soles, the stud locations are marked on them. Beginning with the base line, which in this case is the inside line of the studs for the north wall, mark the plates with an "X" for each stud space. Designate the location of openings in the partitions with a letter "D" for door. Mark "S" for studs alongside openings, and "C" for location of cripples. After the plate and sole have been marked lift the plate from the sole. Most builders will assemble the partitions as shown in Fig. 2.

Lay the studs on the floor in line

203

Fig. 102. Exterior wall sections are built in units and raised into position. This picture shows modular units made by the Unicom method. (National Forest Products)

with the marks on the sole. Lay the plate at the other end of the studs in position with the marks which are identical to those on the sole. Nail the plate to the studs with two 16*d* nails. Transfer the markings for cripples to the headers by laying them alongside the sole in the proper location. Assemble cripples to plate and install headers. True up the frame by adjusting the studs to fit the marks on the sole and nail the studs to the sole. After all studs, cripples, and headers are assembled, nail the second member of the plate on top of the one nailed to the studs

unless it is needed to tie two partitions together. Before the partition is raised into place nail two 1 × 6 temporary braces to the ends of the section in a manner that will permit them to extend to the floor at an angle to prevent the wall from falling and to keep it plumb. After the wall is raised fasten it with 16*d* nails through the sole. When the partition is plumb, nail the brace to a block fastened to the floor.

Second Floor Framing

Second Floor Joists. For the second-floor joists 2 × 10s are to be used. The length of these joists should be measured at the first-floor level. These joists should lap over each other on top of the bearing walls. The pattern for the joists for each portion of the main section of the building can be laid out on the first floor, working from east to west. After the joists have been laid out, they can then be marked, cut, and fitted into place. Using this method for laying out second floor joists tends to prevent errors. As each joist pattern is cut, it should be marked carefully for identification when needed later. Proceed to cut as many joists as required for the second floor.

Before placing the second-floor joists in position, check the bearing partition and corner posts again, to make sure they are plumb. Also check the walls again to make sure they are straight and thoroughly braced. Lay out the joist positions on the plates of the east and west walls and on the bearing partitions.

Begin by placing the second floor joists and headers in area *A*, Fig. 94. Select straight joists for the outside and place them in their respective positions flush with the face of the walls. To raise the joists to the second floor position, first push one end up over the bearing partition, then raise the other end, and step up onto a sawhorse. Lift the joist over the wall plate, leaving it in a flat position until all joists of area *A*, Fig. 94, are on the wall.

Place the joists in a plumb posi-

tion. Nail them to the header on the exterior wall and to the bearing partition plate, sighting each one to make sure the crowned side is up.

Note: When joists are cut at the mill and as they season some of them become crowned. This means that they have a slight curvature from end to end. When used as joists this curvature should be up rather than down. As the joists sag or deflect due to the load put upon them, the tops tend to become level.

Subflooring for Second Floor. The subfloor for the second floor is to be laid using 4 by 8 foot sheets of plywood laid so as to be flush with the outside of the header and joists. They should be cut so that splices fall on joists to permit firm nailing at ends. Half plywood sheets are used in starting alternate rows so that joints are staggered.

Second Floor Wall and Partition Framing. The procedure for framing the walls and partitions of the second floor follows the same routine as that used on the first floor. It would be advisable to do the north and south walls first. Because of the wide extension of the roof at the gable ends, it is necessary to provide special means to support the rafters which extend beyond the building. Two 2 × 6 members replace the last 4 feet of wall plate on each corner and extend to support the rafters. See Fig. 95. The east and west walls have gable ends which make it necessary to increase the length of each stud as it approaches the center. (Chapter V, Roof Framing, will go into detail on cutting rafters.) To frame the east wall mark the position of each stud and cripple stud on the sole. Also mark a 2 × 4 inch piece which will be tacked temporarily in a horizontal position about six feet above the sole to keep the upper ends of the studs in line. Lay a pair of rafters on the studs at the correct slope and mark the studs for cutting to fit the rafters. Frame the header, cripples and subsill for the window. Allow space for the ridge to fall in place. Nail the whole assembly together.

Nailing Sheathing. The sheathing should now be nailed on all walls where the openings have been framed. Nail the sheathing in place up to the height which can be reached by a workman when standing on a sawhorse. The sheathing for the HOUSE PLAN A, as indicated in the specifications, is to be $25\!/\!_{32}$ of an inch by 2 × 8 foot structural insulating sheathing. It is advisable to allow the sheathing to extend from 2 to 4 inches into the fireplace and chimney opening. This procedure will permit cutting of the sheathing down the entire length of the wall, after the bricklayer has laid out the exact opening size. This insures a straight tight joint. Cut the sheathing flush with the studs at all door and window openings. Diagonal

bracing can be omitted if plywood sheathing is used at corners as shown in Fig. 53.

After 4 or 6 feet of sheathing have been applied to the main part of the building, the walls may be framed for the garage B, Fig. 94. The east and west walls of this area can be framed on the floor and raised into place, then plumbed and braced. The fact that trusses are used to support the roof does not modify the wall framing.

The sheathing for the rest of the building can now be carried up as high as the second-floor joists. Erect the necessary scaffolding as the work progresses above the reach of workmen standing on the ground. After the framing has been completed in the gables, the sheathing should be carried up to the louver on the east side and fitted snugly in the corners along the chimney on the west side. Cut the boards flush with the end rafters on the east and west sides. On the eaves sides (north and south) of the house, the sheathing should be carried up to the bottom of the the plates, allowing for fitting of the rafters to the plates. See working drawing Sheet No. 8, Chapter I, typical wall section.

Bay Window Framing. After the outside walls have been sheathed up to the second floor level, the bay window of the dining room can be framed. The framing is shown in Fig. 94. See also the elevation and sectional views of the bay window shown on sheets No. 6 and No. 8 of the working drawings. Prepare the top plate, or header, which is a double 2 × 8 set on edge. This top plate extends around the bay window and forms the window headers. The 2 × 8s for these headers are spiked together, mitered at the corners, and made to fit the shape of the bay at the sill level. Cut six 2 × 4 studs to correct length and erect them at the corners of the bay window. Place and nail the header, or top plate, in position. Frame the subsill and cripple studs below the window, then sheath up the walls.

Second Floor Framing. Not much framing can be done on the second floor until the roof has been framed (Fig. 95).

The open floor space permits ease in handling material for the roof. It is of advantage to the workmen to leave out partitions until after the roof has been framed and sheathed. It is also to the advantage of the workmen to complete the roof of the house as soon as possible, so that they will have a dry place in which to work in case of rain or snow.

Framing Odds and Ends. Up to this time, only the most essential part of the framework of the HOUSE PLAN A has been erected. Our aim has been to erect the skeleton of the building and cover it with sheathing the shingles. With the walls sheathed and the roof overhead, the workman is in a good position to continue his work regarless of weather conditions. Much still remains to be, done on the inside of the building before the framing is completed. Minor partitions must be set, plumbed, tied securely in place, and the corners well nailed to avoid cracking of the plaster. The backing in the corner of walls and ceiling must be installed (see Figs. 36 and 41). Arches must be framed (see Figs. 67 and 68). The rough stairs must be erected and the insulation put in place.[3] Plaster grounds shown in Fig. 54 must be nailed in position. All these odds and ends of framing may be carried on when weather conditions will not permit outside work. If, on the other hand, weather conditions are favorable over an extended period of time, it may be to the advantage of the carpenter to complete the interior framing so other tradesmen, such as the electrician, lather, plasterer, and furnace man can do their jobs. In such a case the carpenter can work on the exterior while the other tradesmen are installing their work.

In other words, a carpenter should plan his work so neither the weather nor the work of other tradesmen will force him to remain idle for any long period of time.

---

3. The subject of insulation is covered in detail in Durbahn: *Fundamentals of Carpentry, Vol. I,* Chapter 7.

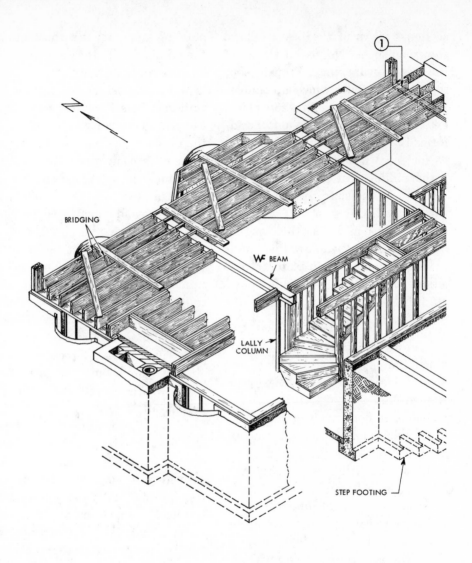

BRIDGING

WF BEAM

LALLY COLUMN

STEP FOOTING

Framing of HOUSE PLAN A:
Balloon Framing

The HOUSE PLAN A can be built using either balloon framing or platform (western) framing. The typical wall sections shown on Sheet No. 8 of the working drawing show both types. The information in this chapter and in Fig. 103, 104 and 105 show that a combination of balloon and platform framing has been used. The outside walls are made with long

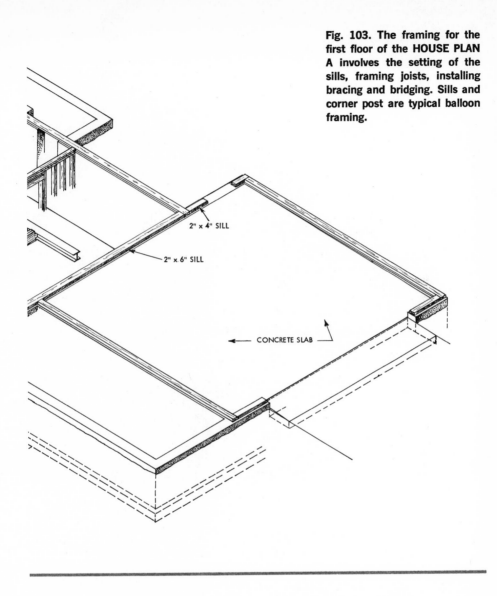

Fig. 103. The framing for the first floor of the HOUSE PLAN A involves the setting of the sills, framing joists, installing bracing and bridging. Sills and corner post are typical balloon framing.

2" x 4" SILL

2" x 6" SILL

CONCRETE SLAB

studs extending from the sill to the plate at the top of the second floor wall. The second floor joists rest on ribbons and are nailed to the studs. These are typical balloon framing de-tails. Some of the features usually found in platform framing are used for partitions. The bearing partitions at the kitchen and at the entrance to the living room rest on the rough

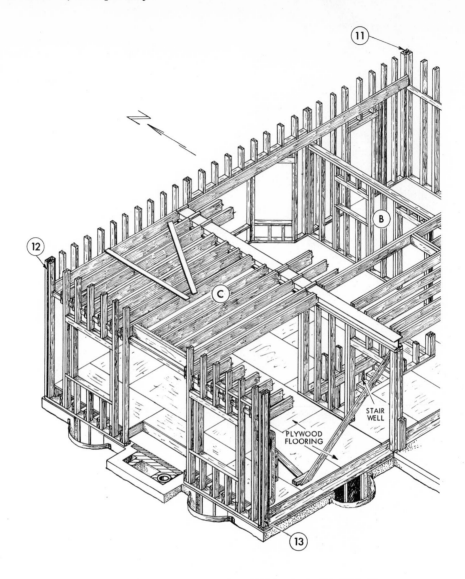

floor. The top member is a double plate which supports the joists for the second floor.

Several alternatives may be used in proceeding with the construction of the frame work above the first floor level. Usually the outside walls are raised first, then the longest in-

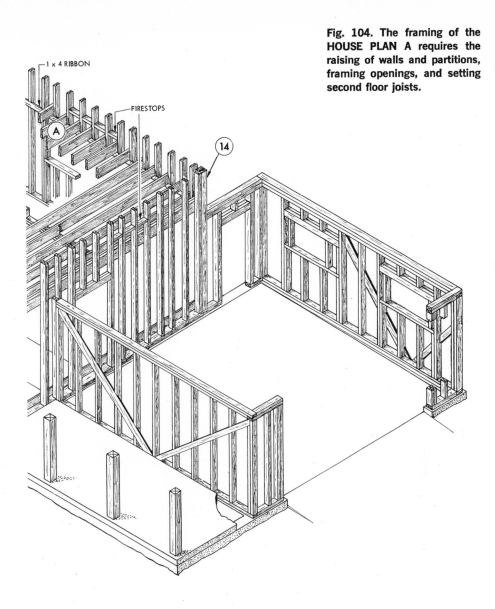

Fig. 104. The framing of the HOUSE PLAN A requires the raising of walls and partitions, framing openings, and setting second floor joists.

1 x 4 RIBBON

FIRESTOPS

A

14

terior partition or bearing partition is raised, working down until the shortest partition is erected last. Interior partitions are generally put to-

gether on the floor and raised into position. Two methods may be used to assemble and raise the outside walls.

211

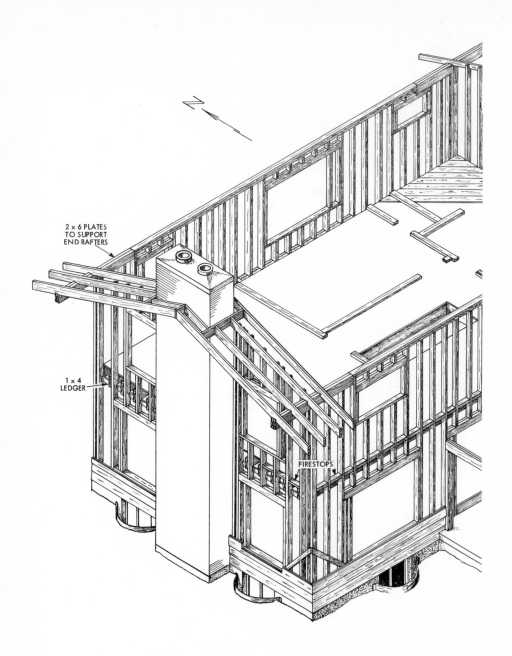

2 x 6 PLATES
TO SUPPORT
END RAFTERS

1 x 4
LEDGER

FIRESTOPS

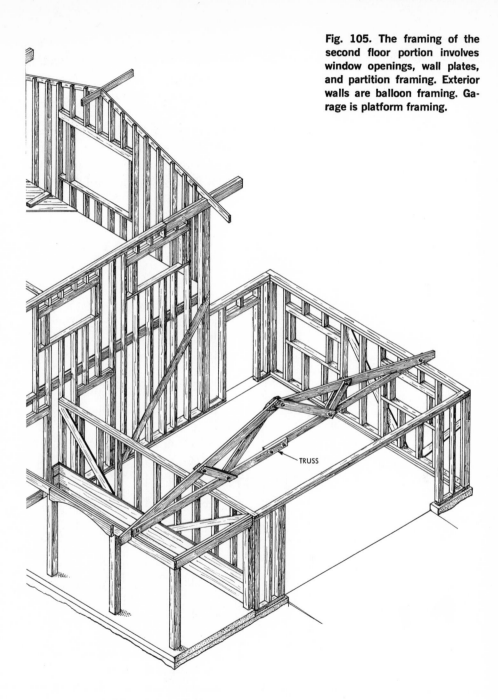

TRUSS

Fig. 105. The framing of the second floor portion involves window openings, wall plates, and partition framing. Exterior walls are balloon framing. Garage is platform framing.

A two story house may be framed in two ways if balloon framing is used. One way is to build the external walls in units without providing for windows or doors. Window and door openings are cut and framed after the walls are erected.

A more common method which builders find quite satisfactory is to build the walls in sections with all openings framed, and then tip them up in place. A number of men are necessary, and even some hoisting equipment may be used to advantage. See Figs. 106 and 107.

In planning the framing for the HOUSE PLAN A the following procedure may be used. After the first floor joists are fastened in place, the rough flooring will be laid. The east and west walls will then be built in units and raised into position. Bear-

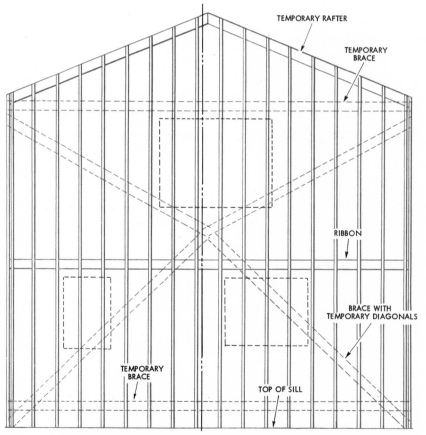

Fig. 106. The wall may be framed and erected in two units. Openings will be framed later.

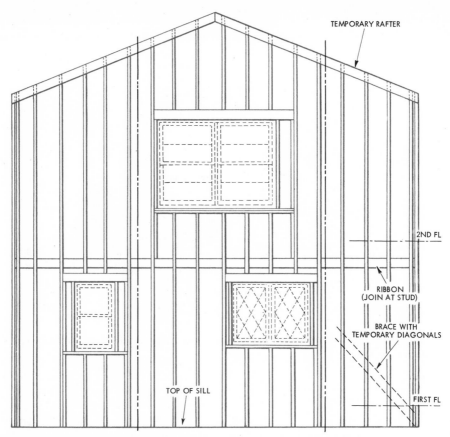

Fig. 107. The exterior walls may be erected in units for balloon framing.

ing partitions will be made on the floor and tipped up. After the east and west walls and the bearing partitions have been erected, the second floor joists will be put in place. The north and south walls will be erected last. The walls of the garage will be framed using typical western framing. This work can be done at any time after the south wall studs are in place.

Sills and Joists. The sills will be cut and placed in the same manner as described for platform framing. The sill construction is shown in Fig. 7. Joists will be placed on the sill as shown in Fig. 108. Subflooring should be laid keeping it back 3½ inches from the east and west joist ends.

Stud Layout. All stud spacing on outside walls and on partitions should start at the same base lines.

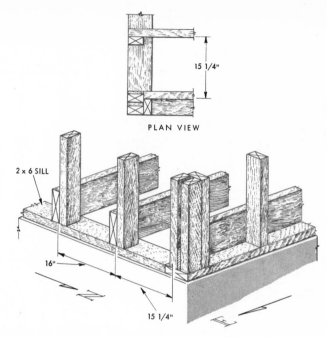

PLAN VIEW

2 x 6 SILL

15 1/4"

16"

15 1/4"

Fig. 108. The framing of the north-east corner of the HOUSE PLAN A shows how the joists and studs are located for balloon framing.

Corner post near point *1* Fig. 103 could serve as the starting point for east-west measurements which should be on 16 inch centers. North-south spacing should be transferred from the joists which are already in place. The studs when erected in place are nailed to the sides of the joists.

Assembling and Erecting Exterior Walls

Whenever possible, the studs for the opposite walls are laid out directly opposite to each other, so that the second floor joists can be nailed to the same side of the studs and extend in a straight line across the bearing partitions. This it not only good construction but also permits pipes and ducts to pass from the walls to second floor joist spaces. The spacing of the studs on the east and west walls of the HOUSE PLAN A is determined by the joists. The first spacing is to be 15¼ inches, as shown in the detail in Fig. 108; all other spacings are 16 inches on center (o.c.). When the stud layout reaches the fireplace on the west wall, a 1 × 6 should be tacked across the opening of the fireplace so that the spacing can be carried across and continued on the south side of the fireplace.

Before starting the stud layout make a master stud pattern. It should be a little longer that the longest stud required for the east and west walls. See Fig. 109. Another master stud pattern may be made for the north and south walls.

Each one of the outside corners *11, 12, 13,* and *14,* Fig. 104, requires a three-stud corner, constructed as shown in Fig. 108. One of these three studs must have a housing for the ribbon. Take the stud pattern, Fig. 109, and cut 12 studs for the four corners. House four of the studs for a ribbon, and nail the studs together for each corner, so the housing will come on the correct side to receive the ribbon.

After cutting and assembling the corner posts, take the master stud pattern and lay out enough studs for the east and west walls. The studs are made longer than necessary so that they may be cut accurately to fit the rafters when the walls are assembled. In order to get an approximate idea of how the studs increase in length beginning at the corner, follow this procedure. Notice that the slope of the roof is 4 inches per foot (unit) of run. Studs are spaced on 16 inch centers. (16 inches $= 1\frac{1}{3}$ feet, 4 inches $\times$ $1\frac{1}{3}$ units of run $=$ $5\frac{1}{3}$ inches, or approximately $5\frac{3}{8}$ inches.) Beginning with the corner studs, each stud will be $5\frac{3}{8}$ inches longer. Cut all of the studs making sure that the bottom end is perfectly square and the cut out for the ribbon is exactly identical on each one.

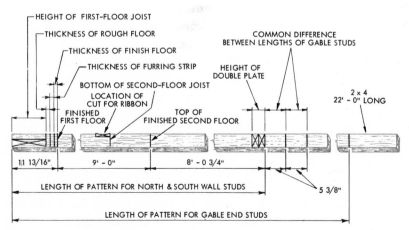

Fig. 109. The master stud pattern for balloon framing shows the location of flooring, ribbon and plates.

Select straight pieces of 1 × 4 inch material to be used for ribbons. Lay the ribbon along the sill of the east wall and transfer the joist spacing to it. Mark the stud locations along side of the joist markings on the ribbon.

Two methods may be used in building the units for the east wall. Many carpenters would make it in two parts with the ribbon spliced on the stud nearest the center of the building. See Fig. 106. All openings would be cut and framed after the rough framing was erected. Other carpenters would proceed in a manner similar to that used in platform framing and would permit the framing of all openings. See Fig. 107. In this case the ribbon would have to be spliced on the stud nearest the division.

In order to explain the procedure we shall assemble the east wall using three units. See Fig. 107. Lay the studs on a level surface with the lower end resting against the sill alongside the joist where they will be finally located. Nail the ribbon to the studs so that they fall in line with the marks on the ribbon. Lay the headers for the various openings against the sill and mark off the places where cripples will be required. Using a story pole marked with the height of the openings, locate the headers and nail them in place. (The story pole is a strip of wood marked to show the height of the opening in relation to the rough floor.) Nail the cripples in place above the headers. Fasten the headers by nailing through the studs on each side of the opening. Mark off the sub-sills for windows and nail them in place in the same manner as the headers. Install cripples under the sub-sills. Cut the short studs which frame the sides of the openings (trimmers) at this time and tack them in place. They are to be nailed securely later. Square the wall and adjust the studs to match the marks on the sill. Nail temporary diagonal braces across the frame and fasten 1 × 6 pieces at each end which will serve to keep the wall upright. Raise the wall into position and toenail the studs into the sill and nail into the first floor joists. Plumb the wall at the corners and fasten the braces to blocks fastened to the floor. Temporary bracing should be left until permanent diagonal bracing can be cut into the studs and the second floor joists are in place. (If plywood sheathing or other structural sheathing is applied the braces may be omitted.) The braces are generally 1 × 3 or 1 × 4 pieces. Lay them across the studs, mark them and make cutouts to fit. Extend the brace to the corner stud and sill. See Fig. 3. Nail the brace at the top only, until the wall has been checked for plumb and alignment.

The west wall should be made in two units because of the fireplace.

It would be advisable to frame for openings after the wall is erected because there would be very few long studs to hold it together.

Bearing partitions parallel to the east and west walls are next in order. Assemble and erect them in the same manner as described for platform framing. The second floor joists are then cut and put in place. One end is lifted to rest on the bearing partition then the other end is raised to rest on the ribbon on the outside wall. See area *A*, Fig. 104. After making sure that the structure is in alignment and the studs plumb, the joists are nailed firmly to the studs and to the plate of the bearing partition. Joists in areas *B* and *C*, Fig. 104, follow using the same procedure.

The north and south walls are now erected in convenient units. There is no ribbon to be let into the studs. Sufficient temporary diagonal bracing will be necessary to keep the units in true shape as they are erected. The outside joists on the first and second floors serve to line up the wall and to provide strong nailing bases.

Framing of other partitions, and framing at the bay and fireplace, is the same as for platform framing which has been discussed earlier in the chapter. For the framing of window and door openings, follow Figs. 43 and 44 or Figs. 104 and 105 which show a variation in the manner of cutting and crippling studs. Firestops must be installed as shown in Figs. 3, 8 and 104.

Framing for Tri-Level House

The HOUSE PLAN C is a typical tri-level house which has gained popularity in cities in cooler climates. See Fig. 110. Generally speaking a split-level house is most practical on a sloped piece of ground so that different grades may be used on opposite sides. However, the tri-level house has found favor in cities and is built on flat ground for several reasons. People feel that they save money by having a basement under half of the house, they like the effect of an open ceiling in the living room and they save steps going up to the bedroom portion rather than going up to a second floor. The HOUSE PLAN C could be built using platform framing in the two-story part. The construction would follow that illustrated in Fig. 1. A typical box sill would be used (see Fig. 9), the rough floor would be laid after the joists are in place, and the exterior walls and partitions would be built in units and tilted up into place. Generally the sole would be fastened to the wall before it is raised into position.

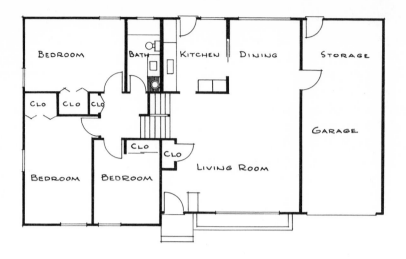

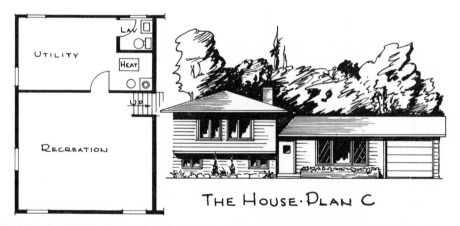

Fig. 110. The HOUSE PLAN C is called a tri-level because floors are arranged on three levels. A special framing problem develops at the bearing partition.

The bearing wall between the two parts of the house can be framed using balloon framing. See Fig. 111. The joists rest on ribbons cut into the studs. When the joists for the living room partition run at right angles to the partition they can be supported on a ribbon also. Similarly, the second floor bedroom joists can also be supported by a ribbon. Note

220

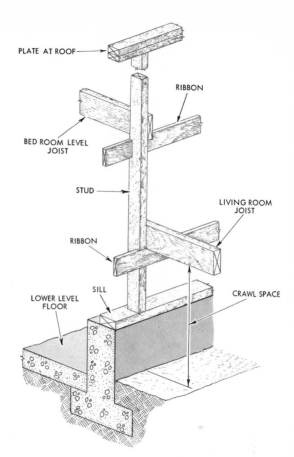

PLATE AT ROOF

RIBBON

BED ROOM LEVEL JOIST

STUD

LIVING ROOM JOIST

RIBBON

SILL

LOWER LEVEL FLOOR

CRAWL SPACE

Fig. 111. The bearing partition in a tri-level house may use some of the features of balloon framing.

that the second floor ribbon is cut into the opposite side of the stud. When the wall gets above the roof of the living room part of the house it becomes an exterior wall projecting up until it becomes the support for the roof over the bedroom area.

221

Checking On Your Knowledge

The following questions give you the opportunity to check up on yourself. If you have read the chapter carefully, you should be able to answer the questions. If you have any difficulty, read the chapter over once more so that you have the information well in mind before you go on with your reading.

DO YOU KNOW

1. What are some of the advantages of platform framing?
2. What are some of the advantages of balloon framing?
3. What are some distinctive features of plank and beam framing?
4. Why is the shrinkage factor so important in framing a house?
5. Why are firestops required in balloon framing?
6. How can the wood members near the ground be protected from termites?
7. What are the functions of the sole and plate in a partition?
8. What is the purpose of bridging between joists?
9. What are the framing members at openings in floors called?
10. What different ways are there to support the framework over openings in exterior walls?
11. When must diagonal bracing be used on exterior walls?

12. What are some advantages of using plywood as exterior wall sheathing?
13. What are plaster grounds?
14. What precaution must be made in framing joists under bathrooms?
15. What means are suggested to cut down sound transmission in a wood stud partition for drywall application?
16. What advantages do steel studs have for drywall application?
17. Why is balloon framing considered good construction with masonry veneer?
18. What is a single-pole scaffold? A double-pole scaffold?
19. Who establishes the safety rules for scaffolding?
20. What is a carpenter's bracket scaffold?
21. What is modular planning?
22. What is a stressed skin panel?
23. What is a box beam?
24. What is a master stud pattern?
25. What are tension, compression, shear and bending stresses?

Roof Framing

The main purpose of the roof is to protect the building from rain, snow, heat and cold. Another purpose equally important is that of enhancing the appearance of the building so that the structure, the details of exterior finish and the roof are architecturally in harmony.

When the building is rectangular in plan, made with perfectly square corners, and with sides which are accurate in length, the roof is simple to frame because all of the members are alike or may be made in pairs. Rafters for a shed roof or gable roof are quite simple. A hip roof requires more skill and know-how because of the number of different rafters and the angle cuts required. Very often however the framing of the roof is one of the carpenter's most difficult problems of construction. This is true whenever the house itself is irregular in shape and the roof has unusual features.

The beginning carpenter should learn about simple roofs, the names of the various rafters, how to lay them out, how to cut them and how to erect them. As roofs increase in complexity he should increase his knowledge to include the layout of the necessary common, jack, hip and valley rafters. He must cut them accurately so that they fit together correctly.

Two things are basic to any approach to roof framing. The student should develop his ability to visualize the whole roof so that he may understand how the various planes will intersect when it is finished. The other thing is a knowledge of the use of the right triangle, a concept which comes from geometry. The framing square, the carpenter's roof layout tool, is stamped with numbers which give the information needed for obtaining lengths and cuts on the rafters. It provides a means of applying the right triangle in step-off and layout techniques.

Styles of Roofs

Important as its utility value may be, the roof, if carefully designed, adds greatly to the beauty of a building. Contemporary houses use a number of roof styles, often in combination. The shape of the house plan and the requirements of the climate are limiting factors. Some owners may want the building to have the flavor of a particular architectural period such as Dutch Colonial or Cape Cod. The roof is very important in bringing out these special effects. A few common types of roofs used in the construction of houses in this country are: *shed*, *gable*, *hip*, *gambrel*, and *mansard*, shown in Fig. 1.

Shed or Lean-to Roof. The simplest type of roof is the *shed* or *lean-to*, usually employed for small sheds, porches, or other structures where appearance is not a matter of primary importance. The shed roof consists of a single plane surface with one side raised to a higher level.

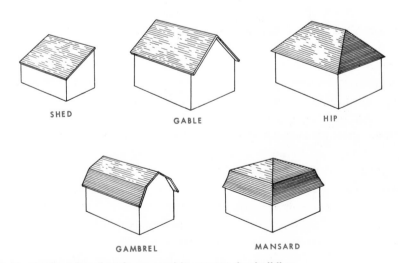

SHED   GABLE   HIP

GAMBREL   MANSARD

Fig. 1. Five basic styles of roofs are used in present day building.

Gable Roof. The *gable roof* has two sloping surfaces. These two surfaces come together in the middle of the roof at the ridge, forming gables at each end. Because of its simplicity of design and relatively low cost of construction, the gable roof is most commonly used for small houses. The slope of the gable roof may vary from an almost flat surface to one which is very steep. (The House-Plan A has a gable roof. See Chapter I.)

Hip Roof. The *hip roof* has four sloping sides. The line where two adjacent sloping sides of the roof meet is called a *hip*. When the plan of the building is rectangular and the roof has the same slope on all four sides, a ridge will occur, as in the illustration of a hip roof in Fig. 1. When the plan of the building is square in shape and the roof has the same slope on all four sides, the roof will come to a point.

Gambrel Roof. A variation of the simple gable roof is the *gambrel roof*, which has two slopes on each side. This type of roof has been used in barns for many years because it provides the best storage space for hay. It is used in residential work in the so-called Dutch Colonial house design.

Mansard Roof. A form of double-sloped roof frequently used in America during Colonial days is known as the *mansard roof*. It came to this country from France. The name is derived from the name of its original designer, the architect François Mansart (1598-1666). The lower portion of this roof is quite steep while the upper portion has a very low slope. This type of roof has the advantage of providing additional space for attic rooms.

A combination of two or more types of roofs is often used to enhance the appearance of a building and give character to the house. Also, some definite purpose may require a combination of different types of roofs.

Roof Framing Terms

The terms used to designate the members of a roof are shown in Fig. 2. The carpentry student should become familiar with the names of these different members or parts of a roof, so he can readily identify them.

Ridge. The highest horizontal roof member is the *ridge*, which helps to align the rafters, and tie them together at the upper end.

Rafter Plate. The framing member at the top of the wall upon which the rafters rest is known as the *rafter plate*.

Rafters. The sloping structural members of a roof designed to support roof loads are called *rafters*.

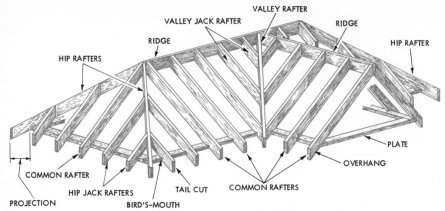

Fig. 2. The names of the members of a roof are important. (Note that the projection is a level dimension, while the overhang follows the rafter line.)

They are spaced at regular intervals in order to distribute the load of sheathing, roofing and snow equally. In a complex roof such as shown in Fig. 2, some of the rafters are shortened and are cut to fit into a particular place. Some of the load is transferred to hip and valley rafters and then to the plate. Rafters are classified as follows: *common, hip, valley, jack* and *cripple jack.*

Common Rafter. The series of framing members which extend at right angles from the plate line to the ridge of the roof are called *common rafters*. The common rafter is so named because it is not cut on an angle at either end as are hip, valley, and jack rafters.

Hip Rafter. The roof member extending diagonally from the exterior corner of the plate to the ridge is known as a *hip rafter*. The hip rafters form the hips where adjacent slopes of the roof meet.

Valley Rafter. The rafter extending diagonally from plate to ridge at the line of the interior intersection of two roof surfaces is called a *valley rafter*, because it is located where adjacent roof slopes meet to form a hollow or *valley*. When two roofs intersect, as shown in Fig. 2, the two valley rafters are alike. It is often true, however, that one ridge is lower than the other. In this case one valley rafter, called a *supporting valley rafter*, is cut to fit from plate to ridge; the other valley rafter, called a *shortened valley rafter*, runs from the plate to the supporting valley rafter. See Fig. 3.

Jack Rafter. Jack rafters are similar to common rafters except

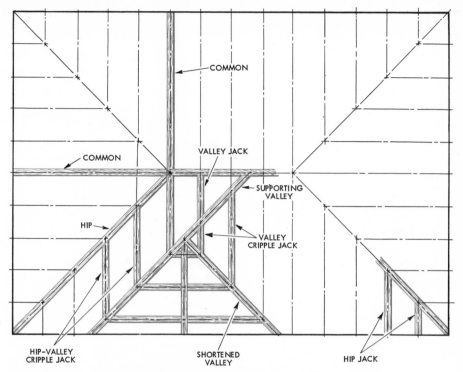

COMMON

COMMON

VALLEY JACK

SUPPORTING
VALLEY

HIP

VALLEY
CRIPPLE JACK

HIP-VALLEY
CRIPPLE JACK

SHORTENED
VALLEY

HIP JACK

Fig. 3. Rafters are named according to their position in the roof and their cuts.

that one end is cut off on an angle to fit against a hip or a valley rafter. Some carpenters use the term *hip jack* to designate those which end against a hip and the term *valley jack* to designate those which end against a valley rafter. See Fig. 3.

Cripple Jack Rafter. A rafter which extends from a hip to a valley rafter or takes a place between two valley rafters is called a *cripple jack rafter*. It is called a *cripple* for short. This rafter touches neither the ridge of the roof nor the rafter plate of the building. See Fig. 3.

Overhang, Lookout, or Tail Piece. The three names *overhang, lookout,* or *tail piece* refer to the same part of the roof. This is the portion of the rafter extending beyond the outside edge of the plate or walls of the building. When laying out a rafter this portion is an addition to what is considered the length of the rafter, and is figured separately.

Bird's-Mouth. The cutout near the bottom of the rafter (when there is an overhang) which fits over the rafter plate is known as the *bird's-mouth.*

227

Principles of Roof Framing

The underlying principle of roof framing is to relate all layout problems to the three sides of a right triangle. The simplest type of common rafter shown in Fig. 4 illustrates how these three sides are related in a roof. The horizontal side is called the run, the vertical side is called the rise and the hypotenuse is called the line length. Each rafter itself, including hip, valley, jack and cripple rafters, may be thought of as being the hypotenuse of a triangle.

When a carpenter has the job of laying out the members of a roof he studies the plans so that he knows about the shape and slope of the roof and its dimensions. He will then use his steel framing square to lay out the rafters and to mark the cuts. Using the blade for the run (unit horizontal measurement), and the tongue for the rise (unit vertical measurement) and by measuring diagonally between these two points he can derive the unit line length. This is called "bridging the square." The framing square has several other valuable features useful for measuring. It has scales divided into ⅛, 1/16, 1/32, 1/10, 1/100 and 1/12 of an inch. It has tables which eliminate most of the mathematics in rafter layout plus some features of value in calculating board feet, the length of diagonal braces, and a means to obtain the length of sides of octagons. See Figs. 5 and 6.

Tables are stamped on one side of the square which give the unit hypotenuse measurement of common, hip and valley rafters for various

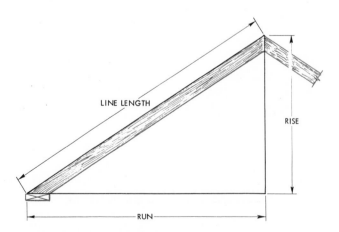

Fig. 4. A simple rafter is part of a triangle.

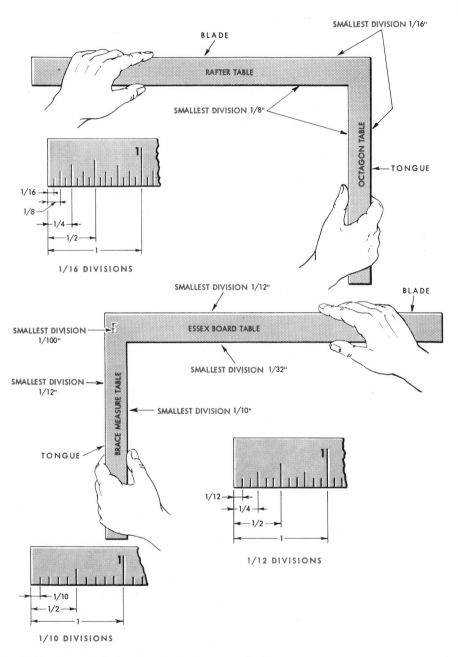

Fig. 5. The carpenter's framing square has many features.

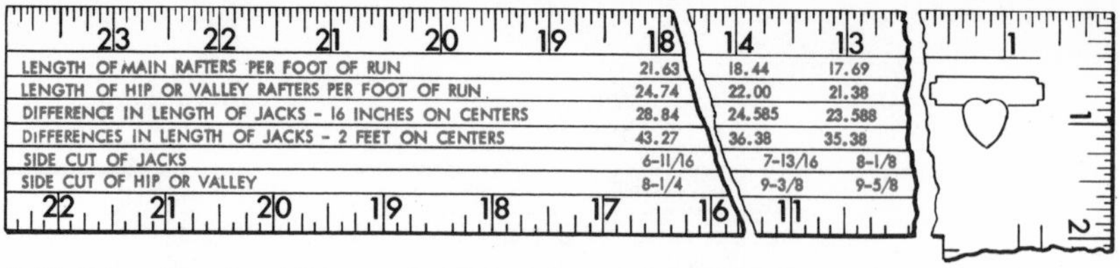

LENGTH OF MAIN RAFTERS PER FOOT OF RUN	21.63	18.44	17.69
LENGTH OF HIP OR VALLEY RAFTERS PER FOOT OF RUN	24.74	22.00	21.38
DIFFERENCE IN LENGTH OF JACKS - 16 INCHES ON CENTERS	28.84	24.585	23.588
DIFFERENCES IN LENGTH OF JACKS - 2 FEET ON CENTERS	43.27	36.38	35.38
SIDE CUT OF JACKS	6-11/16	7-13/16	8-1/8
SIDE CUT OF HIP OR VALLEY	8-1/4	9-3/8	9-5/8

Fig. 6. Unit-length rafter table on the face of the framing square.

units of rise. For example, by referring to the framing square in Fig. 6, if a common rafter had a unit rise of 13 inches per foot of run, the line length would be 17.69 inches or $17^{11}/_{16}$ inches per foot of run. See Fig. 7. The "common difference" for jack rafters spaced at 16 inch and 24 inch centers for various slopes is also shown. This is another application of the triangle, giving the line length of the difference in length of each succeeding jack. If the jacks on the same roof were spaced on 16 inch centers the difference on line length between any two jacks would be 23.588 inches or $23^9/_{16}$ inches. The tables on the square also tell what numbers to use on the blade and tongue of the framing square to mark the actual cuts. Thus the framing square is a great time saver and has become essential in roof layout work.

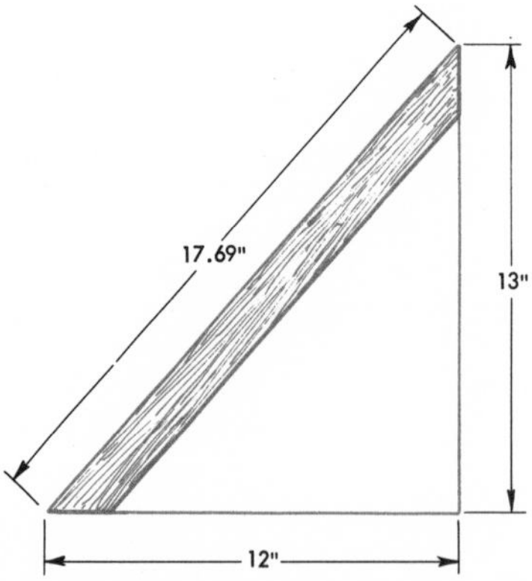

Solving the Right Triangle Mathematically

The framing square has eliminated almost all of the need for mathematics in laying out rafters. Yet it may be of value to be able to understand how the figures in the rafter table on the framing square are derived and how to find the line lengths mathematically for special cases.

The 6-8-10 method of establishing right angles in laying out building lines was discussed in Chapter II. By squaring two sides of the triangle and adding the squares and then extracting the square root of the sum, the hypotenuse is found. See Fig. 8.

Fig. 7. The length of main rafter per foot of run is shown on the framing square table (Fig. 6).

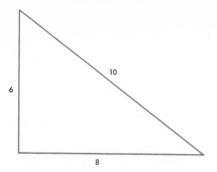

Fig. 8. The 6-8-10 triangle is basic in carpentry.

$$6^2 + 8^2 =$$
$$36 + 64 = 100$$
$$\sqrt{100} = 10$$

The same procedure may be used in roof framing if the unit run of the rafter in Fig. 7 were 12 inches and the unit rise were 13 inches the line length would be found in this manner:

$$12^2 + 13^2 =$$
$$144 + 169 = 313$$

To find the square root of 313 proceed as follows:

1. Place the number under the radical sign. Locate the decimal point.

2. Mark off the digits in groups of two in both directions beginning with the decimal point. (Add as many pair of zeros as you wish to have decimal places to the right.)

3. Mark the decimal point for the answer just above the decimal point of the number.

4. Find the largest perfect square (1) in the left hand group.

5. Place its square (1) above the line for the first number of the answer. Subtract the perfect square (1) from the first group.

6. Bring down the next pair (13).

7. Double the partial answer ($1 \times 2 = 2$).

8. Add a trial digit to the right of the double partial answer. Multiply this new number by the trial digit. Keep trying until you find the highest possible digit that can be used. In this case it is 7. Place the correct new digit in the answer ($27 \times 7 = 189$).

9. Subtract the product.

10. Repeat steps 6 to 9 as often as required.

Referring to the framing square Fig. 6 in the first line "Length of Main Rafter per Foot of Run" for 13 inch unit rise the length given is 17.69 inches.

$$
\begin{array}{r}
1\ 7\ .\ 6\ 9 \\
\sqrt{3\ 13\ .\ 00\ 00} \\
1 \\
\end{array}
$$

27	
7	2 13
189	1 89
	24 00
346	
6	
2076	20 76
3529	
9	3 24 00
31761	3 17 61
	6 39

Applying the Right Triangle to Roof Framing

There are several terms used in applying the idea of rafters as parts of right triangles which must be understood. Fig. 4 shows how a rafter has a horizontal measurement called the *run* a vertical measurement called the *rise* and a hypotenuse measurement called the *line length*. In terms of a gable roof sloping in two directions the two rafters are alike and represent the hypotenuses of two right triangles placed so that they have a common side which is the *altitude or rise*. See Fig. 9.

The Span. The distance from outside to outside of the rafter plates of the building, is known as the *span*. The span distance may be determined by studying the plan view of the floor immediately below the roof of the blueprints of a house. When a building is under construction the span measurement can be found by actually measuring the distance between the outside walls.

Total Run. The base of the triangle is known as the *run* or *total run*. The run is equal to one-half of the span, which usually is one-half the width of the building. The *total*

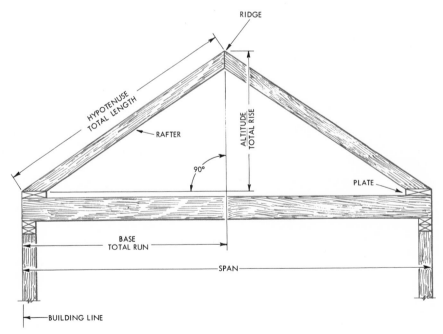

Fig. 9. The basic triangle is developed by the total run, total rise, and total length of the rafter.

run is measured from the outer edge of the plate horizontally to a plumb line dropped from the center of the ridge or highest point of the rafter.

Total Rise of Rafter. The altitude or *total rise* of the triangle is the vertical or plumb distance a rafter extends upward from the plate, as illustrated by the simple rafter shown in Fig. 9.

Total Length of Rafter. The hypotenuse of the triangle in Fig. 9 is the distance between the outside edge of the rafter plate and the high point of the ridge.

Pitch. The pitch of a roof is a means of describing the amount of slope. A true definition of pitch is: Pitch is the ratio of *rise* to *span*. It is expressed as a fraction such as ½, ⅓, ⅜, etc. A roof with a 10 foot *total rise* and a 30 foot *span* would have a ⅓ *pitch*.

It should be observed that the rafter is the hypotenuse, and is the only actual part of the triangle. The base (total run) and the altitude (total rise) are only theoretical; that is, although they have actual values they are not actually represented in pieces of material. Hence they must be visualized through a mental picture of the triangle when applied to roof framing.

Finding the Length of a Rafter

The total length of a rafter can be found in several ways by mathematics or layout. (1) As outlined earlier a mathematical approach can be used by squaring the two sides, adding them, and extracting the square root. Most carpenters would not care to use such a method because it requires too much mathematics. (2) Using the tables on the framing square, the *total length* may be found by multiplying the "length of main rafter per foot of run" by the number of feet of run. (3) Using layout methods the rafter could be laid out full size on the floor or some other large flat surface using the *total rise* and *total run* as sides of a triangle. Except for very special cases this method would be awkward and timetaking. (4) When the building is in the process of building the *total lengths* for hips and other members are frequently taped. However this requires that some of the common rafters and the ridge be installed solidly in place. (5) Carpenters find that the most practical method of determining the length of rafters has been the step-off-method which is based on the concept of unit measurements.[1] This method is both accurate and simple.

---

1. The approximate length of common rafters can be determined by using the 1/12 scale on the framing square. Considering each inch as a foot and each small division as an inch the *total rise* and *total run* points are found. By bridging the framing square with another square also using the 1/12 scale, the *total length* may be found in feet and inches. This method is not accurate enough for use in finding lengths for laying out and cutting rafters, but is useful in estimating quantities of lumber and for checking purposes.

Unit Measurements

If we had a framing square large enough so that we could hold it against the side of a common rafter, as shown in Fig. 10, we could find the total run on the blade of the square and the total rise on the tongue. The seat of the rafter, which fits on the plate, could be found on the blade of the square, and the plumb, or ridge, cut could be found on the tongue. The bridge measure, that is, the distance between these two cuts, would be the *total length of the rafter*. The use of such a large-size framing square would greatly simplify the rafter layout, but since no such square is available, we must use the standard-size framing square in different positions, as shown on the

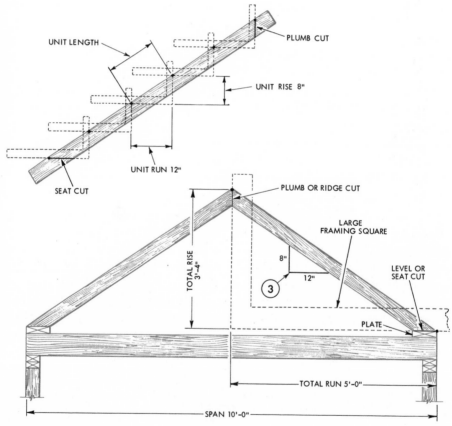

Fig. 10. The rafter is laid out by stepping off the unit run and unit rise five times for a rafter with a five foot total run.

left in Fig. 10, using the same figures on the blade and tongue of the square in each position. The smaller measurements are units or parts of the whole. They are called *unit run, unit rise*, and *unit length*, Fig. 10.

Unit measurements play an extremely important role in rafter layout; by the use of unit measurements the *total length* can be determined. The cut at the ridge, the cut at the rafter plate, and the overhang of the rafter are always laid out by use of unit measurements. In other words, unit measurements are the basis for rafter layout.

Unit Run. Any unit of linear measure may be used for the *unit run*. However, the foot is the established unit of measurement for all common and jack rafters.

Unit Span. Since the run of a rafter is one-half of the span of the building, the *unit span* would be twice the unit run or 24 inches.

Unit Rise. The rise in inches that the rafter extends in a vertical or plumb direction for every foot of unit run is the *unit rise*. The slope of a roof is usually expressed in terms of unit rise, indicated as at (*3*), Fig. 10. This roof has a slope of 8-inch rise per foot of run.

Unit Length of Rafter. The bridge measure or the hypotenuse of the right triangle, formed by the unit run (12 inches) and the unit rise, is the *unit length of the rafter*.

Application of Unit Measurements

The roof shown in Fig. 10 has a 10-foot span (which is a 5-foot run) and a slope of 8 inches per foot of run. Thus there are five 1-foot horizontal steps to be taken with the framing square along the edge of the board. For each horizontal step there will be a vertical step, *unit rise*, of 8 inches: $5 \times 8'' = 40''$ or $3'\text{-}4''$ *total rise*.

The *seat cut* is laid out along the blade of the square and the *plumb*, or *ridge*, cut on the tongue. By taking these unit measurements 5 times in this manner, we can obtain the same results we would obtain if we had a large-sized square on which the total run and total rise could be found. Using this method there is no need to find the actual measurement of the unit length or the total length of the rafter. The total length is determined by layout.

Working with Pitch and Unit Measurements

Many carpenters still describe the slope of a roof as 1/3 *pitch* instead of using unit measurements such as *8 inch rise per foot*. The term pitch is used correctly to express the ratio of the total rise to the total span. Thus a roof with a 5 foot total rise and 20 foot span would have a 5/20 or 1/4 pitch. Another roof with a 7 foot total rise and a 28 foot span would have a 7/28 pitch (which would also be 1/4 pitch). Expressing the slope of a roof by means of pitch has little value because it must be reinterpreted in terms of unit rise and unit run in order to use the framing square to lay out the rafter. However, the carpenter should be familiar with these two expressions and how to convert from pitch to unit measurements. Fig. 11A shows the relationship between some common pitches and their equivalent units of rise per foot.

Rule 1. To find the pitch of a roof divide the rise by the span. Fig. 10 shows a roof with a 3'-4" (3-1/3 feet) rise and a 10'-0" span.

$$\text{pitch} = \frac{\text{total rise}}{\text{total span}} \qquad \text{pitch} = \frac{3\text{-}1/3}{10}$$

$$\text{pitch} = 1/3$$

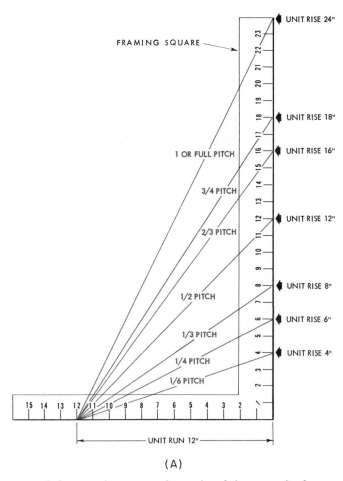

(A)

Fig. 11A. Common pitches may be expressed as units of rise per unit of run.

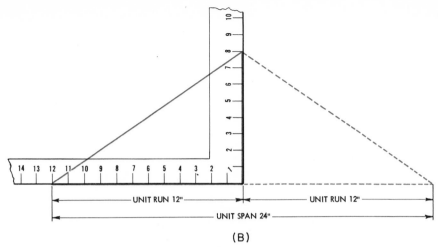

(B)

Fig. 11B. Relationship of unit run to unit span.

Rule 2. To find the total rise of a roof when the pitch and the span are given multiply the pitch by the span.

total rise = pitch × span
total rise = 1/3 × 10
total rise = 3-1/3 feet

Rule 3. To find the unit rise per foot of run when given the pitch multiply the pitch by 24.

unit rise per foot = pitch × 24
             = 1/3 × 24
             = 8 inches

The roof has a unit rise of 8 inches per foot of run. See Fig. 11*B.* Note: The constant 24 comes from the fact that the unit span is always 24 inches.

Rule 4. To find the unit rise when the total rise and total span are given. Divide the total rise by the total span and multiply by 24. In other words find the pitch and multiply the pitch by 24.

Unit rise per foot of run =

$$\frac{\text{total rise}}{\text{total run}} \times 24$$

In the roof of Fig. 10:

Unit rise per foot =

$$\frac{3\text{-}1/3}{10} \times 24 = 8 \text{ inches.}$$

Layout Procedure

The *cut of a roof* is another expression used for reference to the unit rise and unit run. A cut of 11

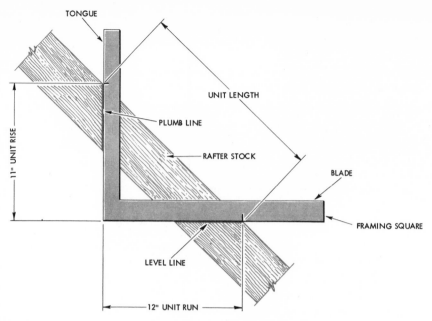

Fig. 12. The cut of the roof is an expression based on the unit run and unit rise.

inches per foot would indicate that the framing square would be placed so that the 12 inch mark on the blade would be located on the edge of the board and the 11 inch mark on the tongue. It is generally good practice to have the unit run (the level lines) on the blade (the longer member of the framing square).

The *plumb cut* is marked along the tongue, as indicated in Fig. 12. The *seat cut*, or *level line*, is marked along the blade. A *plumb line* is any line that is vertical when the rafter is in position in the roof. Any line that is horizontal when the rafter is in the proper position is called a *level line*, as shown in Fig. 12.

It is necessary for the workman, while laying out a rafter, to think constantly of how that rafter will fit into the roof; that is, the carpenter must visualize that particular rafter as it will appear when in its final position in the completed roof. Forming this habit of visualizing the rafter in its proper position will prevent the occurrence of errors in layout. This is particularly true when we understand that most carpenters lay out rafters upside down to the position that rafters take on the roof because it is easier to work with the square in this position. Framing square clips may be attached to the square to facilitate layout.

238

Roof Plan

Generally a set of architect's plans does not include a plan view of the roof unless it is exceedingly complex. The carpenter must learn how to visualize the roof from the information he gets from the floor plan view of the house which shows the shape and dimensions of the building, and from the elevation views which show what the roof will look like from the various sides. The section view will give information on the projection (horizontal measurement) at the eaves and the bird's-mouth. With this meager information he must build the roof with all of its supporting and secondary members. The carpenter may develop his own rough plan by drawing the main framing members, the ridge, hip and valley rafters, directly on the floor plan of the house. (The second floor plan if it has two floors.) He will thus gain an idea as to how the members intersect, how to plan common and jack rafters for the greatest economy of time and material, and what the run of each member will be.

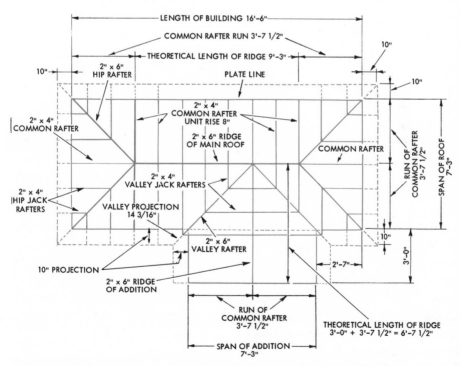

Fig. 13. The plan of the roof shows the arrangement of all rafters. (Roof from Fig. 2.)

For a roof such as the one shown in Fig. 2, a roof plan will look like the plan shown in Fig. 13. Each line represents the center line of a rafter. This drawing shows the over-all dimensions of the building and the amount of the projection, also the location of the major framing members. (The projection is the horizontal distance of the overhang.) The plan also shows the problem that must be solved at the intersection of hips and ridge and at the intersection of the valley and ridge.

The Ridge

The highest framing member of a roof is called the *ridge*. The ridge piece serves a twofold purpose; it helps to align the various roof members and ties them together at the top. A simple gable roof can be built without such a member but it is usually preferred.

Gable Ridge Lengths. Finding the length of the ridge on a gable roof is a simple process, since for a two-slope simple gable roof the ridge piece is the same length as the length of the building plus projection at the gables.

Hip-Roof Ridge Length. The theoretical length of a ridge on a hip roof is equal to the length of the building minus the run of the common rafter on each hipped end. A full-hipped roof requires rafters on all four corners, as in Fig. 13. The theoretical length of the ridge is found by subtracting the width or span of the building from the length of the building. For example, as illustrated in Fig. 13, when the length of the building is 16 feet 6 inches and the span or width is 7 feet 3 inches,

the theoretical length is 9 feet 3 inches (16'-6" minus 7'-3").

True Lengths for Hip-Roof Ridge. Two common methods of framing hip roof rafters at the ridge are illustrated in Figs. 14 and 15. In Fig. 14 the hip rafter is shown framed against the common rafters. When using this method, one half the thickness of the common rafter must be added to each end of the theoretical length of the ridge.

In an equal pitch hip roof the hip rafter always meets the ridge at an angle of 45 degrees. In a plan view such as Fig. 13 the length of the intersection of a hip rafter with the ridge is called *the 45 degree thickness of the rafter*. This is shown in Fig. 15 where the hip rafters are framed against the ridge piece. When using this method of framing the hip rafter, one half the thickness of the ridge piece plus one half the 45 degree thickness of the hip rafter must be added to each end of the theoretical length of the ridge.

Intersecting Roof Ridge. On an intersecting roof that has a gable

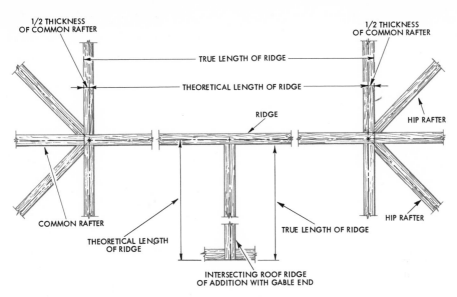

Fig. 14. The true length of ridge members must allow for the thickness of other members at intersections.

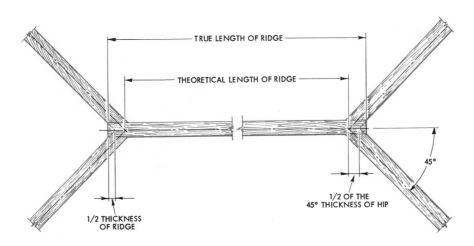

Fig. 15. A second way of framing the hip-ridge connection does not require that common rafters be framed first.

end, as in Fig. 13, the theoretical length of the ridge is equal to the length of the rafter plate of the addition plus the run of the common rafter of the addition.

True Length of Intersecting Roof Ridge. The true length of the intersecting roof ridge is equal to the length of the rafter plate, plus the run of the common rafter, minus one half the thickness of the ridge piece on the main roof, Fig. 14.

When the span of the addition or intersecting roof is smaller than that of the main roof, the ridge of the addition will be lower and will not meet the ridge of the main roof. One valley rafter, called a supporting valley rafter, can be carried up all the way to the ridge of the main roof, as shown by the dotted lines in Fig. 16. If the addition has a gable end, and the valley rafter is carried up to the ridge, the true length of the ridge on

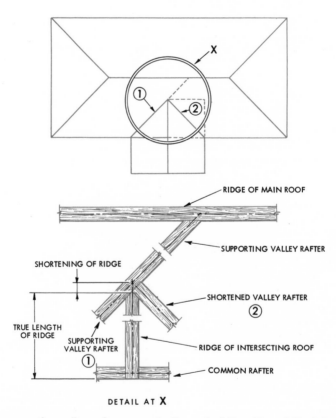

DETAIL AT **X**

Fig. 16. The supporting valley rafter supports the end of the ridge of the intersecting roof and the shortened valley rafter.

the addition will be equal to the length of the rafter plate, plus the run of the common rafter of the addition, minus one-half the 45 degree thickness of the valley rafter, as shown in the detail drawing at *X*, Fig. 16.

Common Rafter

The common rafter is that member of the roof which extends at a right angle from the rafter plate to the ridge. It takes its name, *common rafter*, from the fact that it is the simplest rafter, and is used as a basis for the *layout* process when finding the length and cuts of other rafters. It does not have diagonal cuts on either end.

There are several methods used to find the lengths of rafters. However, the step-off method is most commonly used. This method employs the unit measurements and other roof framing principles previously explained in detail.

Laying Out a Common Rafter

When laying out the rafter pattern by the step-off method the framing square is applied to the piece of lumber as shown at *A*, Fig. 17. The workman must be able to visualize the relation of this layout to the position of the rafter in the roof, as shown at *B*. When completed and cut out the common-rafter pattern will appear as at *C*.

PROCEDURE

Lay out a common rafter for a roof which has a span of 7 feet 3 inches, a unit rise of 8 inches, 2½ inch heel, a projection of 10 inches, a 2 × 6 ridge, and a plumb tail cut. (Figs. 2 and 13.)

1. Finding the total run of the rafter.
2. Determining the unit rise.
3. Selecting rafter stock.
4. Stepping off the rafter length.
5. Laying out bird's-mouth and heel.
6. Laying out overhang and tail cut.
7. Shortening rafter at ridge.
8. Checking the rafter length.

1. Finding the Total Run of the Rafter. In a gable roof the total run of the common rafter is equal to one half the span, as shown in Fig. 10. In our problem the span of the building is given as 7 feet 3 inches. Then *the total run of the rafter* is 3 feet 7½ inches or one-half the span, as shown in Fig. 17.

2. Determining the Unit Rise. The unit rise is usually indicated on the drawings for the building, as shown at *3*, Fig. 10. In our problem the unit rise is given as 8 inches. In case the unit rise is not given, draw a triangle on the profile of the roof on one of the elevation views. Make the level line 12 inches to scale. The

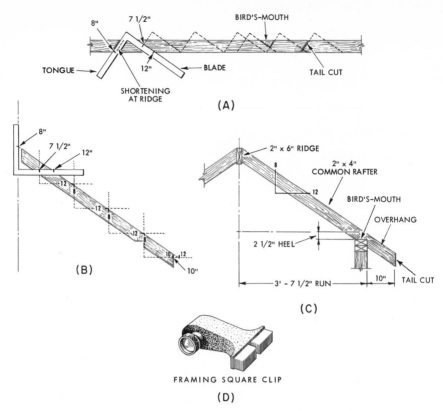

Fig. 17. The framing square is used to step off the rafter. (A) The framing square should be placed on the rafter stock so that the markings are made on the far side of the square. **(B)** The carpenter should think how the rafter will look when it is in the position for installing on the roof. **(C)** The rafter will fit at the ridge and plate if it is laid out correctly. **(D)** Framing square clips are fastened to the square so that it will give the 8-12 measurements for each step.

vertical leg of the triangle, when measured, will give the unit rise in inches.

3. Selecting Rafter Stock. From the stock of lumber available, select a piece of the correct size for the rafter pattern. This should be the best straight piece in the entire pile of stock. Lay the piece on a pair of sawhorses with the crowned edge, or curved side of the stock, turned toward you (the workman). This will place the crowned side upward when the member is erected. It is a good plan to make a record of all the necessary information about the rafter which is to be laid out. This can be done easily by writing the necessary information, such as the length of the span, rise, and run, on the piece of stock near to the left end where you will begin the layout, as shown at *D*, Fig. 18.

4. Stepping Off Rafter Length. When using the step-off method, proceed as follows:

PROCEDURE

a) Lay the framing square on the piece of stock to the *cut of the roof*, that is, 8 inches the unit rise and 12 inches the unit run, near the left end of the piece, Fig. 18. Take the unit rise on the tongue and the unit run on the blade of the square. Extreme exactness is of great importance in this operation. To insure accuracy, it will be necessary to use either a sharp hard pencil or a knife. The figures taken on the square (8 on the tongue and 12 on the blade) must be on the edge of the stock turned toward you (the workman). Greater accuracy can be obtained by the use of framing-square clips, such as the one shown at *D*, Fig. 17.

b) Hold the square in position *1*, Fig. 18. Draw the plumb or ridge line *a* along the tongue of the square.

c) *Odd Unit.* When the total run of a rafter is in even feet all of the

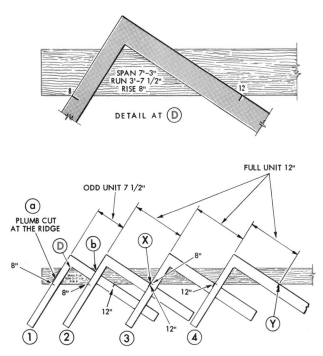

Fig. 18. The rafter layout begins with stepping off the odd unit, followed by three full steps to locate the outside of the plate. Notations about the rafter are marked as at **(D)**.

steps will be equal. Rafters such as this one do not come out even. When the run is given in feet and inches, the inches become what we will call the *odd unit*. To avoid omission it is advisable to allow the first step to be the odd unit. Therefore, while the square is in position *1*, Fig. 18, locate 7½ inches on the blade (the run side of the square) and mark the stock at this point *b*.

d) Full Units. Move the square to position *2*, holding it to the *cut* and up to the *odd unit* mark. Then draw a line along the blade on the edge of the stock at *X*, Fig. 18, thus laying the first full unit. Continue with two more full units *3* and *4*, Fig. 18, holding the square exactly to the marks each time. This will give three full units which are equal to the three feet of run of the rafter. The point *Y*

of the last full unit, Fig. 18 and Fig. 19, is the building line on which the bird's-mouth is to be laid out.

5. Laying Out Bird's-Mouth and Heel. When the rafter has an overhang, the rafter piece is cut out at the plate with a *seat* or *level cut* and a *plumb cut* to fit around the plate. This cut out is called the *bird's-mouth*, Figs. 17 and 19. The plumb line of the bird's-mouth, extended up, forms the *heel* of the rafter, as shown in Fig. 19. It is the heel which establishes a measuring point in laying out the main rafter lengths. Therefore, the heel is of considerable importance.

The size of the heel at the building line is governed by the strength required to carry the overhang. If the overhang is long, the thickness of the rafter at this point must be rela-

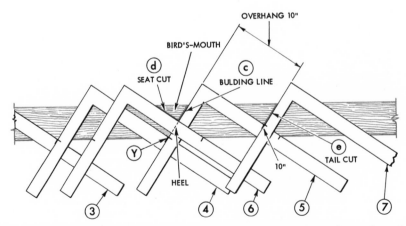

Fig. 19. The bird's-mouth is marked off by measuring the heel dimension and moving the square to make the level cut. The tail cut is made after marking the 10 inch point.

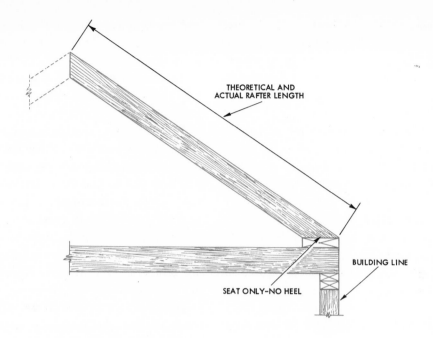

THEORETICAL AND
ACTUAL RAFTER LENGTH

BUILDING LINE

SEAT ONLY—NO HEEL

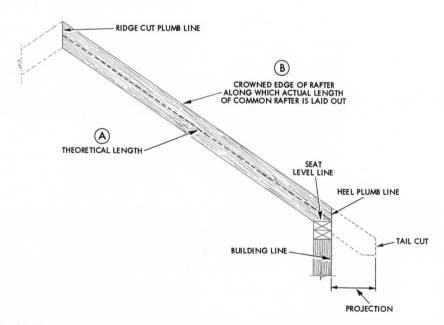

RIDGE CUT PLUMB LINE

Ⓑ

CROWNED EDGE OF RAFTER
ALONG WHICH ACTUAL LENGTH
OF COMMON RAFTER IS LAID OUT

Ⓐ

THEORETICAL LENGTH

SEAT
LEVEL LINE

HEEL PLUMB LINE

TAIL CUT

BUILDING LINE

PROJECTION

Fig. 20. The theoretical length of the rafter does not change whether the rafter has a heel or not.

tively greater. A heel of 2½ inches as given in our problem, is sufficient for the average overhang and will leave a good sized seat or horizontal cut in the bird's-mouth for fastening the rafter to the plate.

The heel on the rafter will raise the rafter, but will not alter the pitch of the roof nor the shape of the basic triangle, Fig. 9, neither will it affect the length of the rafter. The length of the rafter at *B*, Fig. 20, is the same as at *A*, Fig. 20, its theoretical length, because the ridge cut and the heel cut of *B* are both plumb cuts. Therefore, the lines are parallel. The heel, then, merely raises the entire rafter straight up without affecting it in any other way.

To lay out the bird's-mouth, move the square to position 5, Fig. 19. Then draw the building line *c*, which is a plumb line. Lay out the heel on this line, measuring 2½ inches from point *Y*. Move the square to position 6 and draw the seat cut *d*. The bird's-mouth is thus formed by the seat cut and the building line below the heel.

If the rafter did not have an overhang, the layout would be complete and the rafter could be cut along the line through point Y and the seat cut line.

6. Laying Out Overhang and Tail Cut. At the lower end of the rafter, that part which extends beyond the building line is known as the *overhang*. In the layout process, this portion of the rafter is treated separately, since it is an addition to the theoretical length of the rafter. In our problem, the projection (the run of the overhang) is given as 10 inches. Hold the square on the rafter stock so that the tongue is on the building line through point Y and the units 8 and 12 are on the edge of the board. Position 5, Fig. 19. Mark the stock at the 10 inch point on the blade of the square. Then move the square to position 7, use the cut of rafter, and draw the line for the tail cut *e*, Fig. 19. This line will be parallel to the building line,

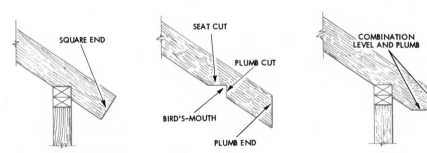

Fig. 21. The overhang may be finished in several ways.

and will allow for a projection of 10 inches. Fig. 20.

The tail cut or rafter end may be finished in one of several ways. Three different methods are shown in Fig. 21. When the finish for the overhang of a roof rafter is not shown on the architectural drawings, then the carpenter or builder must decide upon the type of design to use. The type of cornice, the width of the fascia and the means of support of overhang members are governing factors.

7. Shortening Rafter at Ridge. On a roof without a ridge piece, the common rafters will meet as shown by the dotted lines in Fig. 22. When a ridge piece is used, a part of the rafter stock must be cut away so the rafter will remain in the same position. The ridge cut, then, will be a second line parallel to the first line, at a point on the rafter back one half the thickness of the ridge piece. The ridge piece for a roof can be of either 1 or 2 inch material. However, the 2 inch stock will provide a better

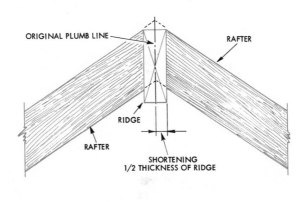

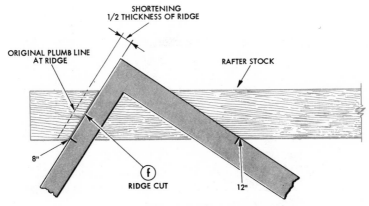

Fig. 22. The shortening at the ridge is made equal to one-half the thickness of the ridge board.

249

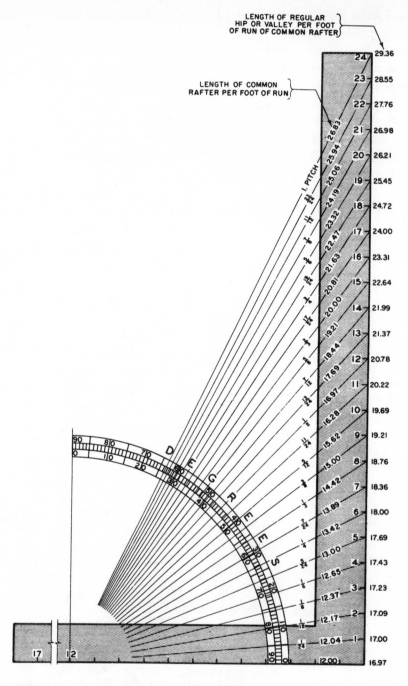

Fig. 23. Roof pitch, unit rise and degree of slope information.

nailing base for the rafters, and will also insure better alignment of the various roof members.

In our problem the ridge piece is specified as a 2 × 6, of which the actual thickness will be 1⅝ inches (or 1½ inches under some standards). Therefore, the rafter pattern must be shortened 13/16 of an inch (or ¾ inch) or one-half the actual thickness of the 2 × 6. Measure 13/16 of an inch at right angles to the original plumb ridge line, Fig. 22. Lay the square to the *cut* of the rafter (8 for unit rise on the tongue and 12 for the unit run on the blade) and draw the plumb line *f*, which will be the true ridge cut; that is, the line on which to cut the rafter. Since the shortening measurements are always taken at right angles to the plumb cut, the slope, or pitch, of the roof does not affect the shortening measurements.

This completes the entire layout of the common rafter pattern. Before cutting the rafter pattern it is advisable to cross out all lines on the rafter pattern stock, except the marks needed for making the cuts.

This precaution will help to prevent errors when making the various rafter cuts.

8. Checking the Rafter Length. It is always advisable to check the rafter length layout by the 12th scale method.[2] This is an approximate method which will help you to detect serious errors if any have occurred during the process of laying out the rafter pattern. If you find your first pattern is not correct in every detail, then a new pattern should be cut in order to avoid undue waste of materials.

A more accurate method to check the line length of the rafter is to refer to the table on the blade of the framing square. The length of common rafters per foot of run for common rafters with 8 inch unit rise equals 14.42 inches.

$3'-7\frac{1}{2}'' = 3.625$ feet

$14.42 \times 3.625 = 52.27$ inches or $4'-4\frac{1}{4}''$ (line length of common rafter)

Note. Fig. 23, *Roof Pitch, Unit Rise and Degree of Slope Information*, has the same information as found on the framing square.

Hip Rafters

Whenever two roof surfaces slope upward from the external corner of two walls of a building, the two surfaces will come together in a sloping line known as a *hip*. If both roof surfaces incline upward with the same slope, the two roofs are said to be of *equal pitch*. If the roofs incline upward with different slopes, they are said to be of *unequal pitch*. An

2. See footnote page 233 regarding the use of the 1/12th scale.

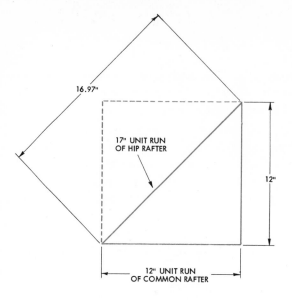

16.97"

17" UNIT RUN
OF HIP RAFTER

12"

12" UNIT RUN
OF COMMON RAFTER

**Fig. 24. The unit run of the hip is
the diagonal of a 12-inch square.**

equal pitch hip roof is illustrated in Fig. 2. The rafters which extend diagonally from the corners of the building to the ridge are called *hip rafters*.

In a plan view, where the observer looks directly down on the roof plan, as in Fig. 13, a hip rafter is the diagonal of a square when the roof has equal pitch. The square is formed by the theoretical total run of the common rafters and the plate lines. The diagonal of this square is the total run of the hip rafter. What the plan view really shows, then, is the total run of the hip, common rafters, and all of her members. Since the unit run of the common rafter is 12 inches, the unit run of the hip rafter

will be the diagonal of a 12 inch square, which is 16.97 inches, as shown in Fig. 24. The number 16.97 is so close to 17 that for all practical purposes you will find it quite satisfactory to use the number 17 instead of 16.97. Hence for every 12 inch unit of common rafter run on an equal-pitch roof, the hip rafter has a unit run of 17 inches.

To find the *plumb cut* of the hip rafter, take the unit run of 17 inches on the blade of the framing square and the figure indicating the same unit rise as for the common rafter on the tongue of the square. Lay the square on the rafter stock in the position shown in the illustration, Fig. 25, with the tongue near the left

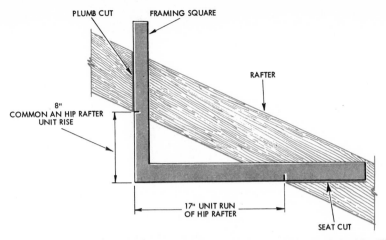

Fig. 25. Plumb and level cuts on the hip rafter are made using the cut of the hip. The unit rise is equal to the unit rise of the common rafter and the unit run is 17 inches. Note: The rafter and framing square are not in layout position but in the position the rafter will take on the roof.

end of the piece. A line drawn along the outside edge of the tongue will give the angle for the *plumb cut* of the hip rafter. To find the *seat cut* of the hip rafter, hold the square to 17 inches on the blade, and to the figure indicating the unit rise on the tongue, in the same position on the rafter stock as shown in Fig. 25. A line drawn along the outside edge of the blade of the square will give the angle for the *seat cut* of the hip rafter.

Basic Right Triangle Applied to Hip Roof

In laying out the common rafter only one right triangle is involved, as shown in Fig. 9. However, in laying out the hip rafter two right tri-angles must be considered, as shown in Fig. 26. The hip rafter is the diagonal of a *square prism*, while the common rafter lies entirely within one plane with only two dimensions.

We have previously found that in an equal-pitch roof, *the length of a common rafter is the hypotenuse of a right triangle, the base of which is the total run of the rafter, and the altitude is the total rise of the rafter,* as shown in Fig. 9. *The run of a hip rafter is the hypotenuse of a right triangle, A B C, Fig. 26, of which the two sides are both equal to the run of the common rafter. The length of a hip rafter is the hypotenuse of a right triangle, A C D, Fig. 26, of which the base is the run of the hip rafter and the altitude is the rise of

253

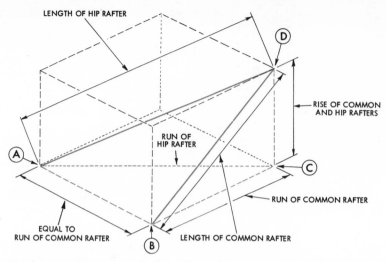

Fig. 26. The theoretical line length of a hip rafter is the diagonal of a prism with a square base.

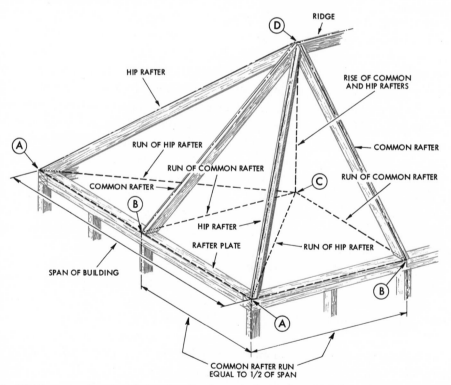

Fig. 27. The carpenter should visualize the theoretical triangles which form the common and hip rafters.

the common and hip rafters. (The rise of the hip rafter is the same as the rise of the common rafter.) The relation of these basic right triangles to the rafters of a hip roof is illustrated in Fig. 27.

Laying Out a Hip Rafter

The layout for a hip rafter, as shown in Fig. 28, is similar to the layout for the common rafter, shown in Figs. 18 and 19. However, when laying out the hip rafter, the figures taken on the framing square are different from those used when laying out the common rafter. Also, the hip rafter has *side cuts* which makes it necessary for the carpenter to work to a *center line*, Fig. 28.

PROCEDURE

The following layout problem is based on the roof plan shown in Fig. 13. This roof has a unit rise of 8 inches and a total common-rafter run of 3 feet 7½ inches. (Span = 7 feet 3 inches.)

1. Finding the total run of the hip rafter.
2. Stepping off length of hip rafter.
3. Backing the hip rafter.
4. Shortening hip rafter at ridge.
5. Making side cuts.
6. Laying out run of the overhang.
7. Checking the hip-rafter lengths.

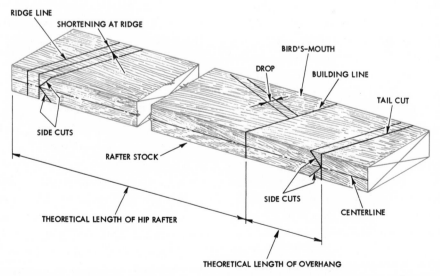

Fig. 28. The hip rafter can be laid out by using the theoretical length or the step off method.

1. Finding the Total Run of the Hip Rafter. As shown in Fig. 24 for each foot unit of run on the common rafter there are 16.97 inches (or 17 inch) run on the hip rafter. The run of the common rafter is $3'\text{-}7\frac{1}{2}''$ = 3-7.5/12 feet or 3.625 feet, $3.625 \times 17 = 61.62$ inches or $5'1\frac{5}{8}''$ run.

2. Stepping Off Length of Hip Rafter. For any rafter, the basis of the step-off method is the unit of run. Stepping off the hip rafter is very similar to stepping off the common rafter except that instead of using 8 inches on the tongue and 12 inches on the blade, 8 inches on the tongue and *17 inches* on the blade are used. The same number of steps are taken as are taken on the common rafter. If a roof had a common rafter with a total run of 15 feet both the common rafter and the hip rafter would have 15 steps, one with a unit run of 12 and the other with a unit run of 17. Odd units must be handled carefully because the run of the odd unit is the *diagonal* of a square.

When laying out the hip rafter, use the same method of procedure as when laying out the common rafter; that is, begin at the top end of the piece of rafter stock and work toward the lower or seat end of the piece. To find the *odd unit* of the hip rafter proceed as follows:

a) *Odd Unit.* The unit run of the hip rafter, as shown at *AC*, Fig. 26, is the diagonal of a square whose

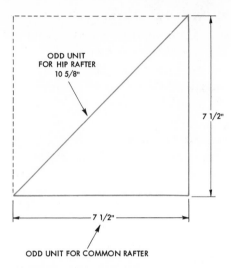

Fig. 29. The odd unit for the hip is the diagonal of a 7½ inch square.

sides are formed by the unit run of the common rafter. Therefore, the odd unit of the hip rafter is a diagonal of a square whose sides are formed by the run of the odd unit of the common rafter, as shown in Fig. 29. The length of the odd unit of run for the hip rafter can be found by holding the square in the position shown in Fig. 30. Take the length of the odd unit of the common rafter ($7\frac{1}{2}$ inches in our problem) on both the tongue and blade of the square, then mark the rafter stock at those points on both sides of the square. Measure the distance between these two points. This will give you the length of the run of the odd unit for the hip rafter. In this problem, this length is $10\frac{5}{8}$ inches.

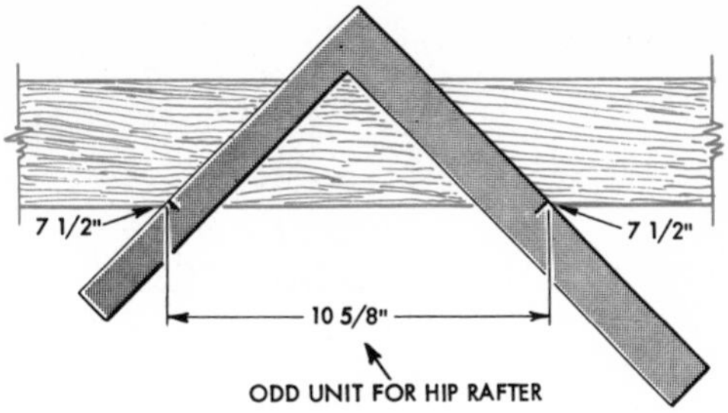

Fig. 30. The length of the odd unit may be determined by bridging the square at the two 7½ inch points.

ODD UNIT FOR HIP RAFTER

7 1/2"　　7 1/2"

10 5/8"

b) Draw a center line on the crown edge (top) of the rafter stock.

c) Hold the framing square to the hip rafter cut, in the position shown in Fig. 31. Take the figure 8 (unit rise) on the tongue of the square and the figure 17 (unit of run of hip rafter) on the blade. Draw the plumb line for the ridge at *A*, Fig. 31, along the tongue of the square. Then, on the blade side of the square, mark the point *B*, indicating the length of the odd unit of the hip rafter. This odd unit is 10⅝ inches.

d) Move the framing square to the position 2, Fig. 31. While holding the tongue of the square to the odd unit point *B*, mark off on the rafter stock the first full unit on the blade side of the square (using 8 and 17), then move the square to position *3*. Now move the square to positions *4* and *5*, Fig. 32. As the square is shifted from one position to the next, mark off the unit lengths until the full three units have been stepped off, in addition to the odd unit length.

e) While holding the square position *5*, Fig. 32, draw the building line as indicated at *C*, along the tongue of the square. On the building line, measure the height of the heel (2½ inches), which is the same as that for the common rafter previously explained. See dimension *Y*, Fig. 33. Move the square to position *6* and draw the seat line, as shown at *D*, Fig. 32. The seat cut is not finished with the drawing of the seat line. Other steps will follow.

3. Backing the Hip Rafter. The *center line* of the hip rafter is the theoretical line where two roof slopes meet. In rafter layout work, all measurements are considered as taken on the center line. To prevent the hip rafter from projecting above the jack rafters, as shown in Fig. 34, the top edge of the rafter must be *backed*, or the rafter may be *dropped*. A rafter is backed by placing a bevel on each side of the top edge, with the high point of the bevel being in the center of the hip,

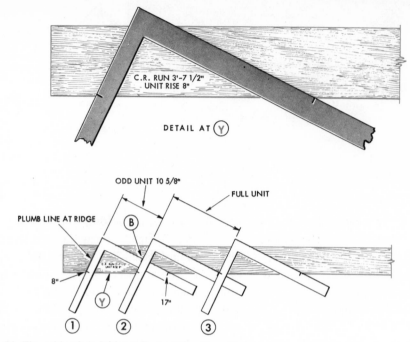

Fig. 31. The odd unit is laid out first on the hip rafter.

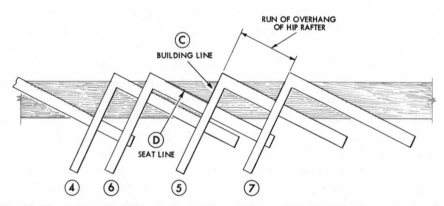

Fig. 32. The seat cut is laid out in a manner similar to that used for the common rafter.

as shown in Fig. 35. If the hip rafter is dropped, as shown in Fig. 36, there will be an open space at the top when the sheathing boards are applied. This method is the most practical and used most often.

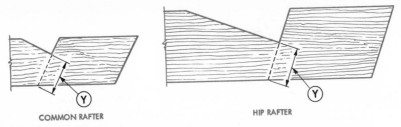

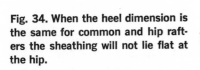

Fig. 33. The basic heel dimension (Y) is the same for common and hip rafters.

Fig. 34. When the heel dimension is the same for common and hip rafters the sheathing will not lie flat at the hip.

Fig. 35. Backing the hip consists of chamfering the edges so that the sheathing will lie flat.

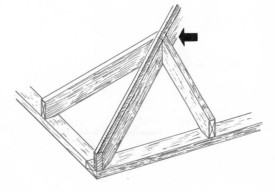

To determine the amount of backing required, lay the framing square to the cut of the hip roof. Take the unit rise of 8 inches on the tongue of the square and the unit run of 17 inches on the blade, as shown in Fig.

259

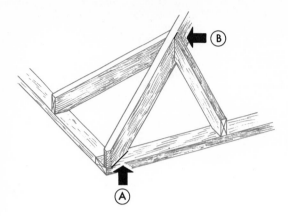

Fig. 36. When the hip is dropped, enough stock is cut away at the seat (A) so that the edge of the hip is level with the top of the jacks (B).

37; then draw the line A along the outside edge of the blade. Measure back one-half of the thickness of the hip rafter to locate point *B*, draw the line *C* parallel to the edge of the rafter stock through point *B*. Bevel the hip rafter between mark and center line.

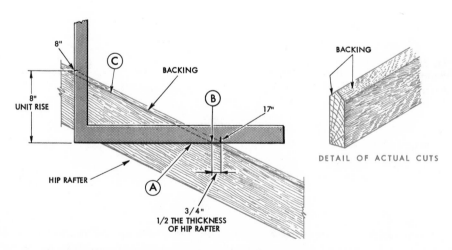

Fig. 37. The amount of backing is found by laying out a level line on the rafter and measuring ½ the thickness of the stock on the line (¾ of an inch).

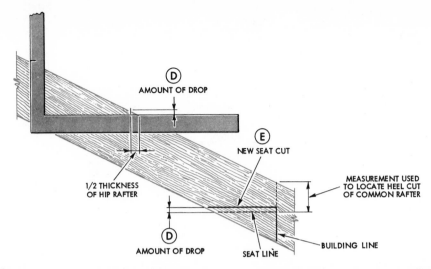

Fig. 38. The amount of drop is determined by laying out a level line anywhere on the rafter, measuring ½ the thickness of the stock (¾ of an inch) and then measuring the plumb distance at that point. The seat line is raised this amount so that the rafter drops accordingly.

If the hip rafter is to be dropped, the amount of drop can be determined by placing the square on the rafter, using units 8 and 17, drawing a level line and marking one half of the thickness of the hip rafter on the line. The plumb distance to the edge of the rafter is the amount of drop to be used at the seat cut E. See Fig. 38.

After finding the amount of drop necessary for the hip rafter at the plate, measure the amount of drop on the building line up from the seat line and draw the line for the seat cut. See Fig. 38.

4. Shortening Hip Rafter at Ridge. If the rafters and the ridge were merely lines or planes without thickness, as they appear on the plan view, Fig. 13, these framing members would all meet at a point X, as shown in Fig. 39. Since these framing members have thickness, the rafters must be shortened at the ridge accordingly.

When the hip rafter is framed against the common rafters, as in Fig. 39, the shortening of the hip rafter will always be one half of the 45 degree thickness of the common rafter regardless of whether or not the ridge is 1 inch or 2 inch material.

To find one half of the 45 degree thickness of the common rafter, lay the framing square across the edge of the rafter stock, using the same figures on each side of the square, as

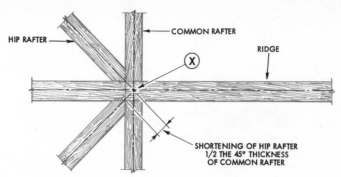

HIP RAFTER

COMMON RAFTER

RIDGE

X

SHORTENING OF HIP RAFTER
1/2 THE 45° THICKNESS
OF COMMON RAFTER

Fig. 39. The shortening of the hip is one-half of the 45° thickness of the common rafter.

shown in Fig. 40. Draw a line, as *A*, and measure the distance from the edge to the center of the stock. This gives one half the 45 degree thickness of the common rafter.

When the hip rafter is framed against the ridge, as shown in Fig. 41, the hip rafter is shortened one half of the 45 degree thickness of the ridge. This is an important fact to remember, since the ridge is sometimes of 1 inch material instead of 2 inch material. After determining the required amount of shortening of the hip rafter at the ridge, lay out this distance on a level line at right angles to the plumb cut, shown at *A*, Fig. 42. Draw a second plumb line *B* and square both lines across the top edge of the hip-rafter stock.

5. Making Side Cuts. If a level cut were taken through the upper end of a hip rafter held in the position it will take on the roof, the faces of the cuts would make an angle of

45 degrees with the sides of the rafter. However, the cuts marked on the top of the rafter, as at *X*, Fig. 43, will not be at 45 degree angles.

Side Cuts at the Ridge. After marking the shortening line B, Fig. 43, measure off one-half the hip-rafter thickness on a level line. This locates a third plumb line *C* half the thickness of the hip rafter from line *B*. Square all three lines *A*, *B*, and *C*, across the top edge of the hip-rafter stock. Fig. 43.

Draw the side cuts from the point where the line *C* intersects the edge of the stock to the center *X*. If the hip rafter has a double side cut, draw another side cut from the opposite side of the rafter stock. Fig. 43. For a single side cut, one of these side-cut lines should be extended all the way across the stock. Which side cut line to be extended will depend upon which side of the hip rafter is to fit against ridge.

262

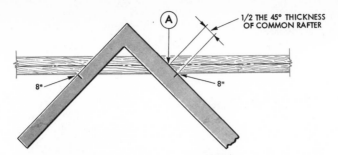

Fig. 40. Take equal measurements on each leg of the framing square to mark a 45° diagonal on the common rafter. Measure one-half of the diagonal.

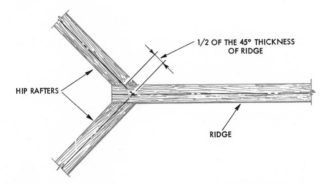

Fig. 41. Shortening of the hip in this case is one-half of the 45° thickness of the ridge.

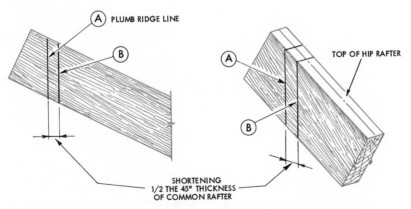

Fig. 42. Mark the shortening by measuring the dimension on a level line.

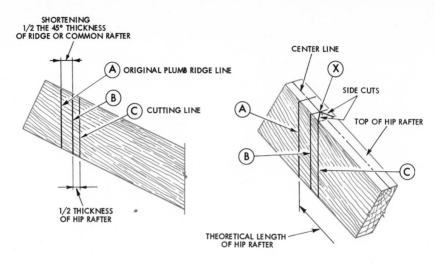

Fig. 43. The side cuts are marked first on the side of the hip rafter on a level line. The points are connected on the top of the rafter to the center X.

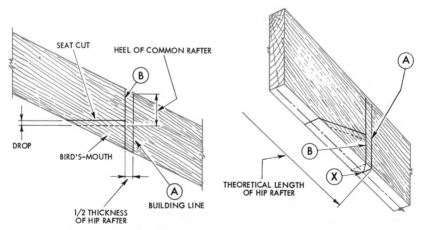

Fig. 44. When side cuts are required at the birds'-mouth, they are laid out in a manner similar to that used at the ridge. (When the hip will not be exposed to view, the saw cuts are made on the seat cut and the building line.) (The drop is shown in Fig. 38.)

Side Cut at Bird's-Mouth. A side cut is seldom made at the bird's-mouth except on work which must be carefully finished. The cut for the bird's mouth is shown at the left, Fig. 44.

Draw a center line on the bottom edge of the rafter stock and square the building line *A* across the bottom edge, as shown in the drawing at the right, Fig. 44. Lay off one half the thickness of the hip rafters on a level line on the side of the building line toward the ridge cut. Then draw the plumb line *B* and square it across the bottom edge of the piece of stock. Draw side cuts from the line *B* to the center line at the point *X*, as shown in drawing at right, Fig. 44.

6. Layout for Run of the Overhang. The run of the overhang of the hip rafter is called the projection. It is the diagonal of a square whose sides are equal to the common-rafter projection. (*Note*: the projection is a level dimension.) You can find the projection of the hip rafter in the same way you found the run of the odd unit of the hip rafter, as shown in Figs. 29 and 30. In the plan-view shown in Fig. 13, the common rafter has a projection of 10 inches. The diagonal of a 10-inch square is approximately $14\frac{3}{16}$ inches which is the projection of the hip rafter for this building.

Lay the framing square on the hip rafter stock in position *1*, Fig. 45, with the tongue of the square held to the building line *A*, and using the cut of the hip 8 and 17. While holding the square in this position, make a mark on the stock at $14\frac{3}{16}$. Then move the square to position *2* and

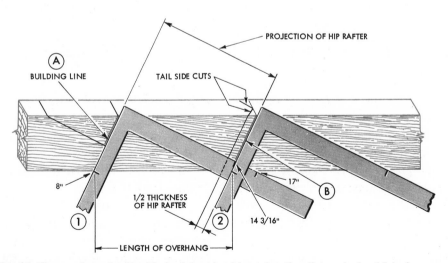

Fig. 45. The overhang for the hip is determined by using the diagonal of a 10 inch square. See Figs. 24 and 29. (The sides of the square are equal to the projection of the common rafter.) Side cuts must be made.

hold it to the cut of the hip. Then draw the line *B*. Square this line across either the top or bottom edge of the rafter stock, and lay out the tail *side cuts* on the end of the overhang.

Side Cuts at Tail. The side cuts at the lower end of the rafter are necessary to accommodate the fascia of the cornice. See Fig. 45.

Side cuts are determined by measuring one half of the thickness of the hip rafter on a level line.

7. Checking the Hip-Rafter Length. The theoretical length of the hip rafter can be checked quickly by using the 12th scale found on the back of the framing square. Using the total run of the hip and total rise, bridge the square using the 12th scale to find the approximate length in feet and inches. The practice of making such a check is recommended because it will help you to

detect any gross errors in layout and will prevent the spoiling of expensive rafter stock.

A more accurate mathematical procedure will give a precise check. The table on the framing square under "Length of Regular Hip or Valley per foot of run of Common Rafter" states that for a unit rise of 8 inches the length dimension is 18.76 inches. (Note that this information is shown on Fig. 23.) The common rafter has a total run of 3'-7½":

3'-7½" = 3-7.5/12 or 3.625 feet
18.76 × 3.625 = 68.005 inches or 5'-8".

After the check has been made, any lines used in the layout should be erased or crossed out, if not needed later. To avoid confusion, leave only those lines on which cuts are to be made.

Valley Rafters

A *valley rafter* is the roof framing member which is placed where two roof slopes meet to form an internal angle, as shown in Fig. 2. In an equal-pitch roof, the basic right triangle, as applied to the hip rafter, shown in Fig. 26, has the same application to the valley rafter; that is, the run of the valley rafter is the hypotenuse of a right triangle whose sides are equal the run of the common rafter. The length of the valley rafter

is a diagonal of a prism in the same manner as the hip. The rise is the same as the rise of the related common rafter.

The intersection of two roof slopes of equal pitch may present several rafter framing situations. The main factors involved are the span of the addition and the method used in framing the ridge of the intersecting roof.

1. When the span of the addition

is the same width as the span of the main roof, the ridge of both roofs will meet on the same level, as shown at *A*, Fig. 46. In this case, the common rafter of both the main roof and the addition will have the same run. The run of the valley rafter will be the hypotenuse of a right triangle whose sides are equal to the run of the common rafters. The valley rafters will have double side cuts to fit against both ridges, as shown in the detail at *A*, Fig. 46.

2. When the span of the addition

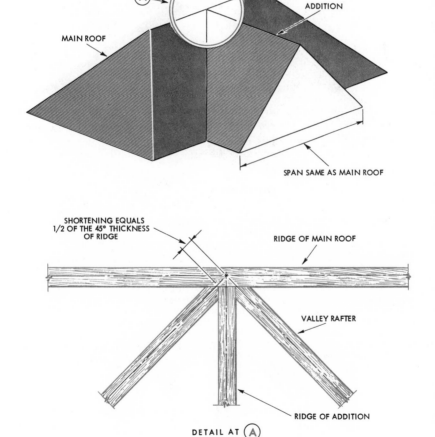

Fig. 46. When the span of the main roof and the addition are the same, the ridges and valley rafters meet.

is less than the span of the main roof, one of the two valley rafters, called a supporting valley, can be framed against the ridge of the main roof with a single side cut, as shown in the detail at *A*, Fig. 47. The length of this supporting valley rafter can be found by the same method used in finding the length of the hip rafter; that is, by using the step-off method. It is related to the common rafter of the main roof in that there will be the same number of steps of the framing square, except that instead of using

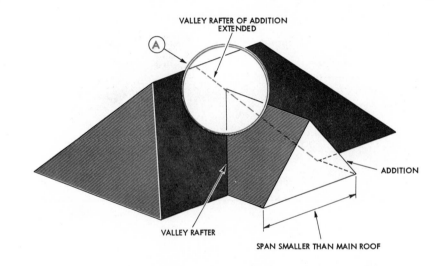

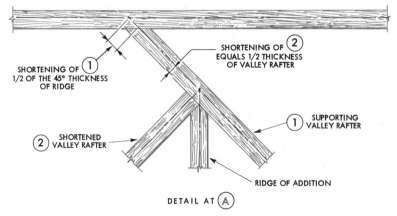

Fig. 47. When the main roof span is greater than that of the addition, one valley rafter is extended to become a supporting valley rafter.

a unit run of 12 inches, a unit run of 17 inches is used. The shortened valley rafter is then framed against the supporting valley rafter with a square cut, as shown in the detail drawing at right, Fig. 47. The run of the shortened valley rafter may be found by taking the hypotenuse of a right triangle with sides equal to the run of the common rafter of the addition. The length of this valley rafter can be stepped off using the same number of steps as used for the common rafter of the addition. The unit run for the common rafter is 12 inches whereas the unit run for the shortened valley rafter is 17 inches.

3. On small roofs such as dormers the ridge is usually framed against

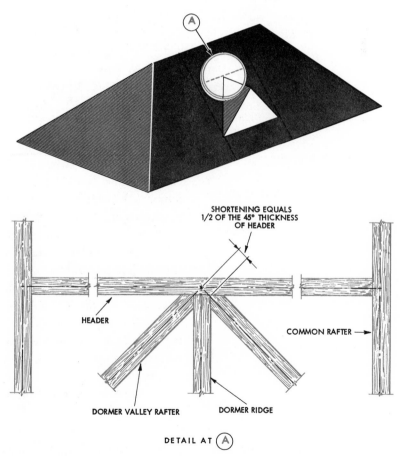

Fig. 48. Valley rafters for small dormers are framed against a header.

a header between the common rafters of the main roof, as shown in Fig. 48. Note particularly the detail drawing shown at *A*. The run of these valley rafters can be found by using the run of the common rafters of the dormers and the step-off method. These valley rafters are framed against the ridge and the header, with a double side cut.

Laying Out a Valley Rafter

The layout of a valley rafter follows the same routine as that of hip rafters except for shortening and side cuts. The supporting valley rafter has the same unit rise as the common rafter of the main roof and the same number of steps and perhaps an odd unit. They differ in the fact that full steps on the common rafter have a unit run of 12 inches whereas full steps on a valley rafter have a unit run of 17 inches. The odd unit must be considered as the diagonal of a square. See Fig. 30.

When a shortened valley rafter occurs the same procedure is required as that for the supporting valley rafter. The same number of steps and the proportional odd unit as needed for the common rafter of the addition are used, but with a unit rise of 17 inches.

PROCEDURE

The following problem is based on the roof plan shown in Fig. 13. This roof has a unit rise of 8 inches and a total common rafter run of 3'-7½" (span = 7'-3"). The span of the addition is also 7'-3" therefore the common rafters are the same as for the main roof.

1. Selecting stock.
2. Finding the total run of the valley rafter.
3. Stepping-off length of the valley rafter.
4. Shortening valley rafter at ridge.
5. Laying out the bird's-mouth.
6. Making side cuts.
7. Laying out for run of the overhang and tail cut.
8. Checking the valley-rafter lengths.

1. Selecting Stock. Valley-rafter stock must be selected with great care, because the valley rafter must support the weight of the valley jacks and the roof load in the near-by area. Usually the valley-rafter stock is one or two sizes larger than the common rafters. In roofs of large span, the valley rafters are often doubled.

2. Finding the Total Run of the Valley Rafter. As shown in Fig. 24 for each foot of run on the common rafter there are 16.97 inches (or 17) run on the valley (or hip) rafter. The run of the common rafter of the addition to the building is 3'-7½":

3'-7½" = 3-7.5/12 or 3.625 feet.
3.625 × 17 = 61.62 inches or 5'-1⅝" run.

3. Stepping Off Length of Valley Rafter. The basis of the step-off method for any rafter is the unit of run. The unit of run for the common rafter is 12 inches and the unit of run for the hip rafter and valley rafter is 17 inches. When stepping off the valley rafters, proceed the same as you did when stepping off the hip rafters. First, lay the rafter stock on two sawhorses with the crown edge turned toward you (the workman). Lay the framing square on the stock near the left end, which will be the upper end of the rafter when it is in position on the roof. Hold the square to the unit rise, 8 inches (in our problem), on the tongue and the unit run, 17 inches on the blade, as shown in Fig. 31. Draw the plumb line along the tongue of the square, and lay off the odd unit. (The odd unit will have

a 10⅝″ run as shown in Fig. 29.) Continue as you did when laying out the hip rafter, with the square in the positions shown in Fig. 31. In addition to the odd unit step off three full units.

4. Shortening Valley Rafter at Ridge. The amount the valley rafter should be shortened at the ridge will be one-half the 45 degree thickness of the ridge when the span of the main roof is the same as the span of the addition as it is in our problem, Fig. 46. The shortening of the rafter is measured on a level line, as shown in Fig. 49.

5. Laying Out the Bird's-Mouth. The valley rafter is laid out in steps in the same manner as the hip rafter. (See Figs. 29, 30, 31 and 32.) The odd step with 10⅝ inch run is taken

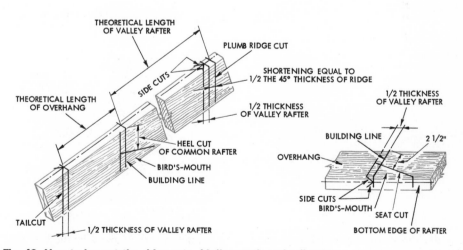

Fig. 49. How to lay out the ridge cuts, bird's-mouth and tail cuts.

first then three steps with 17 inch run. The last step will give the plumb line which is the building line. Measure down 2½ inches from the top edge of the rafter and draw the level line for the bird's-mouth. See Fig. 49.

6. Making Side Cuts. The side cuts for the valley rafter are laid out in the same way as for the hip rafter; that is, by measuring one half the valley-rafter thickness on a level line from the shortening line at the top end, as shown in Fig. 49. The side cuts at the plate run from building line toward the overhang instead of toward the ridge as in the hip rafter.

The angle side cuts are usually omitted because they take time and are not necessary unless the work is to be exposed to view. The bird's-mouth is cut straight across, using the side cut line, as shown in Fig. 50. (However if there is no overhang the two angle side cuts should be made

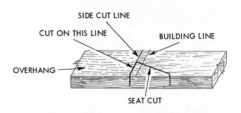

Fig. 50. The bird's-mouth of the valley rafter need not have side cuts if the rafter will not be exposed to view.

at the lower end to provide nailing for the fascia.)

When the ridge of the addition is lower than that of the main part of the building, a supporting valley as shown in Fig. 47 is used. A special problem in side cut layout develops as shown in Fig. 51.

7. Laying Out for Run of the Overhang and Tail Cut. The run of the overhang of the valley rafter is the hypotenuse of a right triangle whose two sides are equal to the run

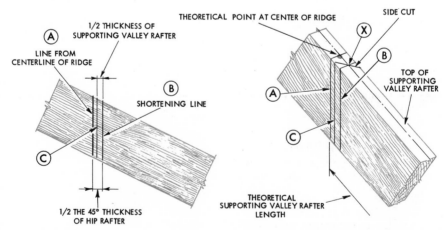

Fig. 51. The shortening for the supporting valley is marked first, followed by the side cut, line (C). The cutting line is drawn through point (X).

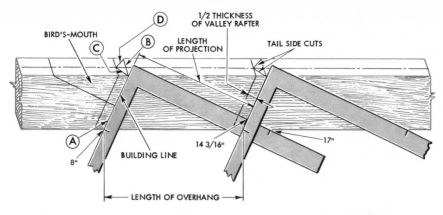

Fig. 52. The overhang for the valley rafter is determined by using the diagonal of a 10 inch square. (See Figs. 24 and 29.) (The sides of the square are equal to the projection of the common rafter.) The bird's-mouth is cut on lines A and B if the rafter is to be concealed in a cornice. It is cut on lines A, C and D if it is exposed to view.

of the overhang of the common rafter. Since the run of the overhang of the common rafter, as shown in Fig. 13, is 10 inches, the run of the valley-rafter projection will be approximately 14³⁄₁₆ inches. This length is laid out from the building line as shown in Fig. 52.

The tail cut at the end of the overhang consists of two side cuts to receive the fascia board of the cornice laid out beyond the line indicating the full length of the rafter. See Fig. 52.

8. Checking the Valley Rafter Length. The theoretical length of the valley rafter is the same as that of the hip rafter because the ridge and plate levels of the main roof and the roof of the addition are at the same height. The explanation on page 266, *checking the hip rafter length,* applies to the valley rafters also.

Jack Rafters

In a sense a jack rafter is a common rafter with either the lower or upper end cut diagonally to fit against a hip or valley rafter. In spe-

cial cases both ends may be cut diagonally.

There are three types of jack rafters. Two of these types—the hip jack and the valley jack—are shown in Fig. 2. The *hip jack* extends from the rafter plate to the hip rafter, as shown at *1*, Fig. 53. The *valley jack* extends from the valley rafter to the ridge of the roof, Fig. 59. The third type of jack rafter is the *cripple jack*, which may be classified into *hip valley cripple* and *valley cripple* (see Fig. 62). Neither one of these cripple jack rafters touches the ridge or the plate. The hip valley cripple extends between the valley and the hip rafters. When the ridges of the two roofs are on different levels the valley cripple jack is framed from the sup-porting valley rafter to the valley of the addition, as shown at *7*, Fig. 53. (See also Fig. 62.)

The unit run, unit rise, and unit length of all jack rafters are the same as the unit run, unit rise, and unit length of the common rafters on the particular roof. Like the common rafter, the run is the basis for jack-rafter layout. The run of any one of the various jack rafters is one side of a square. One side of the square for jack *1* Fig. 53 is shown with a dotted line. The square for jacks *3*, *5* and *7* may be traced in the same manner. When the total run of any jack rafter

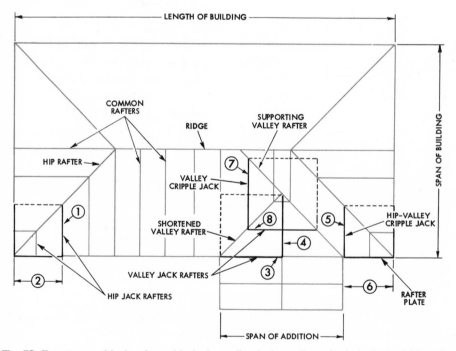

Fig. 53. Four types of jack rafters: hip jacks, valley jacks, valley cripple jacks and hip-valley cripple jacks.

is known, its length and the cuts can be easily laid out.

The total run of the hip-jack rafter *1*, Fig. 53, is the same as the distance *2*, which is the distance the jack is set from the corner of the building.

The total run *3* of the valley jack is equal to the distance *4*, which is the same as the distance the valley jack is set from the point of the valley and ridge intersection.

The total run *5* of the hip-valley jack rafter is equal to the rafter-plate length *6*, Fig. 53, which is the distance the hip-valley jack is set from the corner of the building.

The total run *7* of the valley cripple jack is twice the run of the valley jack *8*, Fig. 53.

Laying Out a Hip Jack Rafter

The jack rafters meeting a hip rafter, as shown in Fig. 54, are a series of rafters spaced the same distance apart as the common rafters. Jacks are spaced uniformly to permit proper support of roofing, snow load, and the nailing of sheathing. Since this spacing is uniform, the length of each successive jack rafter will be uniformly shortened. This shortening is known as *the common difference of jack rafters*, as shown in Figs. 54 and 55. To insure this equal spacing and uniform common difference, a jack rafter pattern should be laid out for the longest jack rafter, as shown in Fig. 55. On this pattern rafter the other jacks are marked

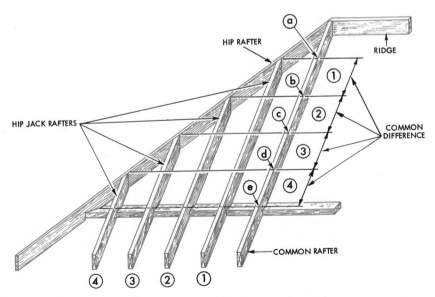

Fig. 54. Hip jacks which are evenly spaced along the plate have a common difference in length.

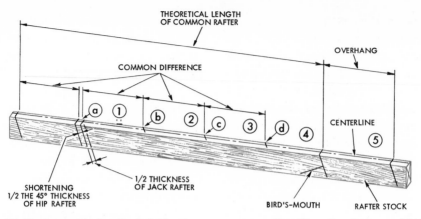

Fig. 55. The longest jack rafter is laid out on a common rafter. The other jacks are laid out from the long point using the common difference measurement.

showing their cutting lines. The bird's-mouth and overhang will be the same for all of them. This jack rafter, then, becomes a layout pattern from which as many pairs of jacks can be cut as are needed for the roof under construction. Each hip requires one pair, or two jacks, for each of the jack rafter lengths required. Very often the pattern works out so that the jacks are the same at all four hips.

PROCEDURE

The following problems in jack rafter layout are for a roof with an 8 inch unit rise and with the common rafters spaced 16 inches on center (o.c.).

1. Laying out pattern for the longest hip jack-rafter length.

2. Finding the common difference for the jack rafters.

3. Laying out the first common difference from the ridge line.

4. Shortening the jack for the hip rafter.

5. Laying out the side cuts.

6. Laying out lengths of other jack rafters from longest point.

7. Laying out and cutting jack rafters.

1. Laying Out Pattern for the Longest Hip Jack Rafter Length. The total run, unit rise, and overhang for the jack rafter must be determined as they were for the common rafter. To do this, a full-length common rafter should be laid out first. This layout should include the plumb cut at the ridge, the cut for the bird's-mouth, the length of the overhang, and the tail cut. However, there should be no shortening at the ridge, since this rafter length is the theoretical length of the common rafter, as shown in Fig. 55.

Since the jack rafter has a side cut, a center line is required along the top edge of this pattern, Fig. 55.

2. Finding the Common Difference for the Jack Rafters. The jack rafters vary in length because they fill a triangular-shaped space in the roof. Beginning with the shortest jack rafter, these rafters increase in length regularly. If evenly spaced along the plate from the corner, the second rafter is twice as long as the first, the third rafter is three times as long as the first, and so on. You can find this common-difference

length of the jack rafters by the following procedure:

A. Finding the Common Difference by Layout. *a*) Place the framing square on a piece of rafter stock having a straight, smooth edge. Hold the square to the cut of the common rafter (8 inches on the tongue and 12 inches on the blade), as shown at *A*, Fig. 56.

b) While holding the square in this position, draw a line along the blade of the square. Then slide the square along this line to the figure 16 on the blade, position *B*, for 16-inch spacing.

c) While holding the square in this position, mark at *X* on the tongue side of the square, as shown in Fig. 56.

d) The distance between these two

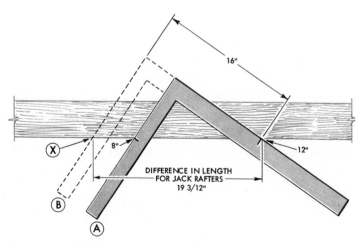

Fig. 56. The common difference is found by layout procedure.

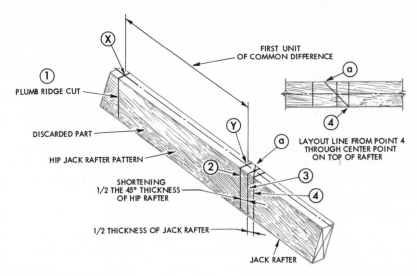

Fig. 57. The layout of the side cuts begins with a line squared from the common difference point (Y).

points will be 19¼ inches, the common difference in length for jack rafters, spaced 16 inches on center and having a unit rise of 8 inches.

B. Finding the Common Difference Using the Rafter Tables. The table on the framing square has a line designated *Difference of Length of Jacks 16 inches on centers.* Under each whole inch mark a number appears. Under the number 8, which represents a unit rise of 8 inches per foot of run on the common rafter, the figure 19.23 appears. This is the common difference. (Another line gives information on the *Difference in Length of Jacks for Rafters Spaced 2 feet on centers.*)

3. Laying Out the First Common Difference from the Ridge Line. Square the line for the plumb ridge cut across the top edge of the jack rafter stock, as shown at *1*, Fig. 57. Measure the length of the common difference (19¼ inches) from the point X along the center line, and mark point Y. Square a line through point Y to the edge of the rafter stock and then draw a plumb line *2*. This will give you the first unit of common difference of the jack rafter, measured from the ridge line.

4. Shortening the Jack for the Hip Rafter. Since the hip rafter has thickness, it becomes necessary to shorten the jack rafter one half the

45 degree thickness of the hip rafter stock, as shown in Fig. 58. Measure this required shortening distance on a level line from the plumb line and draw a third plumb line, as shown at *3*, Fig. 57. Square this line across the top edge of the rafter stock. This will give you the amount of shortening necessary for the jack rafter which fits against a hip rafter.

5. Laying Out the Side Cuts. The side cuts for jack rafters are laid out in the same way as side cuts for any other rafter. Take one half the thickness of the rafter stock, measured on a level line, as shown in Fig. 57. Draw a fourth plumb line *4*. Extend the side cut across the top edge of the rafter stock through the center point. This will give you the side cut at the top for the longest hip jack rafter.

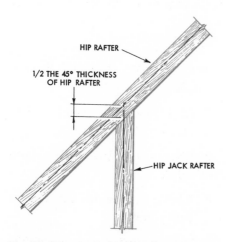

Fig. 58. The side cuts are laid out to provide for the thickness of the hip rafter.

HIP RAFTER

1/2 THE 45° THICKNESS OF HIP RAFTER

HIP JACK RAFTER

6. Laying Out Lengths of Other Jack Rafters. It is not necessary to lay out each jack independently on the pattern jack. By using the common difference measurement and measuring from the long point marked *a*, shown on Fig. 55 and Fig. 57, the location of each jack can be drawn on the pattern jack. Lay out lines across the top edge of the rafter stock at each point, as shown in Fig. 55. Make side cuts parallel to line at *a*.

7. Laying Out and Cutting Jack Rafters. Lay out a pair of jacks, or as many as required, for each jack length from the pattern rafter. It must be remembered that they are right and left on each side of the hip. The side-cut layout can be simplified by the use of a *layout tee* (illustrated in Fig. 86).

Laying Out a Valley Jack Rafter

The valley jack rafters, as shown in Fig. 59, like the hip jacks, are a series of rafters spaced the same distance apart as the common rafters. This spacing is uniform and is usually measured from the common rafter. The valley jacks have a common difference obtained in the same way as the common difference was obtained for the hip jack rafters. First, a pattern is laid out for the longest valley jack, then on this pattern spacings are laid out for the different valley jack lengths.

The valley jack extends from the

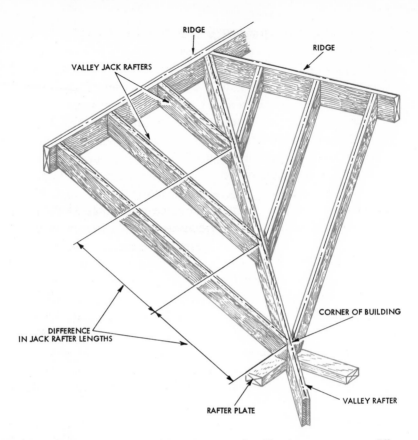

Fig. 59. Valley jacks which are evenly spaced along the ridge have a common difference in length.

valley rafter to the ridge. The valley jack does not have a bird's-mouth cut nor an overhang, but it does have a ridge cut to fit against the ridge piece and a side cut to fit against the valley. From the valley jack pattern, a pair of jacks is cut for each jack length required.

PROCEDURE

Using the same figures, 8 inch unit rise and common rafter spaced 16 inches on center, work out the following problems.

1. Laying out the longest valley jack rafter length.

2. Shortening the valley jack rafter.

3. Laying out the side cuts for the valley jacks.

4. Laying out the common difference of the valley jacks.

5. Shortening the valley jack at the ridge.

6. Laying out and cutting the necessary valley jack rafters.

1. Laying Out the Longest Valley Jack Rafter Length. In the case (Fig. 59) the longest valley jack rafter is the same as a common rafter except for the cut at the bottom, which fits against the valley rafter. It has the same unit run, unit rise, unit length and total run. The run of the valley jack starts at the corner of the building where the valley meets the plate. Therefore, a full common rafter length is laid out with a plumb line at the ridge and a plumb line at the building line. There is no bird's-mouth cut nor any overhang.

See Fig. 60. Because the valley jack has a side cut, it becomes necessary to draw a center line on the top edge of the rafter stock.

2. Shortening the Valley Jack Rafter. Since each valley jack rafter is intersected by the valley rafter, they must be shortened at the bottom end one half the 45 degree thickness of the valley rafter stock, as shown in Fig. 61.

3. Laying Out the Side Cuts for the Valley Jacks. The side cuts for the valley jack rafters are laid out in the same manner as for hip jacks. From the shortening plumb line, measure one half the thickness of the jack rafter stock on a level line, as shown in Figs. 60 and 61.

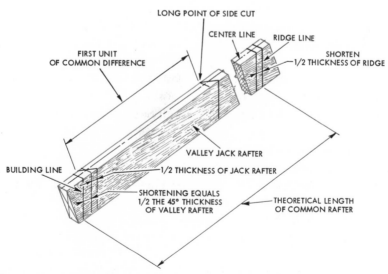

LONG POINT OF SIDE CUT

CENTER LINE   RIDGE LINE

FIRST UNIT
OF COMMON DIFFERENCE

SHORTEN
1/2 THICKNESS OF RIDGE

VALLEY JACK RAFTER

BUILDING LINE   1/2 THICKNESS OF JACK RAFTER

SHORTENING EQUALS
1/2 THE 45° THICKNESS
OF VALLEY RAFTER

THEORETICAL LENGTH
OF COMMON RAFTER

Fig. 60. The longest valley jack is laid out first.

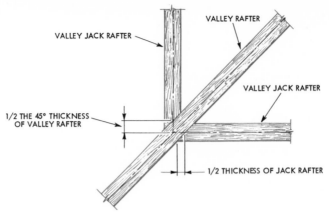

Fig. 61. The valley jack is shortened to provide for the thickness of the valley rafter.

4. Laying Out the Common Difference of the Valley Jacks. To find the common difference of the valley jacks, proceed in the same way as you did when obtaining the common difference for the hip jacks. The common difference for the valley jack is laid out from the longest point of the first side cut, as shown in Fig. 60. Lines are laid out across the top edge of the pattern rafter stock to indicate the different lengths of subsequent valley jack rafters. See Fig. 59.

5. Shortening the Valley Jack at the Ridge. The valley jack must be shortened to fit against the ridge. To find the cutting line for this shortening, measure one half the thickness of the ridge on a level line from the plumb line of the ridge in the same way as for the common rafter. See Figs. 59 and 60.

6. Laying Out and Cutting the necessary Valley Jack Rafters. After the pattern for the valley jack rafter has been laid out, make the cut at the top where it fits against the ridge, then make the side cuts at the bottom end where the jack fits against the valley rafter. The remainder of the valley jacks needed should be laid out in pairs. Use the pattern to find the length and the cutting line at the ridge. The side cuts can be laid out by using a layout tee. (See illustration, Fig. 86.)

Laying Out a Valley Cripple Jack Rafter

The rafter framed between the shortened valley rafter and the supporting or main valley rafter is known as the *valley cripple jack,* as shown in Fig. 62. The angle of the

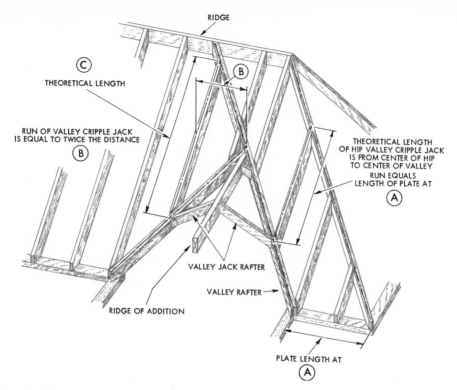

RIDGE

C

THEORETICAL LENGTH

RUN OF VALLEY CRIPPLE JACK
IS EQUAL TO TWICE THE DISTANCE

B

B

THEORETICAL LENGTH
OF HIP VALLEY CRIPPLE JACK
IS FROM CENTER OF HIP
TO CENTER OF VALLEY
RUN EQUALS
LENGTH OF PLATE AT

A

VALLEY JACK RAFTER

VALLEY RAFTER

RIDGE OF ADDITION

PLATE LENGTH AT

A

Fig. 62. The run of the hip-valley cripple jack is related to the plate length (A). The run of the valley cripple jack is related to the distance (B) to the theoretical center line: 2 B = C.

cut at the top end, where the jack fits against the supporting valley rafter, is the reverse of the angle of the cut at the lower end, where it fits against the shortened valley rafter. The run of the valley cripple jack is one side of a square, as shown at 7, Fig. 53. This run is twice the run of valley jack 8 Fig. 53. The theoretical length of the valley cripple jack is the distance from center to center of the two valley rafters, as shown in Fig. 62.

PROCEDURE

1. Layout Using the Valley Jack Pattern Rafter. To lay out a typical valley cripple jack such as number 7, Fig. 53, it is essential to obtain the theoretical length first. If valley jack rafter number 8 has a run of 16 inches then rafter 7 would have twice that amount or two units of common difference on the pattern rafter. Fig. 57 shows how to proceed once the theoretical length is established.

283

2. Layout Using the Step-Off Method. Fig. 3 shows valley cripple rafters which are not spaced so that their unit runs fall on multiples of 16 inches. The run of the shortest valley cripple is twice the length of the smallest valley jack on the small gable roof. If the run of this jack were 1'-2", the total run of the valley cripple would be 2'-4". The framing square would be used stepping off 2 full steps of 8 inch rise and 12 inch run, and a fractional step with a 4 inch run. Thus the theoretical length would be laid out. (The same procedure would be used for the second valley cripple jack.) Fig. 57 shows the details of laying out the shortening and side cuts. When the two valley rafters are of the same thickness, as is usually the case, twice the 45 degree thickness of the rafter can be

taken off of one end, thus saving one operation. However, the carpenter should avoid short cuts unless he is very familiar with what he is doing.

The side cuts, one at each end, are laid out in the same way as the side cuts of other jack rafters. However, it must be remembered that the angles for these side cuts extend in opposite directions, as shown in Figs. 62 and 63.

Laying Out a Hip Valley Cripple Jack Rafter

The run of the hip valley cripple jacks is one side of a square, as shown at 5, Fig. 53. It is equivalent to the distance 6 from the plate corner to the center line of the valley rafter.

In laying out the hip valley cripple jack use the *cut* of the common rafter. The theoretical length of this

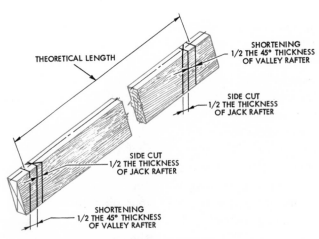

Fig. 63. Shortening and side cuts laid out for a valley cripple jack.

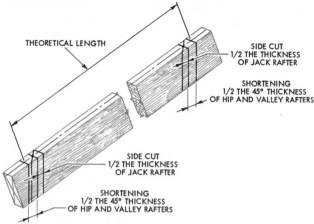

THEORETICAL LENGTH

SIDE CUT
1/2 THE THICKNESS
OF JACK RAFTER

SHORTENING
1/2 THE 45° THICKNESS
OF HIP AND VALLEY RAFTERS

SIDE CUT
1/2 THE THICKNESS
OF JACK RAFTER

SHORTENING
1/2 THE 45° THICKNESS
OF HIP AND VALLEY RAFTERS

Fig. 64. Shortening and side cuts laid out for a hip-valley cripple jack.

rafter can be obtained by using a hip pattern rafter or a step-off method as outlined under valley crippled jack procedure. The hip valley cripple jack must be shortened at both ends, one-half the 45-degree thickness of the hip and valley rafter stock, as shown in Fig. 64. If the hip and valley rafters are of the same thickness, twice this thickness can be taken off of one end of the rafter, thus saving one operation.

The hip valley cripple jack has a side cut on each end, as shown in Fig. 62 and 64. These cuts are parallel to each other and are laid out in the same way as other side cuts on jack rafters.

Erection of the Roof

The assembly of a roof which has a ridge which is too high to reach conveniently, such as the one shown in Fig. 65, usually requires the erection of a scaffold or staging. To make this scaffold, build as many two-legged horses as will be needed for the entire length of the roof. These horses should be spaced about 10 feet apart. The height of the cross ledgers for the scaffold can be determined by finding the ridge height on the building plans. The staging should be about 4 feet below the top of the ridge piece. Adequate guard rails should be provided.

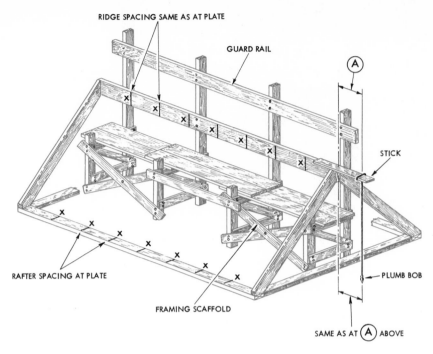

RIDGE SPACING SAME AS AT PLATE

GUARD RAIL

(A)

STICK

RAFTER SPACING AT PLATE

PLUMB BOB

FRAMING SCAFFOLD

SAME AS AT (A) ABOVE

Fig. 65. A scaffold helps in the erection of a roof. Rafter spaces are marked on the plate and the ridge. (The rafter spacing is not to scale.)

Erecting Gable Roof Frame

For the erection of the ordinary gable roof proceed as follows.

PROCEDURE

a) Lay out the rafter spacing on one of the rafter plates, by squaring lines across the plate and placing an X on the side of each line, where the rafter is to be nailed, as shown in Fig. 65.

b) Select a straight piece of ridge stock. Set this ridge piece on edge on the rafter plate flush with one end of the building, then transfer the rafter spacing to the ridge piece. The length of the ridge piece for a gable roof is equal to the length of the building, measuring from outside to outside of the rafter plates. If more than one piece of stock is required to satisfy the ridge length, the joint must be made on the center of a rafter.

c) Select a pair of straight rafters for each gable end. Three men can work to advantage when erecting the four end rafters. Two men standing on the scaffold can hold the ridge piece in position while a third man nails the rafters at the bird's-mouth.

d) Brace this frame and fill in the rest of the rafters by nailing them opposite each other. As the nailing progresses, sight the ridge for trueness.

e) After all the rafters are in place, plumb the ridge at the gable end with a straightedge and level, by hanging a plumb bob on a stick fastened to the top of the ridge. The plumb bob should be held at the same distance from the plate, at plate level, as the line is from the ridge at the top, as shown at *A*, Fig. 65. After the gable has been plumbed, brace the roof frame se-

curely in position. The bracing may be removed after sheathing is nailed on.

Erecting a Hip Roof

On an equal pitch hip roof, the run of the hip rafter is the diagonal of a square formed by the run of the common rafters, which is equal to one half the span of the building, as shown in Fig. 13. The first full common rafter is placed at a distance equal to one half the span, from the corners of the building. The following procedure may be used.

PROCEDURE

a) From the corner of the building, measure and mark on the rafter

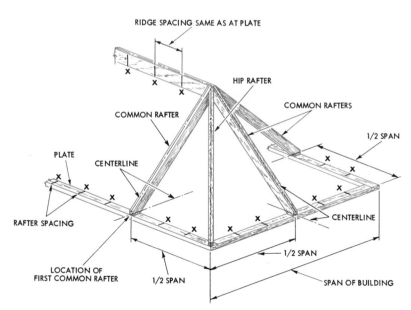

RIDGE SPACING SAME AS AT PLATE

HIP RAFTER

COMMON RAFTER

COMMON RAFTERS

1/2 SPAN

PLATE

CENTERLINE

CENTERLINE

RAFTER SPACING

LOCATION OF
FIRST COMMON RAFTER

1/2 SPAN

1/2 SPAN

SPAN OF BUILDING

Fig. 66. The erection of a hip roof begins with common rafters and ridge. (The rafter spacing is not to scale.)

plate of the building a distance equal to one half of the span. See Fig. 66. This point will locate the center of the first common rafter. The thickness of the common rafter is laid out at this point, one half on each side of this line. All other rafters, both common and jacks, are spaced from this rafter and their location marked by squaring a line across the plate, with an *X* on one side of the line to indicate the side on which the rafter is to be nailed.

b) Select the ridge stock and lay out its length as previously explained, then transfer the spacings from the plate to the ridge.

c) Erect a set of common rafters at the end of the ridge and place one common rafter at the center of each end also, Fig. 66.

d) Fill in all of the other common rafters, nailing them opposite each other, keeping the ridge straight as the nailing progresses.

e) Nail the hip and jack rafters in place.

f) The ridge of a hip roof does not need to be plumbed, as it automatically will be placed and held in the proper position by the end common rafters and the hip rafters.

Erecting Intersecting Roof

When a building is to have an addition, or intersecting roof, the main roof is partly framed before the frame of the addition is started. As shown in Fig. 67, a point must be located on the main ridge where the ridge or supporting valley of the addition is to tie in to the main roof. The ridge of the addition and a set of end rafters are erected. The valley rafters are next in order—followed by all of the remaining common rafters.

Hip jack rafters are nailed flush with the top edge of the hip rafter, but the valley jacks must be held up so the top will line up with the center of the valley rafters in order that the sheathing may lie flat. The method of nailing the valley jack rafters in position is shown in Fig. 68.

Shed Roof

The single slope roof, such as the shed or lean-to, has several applications in building construction. Some of them, illustrated in Fig. 69, are the roof of an independent building, the roof of a porch, a dormer roof, and a lean-to roof. It is an application of the common rafter.

In framing a shed roof, such as shown in Fig. 70A, it is necessary to establish the plate height of the highest wall according to the pitch of the roof. The difference in plate height is found by multiplying the unit rise of the rafter by the number of feet in the run of the rafter. The run of the rafter should be taken to the inside of the plate of the high wall.

The rafter is laid out by starting with the outside building line of the

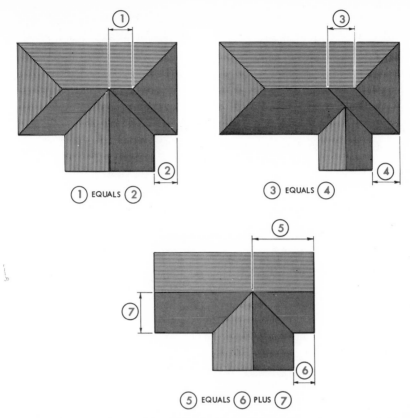

Fig. 67. After a portion of the main part of the roof has been framed, the point of intersection or support for the addition is located.

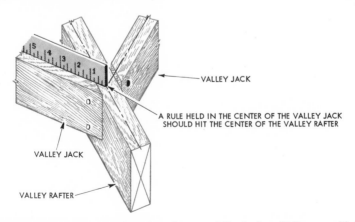

Fig. 68. Valley jacks must be nailed so that the top of the jacks will line up with the center line of the valley rafter.

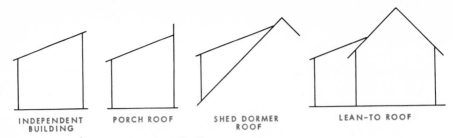

Fig. 69. Shed roofs have several applications.

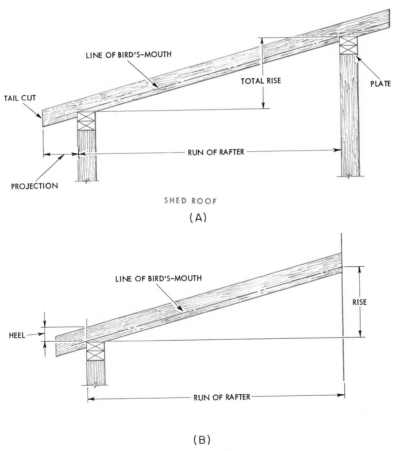

SHED ROOF

(A)

(B)

Fig. 70. (A) The shed roof rafter is a common rafter with two bird's-mouths and overhangs. (B) The porch roof rafter is essentially a common rafter.

low wall (laying the square to the unit rise and unit run of the rafter). The length of the rafter is stepped off the same as any common rafter. The bird's-mouth and overhang at the bottom and top are then laid out.

Porch Roof

A shed roof such as the one illustrated in Fig. 70B is commonly used on porch roofs. The rafters for this roof are laid out in the same way as the rafters for the shed roof, except there is no bird's-mouth cut at the top end. The total rise of such a roof frequently is governed by a second story window sill. In such a case the total rise is determined by taking into consideration the heel and the thickness of the roof sheathing, also the thickness of the shingles. It is necessary for the carpenter to know the thickness of the finished porch roof in order to make sure it will come under the window sill.

Dormer Roof

A dormer roof such as the one shown in Fig. 71 presents three different problems for the carpenter: *(a)* determining the meeting point of two slopes; *(b)* finding the top cut of the dormer rafter; and *(c)* finding the common difference of the stud lengths.

a) Meeting Point of Two Slopes. The location of the meeting point of the dormer roof and the main roof is determined by the run of the dormer rafter. Dividing the height of the dormer (expressed in inches) by the difference in unit rise of the two roof slopes will give the number of feet in the run of the dormer rafter.

For example, in the case of the dormer roof in Fig. 71, the unit rise of the dormer rafter is 4 inches per foot of run, and the unit rise of the main-roof rafter is 14 inches per foot of run. As the two rafters approach the meeting point at the main roof they are closer together at the end of each unit of rafter run. If the dormer rafter were on a level line and did not have a rise, the two rafters would be 14 inches closer together at the end of each unit of run. However, since the dormer rafter has a rise of 4 inches per foot run, the two rafters are only 10 inches closer together at the end of each unit of run. This 10 inches is the difference in the unit rise of the two rafters. Since the height of the dormer is 4 feet, or 48 inches, this number divided by 10 would give 4.8 units. The unit of run is 1 foot; $4.8 \times 1 = 4.8$ feet, or 4 feet $9\frac{5}{8}$ inches, which is the run of the dormer rafter. See Fig. 72.

b) Finding Top Cut of Dormer Rafter. In the dormer shown in Fig. 71 the dormer rafter with a unit rise of 4 inches must fit against a roof with a unit rise of 14 inches. Adjustments must be made so that the dormer rafter fits against the roof rafter. This is done by laying the framing square on a straight piece

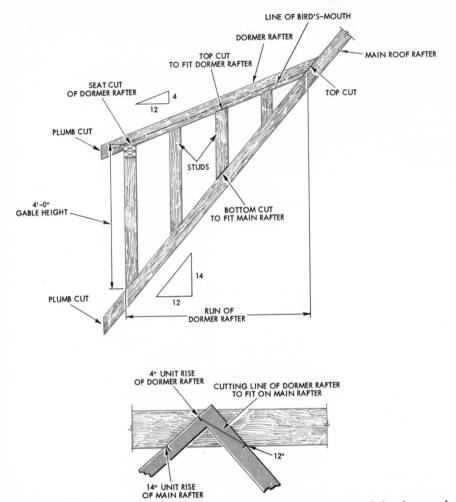

Fig. 71. The problems involved in framing dormers are: finding the run of the dormer; determining the cuts on the rafter; and finding the length and cuts on the studs.

of rafter stock in the position shown in Fig. 71 (bottom). The square is laid to the cut of the unit rise of the main roof (14 inches) and the unit run (12 inches). While holding the square in this position a mark is made on the blade side at 12 and another mark on the tongue side at 4 (the unit rise of the dormer rafter). Draw a line through the points at 4 and 12. This gives the angle for the top cut of the dormer rafter.

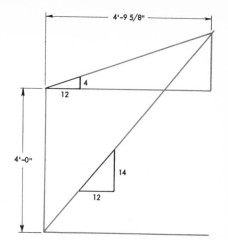

Fig. 72. A schematic diagram of the dormer shows how the run is derived.

c) Finding the Common Difference of Stud Lengths. For the dormer shown in Fig. 71 the top cut on the side studs is the same as the plumb cut at the end of the dormer rafter. The cut at the lower end of the same stud is the same as the plumb cut at the end of the main roof common rafter.

The common difference in lengths of the side studs for every 12 inch spacing is the difference between the rise of the two roofs, or 10 inches, in this case. When the studs are spaced 16 inches on center (o.c.), the difference is found by sliding the square in a way similar to that used in the case of the jack rafters illustrated in Fig. 56. This is done by taking the difference in unit rise (10 inches) on the tongue side of the square and the unit run (12 inches) on the blade of the square. Draw a line along the

blade, then slide the square along this line to the number 16 (the spacing) on the blade, and read the figure on the tongue. This measurement is 13⅜ which is the *common difference* of the stud lengths for the dormer shown in Fig. 71.

Gambrel Roof

The method used in framing a gambrel roof is much the same as for any gable roof. The slope of the roof is broken at a point somewhere between the plate and the ridge, as shown in Fig. 73. The part of the roof above this break makes an angle with the horizontal plane of less than 45 degrees, generally between 4 and 7 inch unit rise, while the portion below this break makes an angle greater than 45 degrees, generally between a 20 and 24 inch unit rise. See Fig. 23.

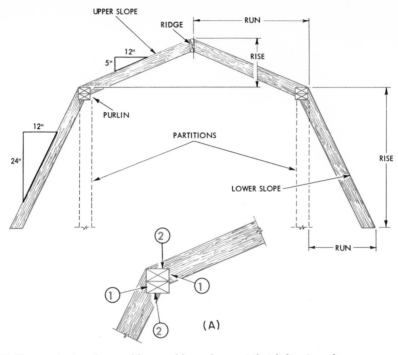

Fig. 73. The gambrel roof resembles a gable roof except that it has two slopes.

The gambrel roof may be considered as two separate roofs, with the unit rise of the upper slope much less than the unit rise of the lower slope. The main difference in the method of framing this type of roof is at the point where the rafters of the two slopes join. This point may be framed with purlin plate which is supported by partitions. The rafters of both slopes of a gambrel roof are cut to fit around the purlin. The cuts *1* and *2* of each rafter, as shown at *A*, Fig. 73, are plumb and level cuts similar to the ridge and seat cuts of a common rafter.

Chimney Saddles

The purpose of a saddle is to shed water away from the chimney. If the width of the chimney and the unit rise of the main roof are known, it is a simple matter to cut the various members of a chimney saddle, to nail

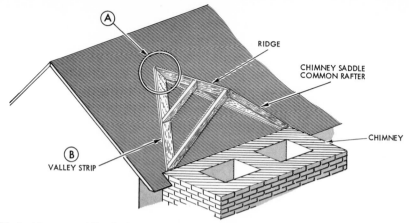

Fig. 74. A chimney saddle sheds water from behind a chimney. It may be assembled on the ground and installed after the roof is sheathed.

them together, and then slip the saddle behind the chimney in the position shown in Fig. 74. All of this work can be done on the ground or the floor of the building, where it is more convenient to work. A 1×4 or 1×6 can be nailed on the roof sheathing in place of a valley rafter. This *valley strip*, shown at *B*, Fig. 74, serves as a ledge to which the rafters and the roof sheathing of the dormer can be nailed.

Common Rafter Run for Saddle

The width of the chimney is the span of the saddle. One half of the span is the run of the common rafter. It is necessary to shorten the run of the common rafter a distance shown as *5*, Fig. 75, to allow for the valley strip and roof boards, in order to keep the flashing in line with the chimney corner.

PROCEDURE

The distance *5* is found by laying the square on a board, with a straightedge, to the cut of the roof, as shown in Fig. 76. Draw the line *1* along the blade, or run side, of the square. From the line *1* measure the thickness of the roof board and draw the line *2*. From the edge of the board, measure back the thickness of the valley strip and draw the line *3*, then draw the line *4* at the intersection of line *1*. The distance shown as *5* is the amount to deduct from the run of the common rafter, to prevent the roof boards from extending beyond the sides of the chimney.

Valley Strips for Saddle

To find the valley strip required for the saddle, proceed as follows:

295

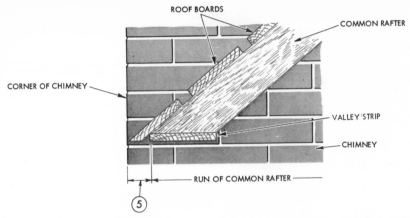

Fig. 75. The saddle is made less wide than the chimney so that when sheathing and flashing are installed they will not project.

PROCEDURE

Take a piece of 1 × 4 or 1 × 6 and step off the length of the valley strip shown at *B*, Fig. 74, using the same method as for laying out a valley rafter (no shortening required). Take the unit rise on the tongue of the square and 17 on the blade and

THICKNESS OF ROOF BOARDS

12"

UNIT RISE

THICKNESS OF VALLEY STRIP

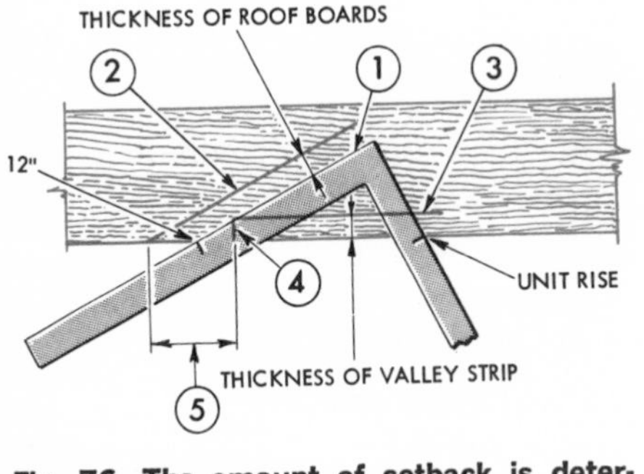

Fig. 76. The amount of setback is determined by layout.

step off as many units as there are feet in the run of the common rafter. To get the top cut, use the unit length of the common rafter on the tongue of the square and 12, the unit run, on the blade. Mark along the tongue side of the square, that is, the length side, as shown in Fig. 77. Use the same figures for the bottom cut, but mark along the blade, or run side, of the square, as shown in Fig. 77.

Ridge Piece of the Saddle

The ridge of the saddle fits against the valley strip as shown at *A*, Fig. 74. To make this cut, lay the square on the ridge piece, using the figures for the cut of the main roof and mark along the blade, or run side of the square (the seat cut for the common rafter of the main roof). The length

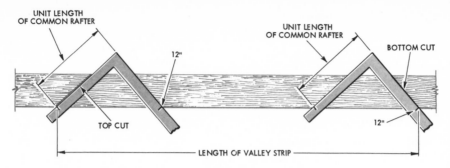

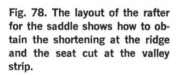

Fig. 77. The top and bottom cuts for the valley strip are shown in detail.

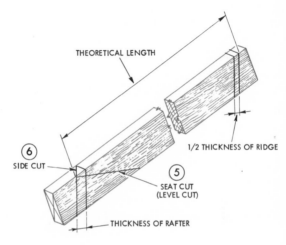

Fig. 78. The layout of the rafter for the saddle shows how to obtain the shortening at the ridge and the seat cut at the valley strip.

of the ridge is equal to the run of the common rafter less about ⅝ of an inch to allow for the drop of the ridge, if the ridge is made out of one-inch material. (This amount will be less if the roof has a low unit rise).

Rafter Layout for the Saddle

The rafters for the saddle are similar to valley jack rafters with a seat cut, instead of a plumb cut, at the lower end. To lay out the saddle rafters, step off the length of the common rafter. Then deduct ½ the thickness of the ridge for the shortening. Lay out the side cut, as shown at 6, Fig. 78. Lay out Line 5, the seat cut line. Square the side cut line over the top of the member to locate a point on the opposite edge 6. Connect the points as shown and saw on the lines.

297

Length of Other Saddle Rafters

Find the common difference for the jack rafters. Then lay out this common difference on the longest rafter and cut as many pairs of rafters as will be required for the saddle.

Bay Window Roof Framing

Some roofs have the features of an octagon or polygon because of the unusual shape of the floor plan of the building. The roof over a bay window brings out this problem. It is advisable to make a sketch layout to scale or full size in order to decide on the best arrangement of members and to find information on the cuts. The methods used to find the total rise, run and length of the rafters generally apply in this special area as well.

Bay Window Roof Plan

The roof plan, Fig. 79, shows the location and length of run of all of the rafters for the bay roof. A layout such as this should be made either at a scale of 3 inches equal 1 foot or full size. When the bay is a part of an octagon, the distances Ob and Oe are equal. The run of the hip rafter on a polygon roof should bisect the angle at the plate. Therefore, the angle abc is divided into two equal angles Aba and Abc, each of the lines Aa and Ac represent the run of a common rafter, while Dd represents the jack-rafter run.

The unit run and unit rise of common rafters are established on the architect's drawing. The unit rise and total rise of the hip are the same as that of the common rafter, but because the run of the hip is not the diagonal of a square the unit run and total run will differ from the usual

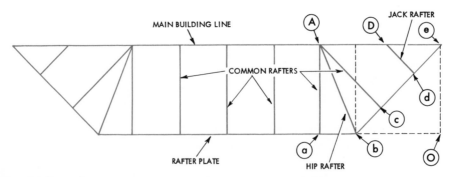

Fig. 79. A bay roof plan laid out to scale shows the run and center line of the rafters.

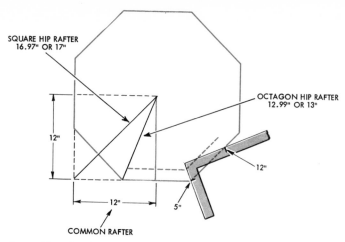

Fig. 80. An octagon hip rafter has a run of 13 inches for each 12 inches on a common rafter.

12:17 ratio. On the octagon roof the unit run of the hip is 13 inches for every 12 inches of common rafter run, as shown in Fig. 80. The miter cut at the plate of an octagon can be found by taking 5 inches on the tongue of the square and 12 inches on the blade, as shown in Fig. 80. Draw the line for the miter cut along the tongue side (5 inches) of the square.

The necessary dimensions and cuts of the rafters can be found by making a scale drawing, as shown in Fig. 81. This scale drawing should be made as large as convenient for handling, full size if possible. The outline of the corner of the bay window roof is drawn first, followed by the center line for each rafter. The center lines of the rafters I, II, and III

converge at the point *F*, while the center line of the jack rafter IV is drawn at the required spacing (usually 16″) and parallel to rafter III. The wall rafter V is nailed against the building and acts as a roof-board support. Each rafter is drawn to the *full width of the rafter stock*, in order that the full-size run can be obtained for each rafter side cut, as shown at *1, 2, 3, 4,* and *5,* Fig. 81.

Since there are a number of dimensions which must be worked out, it is advisable to make a schedule, as shown in Fig. 82, where the different dimensions can be recorded for later use. The total run of each rafter is scaled from the drawing shown in Fig. 81, and listed under the heading *Total Run*. The unit rise of the roof

299

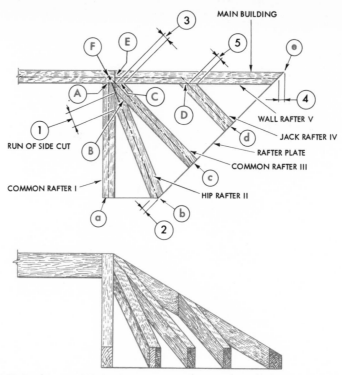

Fig. 81. A full size layout of the rafter connections gives information on cheeks and direction of cuts.

	Total Run	Total Rise	Total Length
(I) Common Rafter (A) to (a)			
(II) Hip Rafter (B) to (b)			
(III) Common Rafter (C) to (c)			
(IV) Jack Rafter (D) to (d)			
(V) Wall Rafter (E) to (e)			

Fig. 82. A schedule of dimensions for each rafter helps prevent errors.

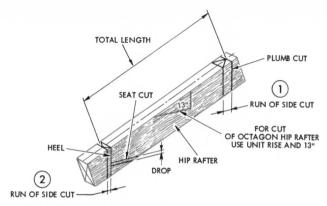

Fig. 83. The hip rafter is laid out using the information from the plan view (Fig. 81) for side cuts.

is found on the drawings for the building. The total rise and total length can be worked out by sliding the framing square in a step-off method as previously explained. These dimensions can then be recorded in the schedule above.

Laying Out the Rafters

To find the *cut* for the common and jack rafters I, III, and IV, take the unit rise and unit run of the common rafter. Rafter I has a square cut at the top. Rafters III and IV have side cuts at the top. The bottom cut, both seat and heel, are the same on all three rafters.

For the *cut* of the hip rafter, take the unit rise of the common rafter, and a unit run of 13. This hip has a double side cut at the top and bottom. The run of these side cuts,

shown at *1* and *2*, Fig. 81, is taken from the scaled drawing and measured at a right angle to the plumb cut, as shown in Fig. 83. It is not necessary to shorten the rafter, since this is taken into consideration when the run of the rafter was measured from the sketch. The hip rafter must be dropped. The amount of drop will be slight because the corner is not a 90 degree angle.

Rafter V has a square cut at the top and a side cut at the bottom. The *cut* of this rafter is different from that of any of the others. However, the proportions of this cut are the same as its total rise and total run. Since this rafter is not at a right angle to the plate, it must be dropped also. If the roof had a unit rise of 8 inches the drop would be approximately ½ inch.

Collar Beams and Ceiling Joists

The horizontal framing members used to stiffen the rafters of a roof are known as *collar beams*. Where rafters form part of the walls of a second-floor room, these collar beams may become the ceiling joists of such rooms. The length of these collar beams, or ceiling joists, depends upon the span of the building, their distance above the plate, and the unit rise of the roof.

Layout for Collar Beam

The length of the collar beam is shorter than the span of the roof. The amount to shorten the beam is indicated by *A*, Fig. 84. To find *A*

divide the distance *B*, the height at which the beam is set above the plate, in inches by the unit rise per foot of run of the common rafter. The result will be the number of units of rise in dimension B. Multiply this number by the unit of run to get the shortening A.

PROCEDURE

The problem: A building has a span of 16 feet; the unit rise of the common rafter is 10 inches. What will be the length of a collar beam placed 4 feet above the rafter plate level?

To find the length of the collar

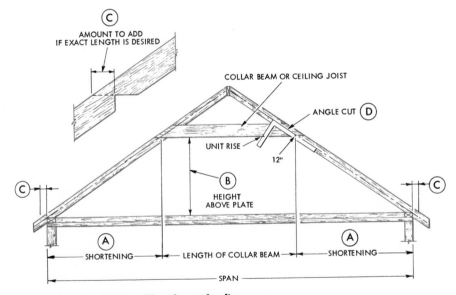

Fig. 84. The collar beams stiffen the roof rafters.

beam, divide the distance of the beam above the rafter plate, 48 inches, by 10 inches, the unit rise of the common rafter. The result is 4.8 units of rise. The unit of run is 1 foot; 4.8 units of run equals 4.8 feet or 4 feet $9\frac{9}{16}$ inches, which is the amount of shortening required on *each* end of the piece shown as dimension A, Fig. 84. Two times 4 feet $9\frac{9}{16}$ inches equals 9 feet $7\frac{1}{8}$ inches.

Subtracting this amount from 16 feet, the length of the span, leaves 6 feet $4\frac{7}{8}$ inches, the length of the collar beam.

In order to have the collar beam fit tightly against the roof boards, it will be necessary to add two times the distance C, Fig. 84, to the length of the beam. The actual cut is made using the unit rise and unit run as shown at D.

Gable End Framing

The studs on the gable end of a roof have a common difference in length. If the studs are spaced 12 inches on center (o.c.), then the

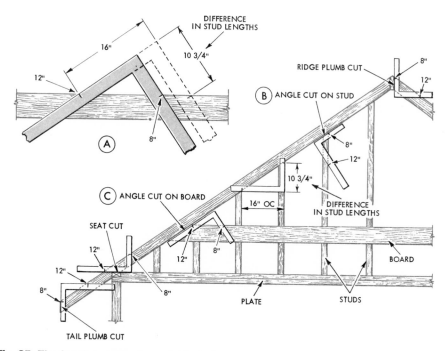

Fig. 85. The framing square is useful in laying out the studs and sheathing for gable ends.

common difference will be the same as the unit rise of the rafter. For other spacing, for example, 16 inches on center (o.c.), the common difference can be found by sliding the square, as shown at *A*, Fig. 85. Place the square to the cut of the roof, with 8 inches (the unit rise) on the tongue and 12 inches (the unit run) on the blade, as shown in the illustration, Fig. 85. Draw a line along the blade, or 12 inch side of the square, then slide the square along this line to 16 inches. Hold the square on the line and read the figure on the tongue side of the square to find the common difference of stud lengths when the studs are spaced 16 inches on center (o.c.). When the unit rise is 8 inches, the unit run 12 inches, and the stud spacing is 16 inches (o.c.), then the common difference of stud lengths is 10¾ inches. See *A*, Fig. 85.

The angle cut on any stud or board in a vertical position, on gable ends, is the same as the ridge, or plumb, cut of the rafter. This cut will fit against the rafter and have the same slope as the roof. Therefore, to find the top cut of a gable stud to fit against the rafter, hold the square to the figure 12 on the blade and the unit rise on the tongue, as shown at *B* Fig. 85. Draw a line along the tongue or rise side of the square to find the correct angle for the cut.

For a horizontal board, or any framing member in a level position, which is to fit against the rafter, the end angle cut is the same as the seat cut of the rafter. This angle is also the correct cut for horizontal sheathing boards. See *C*, Fig. 85.

Layout Tee

The framing of every roof requires the duplication of some rafters. They are laid out from a pattern which is made for each kind of rafter. The over-all lengths can be determined readily from the master pattern, but the cuts cannot be transferred as easily. The carpenter will find a *layout tee* (shown in Fig. 86) a very useful device. It will help him lay out the side cuts as well as the tail cuts, ridge cuts, and bird's-mouths with a high degree of accuracy and speed.

On roofs having hip or valley rafters, it is advisable to make two *layout tees:* one for the common and jack rafters and another for the hip and valley rafters. The correct length of the overhang can be laid out on the *tee* if the length of the overhang is not too great.

It is also advisable to make the layout tee from one-inch material, so it will be light in weight and easy to handle. The 12 inch length is convenient unless a longer overhang is to be included. The stem should be as wide as the rafter stock, while the

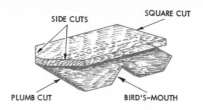

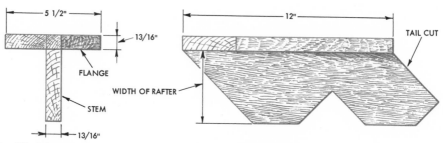

Fig. 86. A layout tee is a device used for marking rafter cuts.

flange, or top, must be at least twice as wide as the thickness of the rafters, plus the thickness of the stem of the *tee*. The cuts on the *tee* are transferred from the rafter pattern with the framing square or **T** bevel. If these cuts are accurately laid out, and if they are cut and planed smooth to the lines, better layout results will be obtained.

The Unequal Pitch Roof

An unequal pitch roof develops whenever two parts of a roof, each having a different slope, intersect. At times it is necessary to have different slopes on a roof; at other times it is used in order to create certain architectural effects. A common unequal pitch roof is required when a rectangular house is to have a roof which comes to a point. See Fig. 87. Another unequal pitch roof which a car-penter may encounter involves two roofs which intersect, each with a different span but with the same plate and ridge heights. See Figs. 88 and 89. Dormers often bring about unequal pitch problems because the dormer roof has a low slope compared to the steeper slope of the main roof. See Fig. 90. The usual procedure is to frame the two parts of the roof in the same manner as

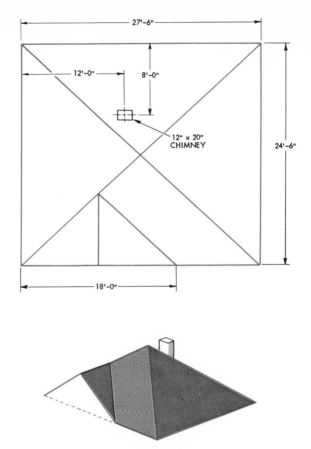

Fig. 87. An unequal pitch roof develops whenever a rectangular roof comes to a point.

outlined in this chapter except for the parts of the roof where unequal pitch hips and valleys develop. Because the problem becomes very complex, many builders will fall back on a taping method to obtain the length of the hips and valleys, and will use a layout only to determine the shape of the cuts. Others will use a full, half, or quarter size layout made on the floor or other convenient place, to find the run of various members and then will use a step off method to lay out the rafters. Seventeen inches cannot be used as the unit of run for hips and valleys on unequal pitch roofs because the unit run is not the diagonal of a square

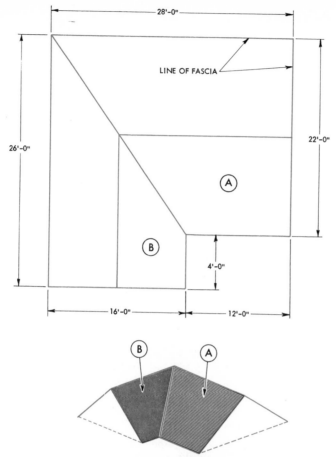

Fig. 88. Intersecting roofs with the same ridge and plate heights and different spans require unequal pitch rafters.

but is the diagonal of a rectangle. See Fig. 91. The layout not only gives the carpenter the shape of the cuts as they appear in a plan view but gives the run of the various members.

New problems arise in laying out an unequal pitch hip rafter regarding backing and dropping. Because the roof slopes at a different angle on each side of the hip, the amount of backing or dropping will therefore not be the same on each side of the rafter.

The jacks, if evenly spaced along

307

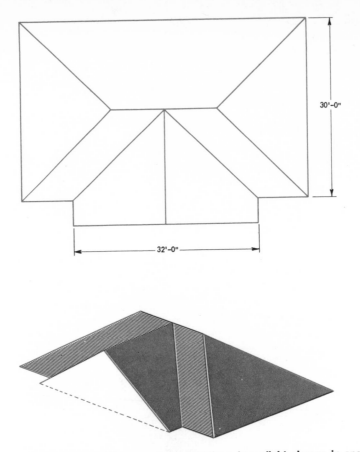

30'-0"

32'-0"

Fig. 89. An unequal pitch roof is necessary when there is a slight change in span and the ridges and plates are kept at the same elevations.

the plate or ridge, will not line up in a herringbone pattern. See Fig. 92. The jacks, however, can be laid off using a step off method, using the same steps as the common rafter on that side of the roof.

One other problem to be solved by the carpenter is peculiar to unequal pitch roofs with overhangs. If the two pitches used on the roof are a great deal different, it will be found in many instances that the common and jack rafters of one of the roofs will not rest with sufficient bearing on the plate. It is then necessary to build up the plate by adding another member to bring it up to make a satisfactory bird's-mouth possible.

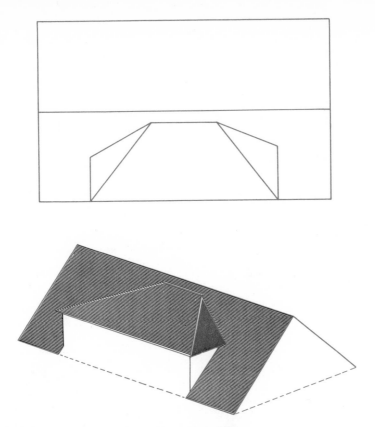

Fig. 90. Hipped dormers bring about unequal pitch valleys.

PROCEDURE

The problem is a typical unequal pitch roof with no overhang. See Fig. 92. (*Note:* The difference in pitch between the two parts of the roof is more than that which is usually found in practice. The pitches were chosen in order to bring out the layout problem and show the cuts in greater contrast.)

1. Laying out and building the equal pitch portion of the roof.

2. Making a plan layout for the unequal pitch hip and hip jack rafters.

3. Finding the slope and laying out the line length of the hip rafter.

4. Laying out the plumb cut (heel).

5. Shortening the hip rafter at the ridge and making side cuts.

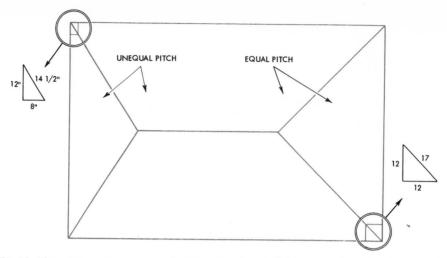

Fig. 91. The unit run of an unequal pitch rafter is not 17, because it is the diagonal of a rectangle instead of a square.

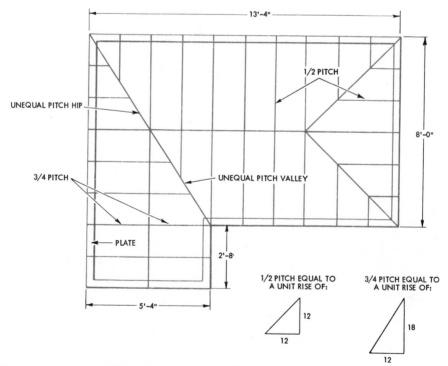

Fig. 92. The plan of a roof with an unequal portion should be laid out to scale in order to find the location and run of rafters.

6. Backing and dropping the hip rafter.

7. Laying out the hip jacks.

8. Laying out the unequal pitch valley rafter.

9. Laying out the unequal pitch valley jack rafters.

1. Laying Out and Building the Equal Pitch Portion of the Roof. The roof can be considered as two separate roofs, one with a gable end and a ¾ pitch, and the other with a hip end with ½ pitch. Using the instructions given earlier in this chapter, lay out all the common rafters for the ¾ pitch roof using 18 inches as the unit rise, 12 inches as the unit run and a total run of 2 feet 8 inches. Make the deduction for the ridge and use a 3 inch heel. Make all of the common rafters for the ½ pitch portion of the building, using a unit rise of 12 inches and a total run of 4 feet. Erect the common rafters and the ridges at this time. Brace the ridges where they meet so that they keep in proper place. Lay out, cut, and install the hips and jacks for the ½ pitch end. See Fig. 92.

2. Making a Plan Layout for the Unequal Pitch Hip and Hip Jack Rafters. A full, half or quarter size layout of the hip and jack rafters is essential to determine the run and the cuts on each member. First draw the plates, starting at the corner and extending beyond the common rafters which support the ends of the ridges. See Fig. 93. The next step is to lay out the center lines for the common rafters, the hip, and jacks. Space the jacks 16 inches o.c. along each plate. Notice that even though they are measured the same distance from the corner, the center lines will not meet at the hip. After the center lines have been laid out, proceed to lay out the common rafters, ridge, hip, and jacks in that order, using the exact thickness of the stock (1½ inches). The side cuts on the hip will no longer be equal and the side cut of the jacks on each side of the ridge will vary greatly.

3. Finding the Slope and Laying Out the Line Length of the Hip Rafter. It is possible to find the unit run and unit rise of the hip by scaling the layout and finding the diagonal of a proportional rectangle. After the layout for the hip and valley rafters has been made (see Fig. 93), measure a distance of 1 foot from the plate corner and draw a line to the hip and back to the other plate. You will have made a rectangle 1 foot by 8 inches. See Fig. 91. The diagonal will measure 14½ inches, which is the unit run. The 1 foot measurement was measured parallel to the ½ pitch roof rafters; therefore the rectangle is related to the common rafter on the ½ pitch side. To find the total rise and total run of the hip, step off four steps (the run of the common rafter is 4'-0") with a unit run of 14½ inches and a

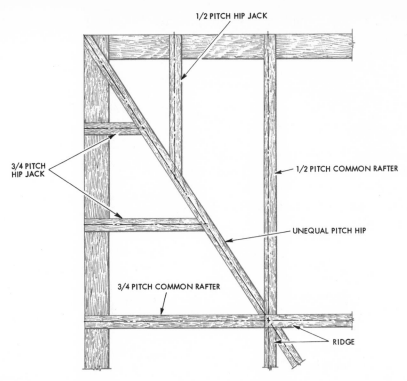

1/2 PITCH HIP JACK

3/4 PITCH HIP JACK

1/2 PITCH COMMON RAFTER

UNEQUAL PITCH HIP

3/4 PITCH COMMON RAFTER

RIDGE

Fig. 93. The rafters should be drawn in place to show how the cuts are to be made. This is the hip area.

unit rise of 12 inches (the unit rise for the ½ pitch roof is 12 inches).

An easier method of laying out the hip line length, if the plan view Fig. 93 has been drawn accurately at full size or half size, is to take the total run and the total rise and draw the triangle for the whole rafter at once. The total rise is the same as the rise for the common rafter (12 inch unit rise × 4 feet run = 4 feet total rise). Make a right triangle with the total run of the hip as the base and the

total rise of the hip (the same rise as the common rafter) as the altitude. The hypotenuse is the line length of the hip. See Fig. 94, Step 1.

4. Laying Out the Plumb Cut (Heel). Before any side cuts, backing, or dropping are considered, the plumb cut (heel) should be made. The top edge of a fascia, which goes around the roof, must be level and line up with the top of the plumb cut on all of the rafters. Therefore the plumb cut at the plate (heel), es-

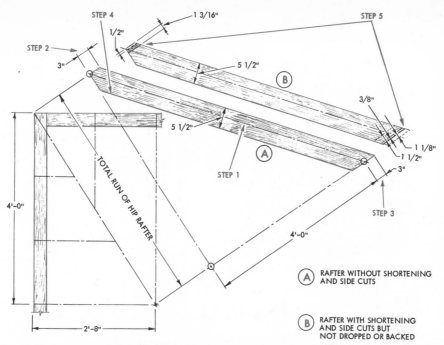

Fig. 94. The unequal pitch hip can be laid out using the total run from the plan layout and the total rise of the common rafter. Cuts can be transferred from the layout.

tablished on the common rafters must be used. We are assuming that this measurement on the roof is 3 inches. Draw a plumb line above the plate corner and measure a 3 inch distance (Step 2). Do the same thing at the ridge and connect the two points to give the top edge of the rafter (Step 3). Measure 5½ inches at right angles to this line at two places and connect these points to give the bottom line of the hip rafter (Step 4). Note carefully whether there is sufficient bearing or not at the plate.

5. Shortening the Hip Rafter at the Ridge and Making Side Cuts. Draw lines at right angles to the center line of the hip rafter to indicate the shortening at the ridge and dimensions of the side cuts (Step 5, Fig. 94). See Fig. 95 for shortening and side cuts. Measure the spaces between points carefully and show the dimensions on the layout. Transfer the dimensions to the layout of the rafter, making all measurements on a level line. See Fig. 95. Draw plumb lines through the points to indicate the cuts to be made. Take

313

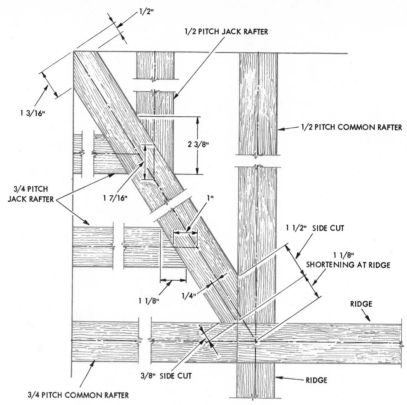

Fig. 95. A step by step method for laying out the cuts for the unequal pitch hip.

care to see that the lines are on the proper side of the rafter corresponding to the plan view, Fig. 95. Also note that the cut at the ridge does not fall on the center line, but must be offset ¼ of an inch when viewed from above.

6. Backing and Dropping the Hip Rafter. The methods of backing and dropping the hip shown in Figs. 37 and 38 are satisfactory if the difference in pitch between the two

sides of the roof is comparatively slight. If this method is used when the difference in pitch is great, the sheathing will not lie flat because one edge of the hip will be much too high. It becomes necessary to use both backing and dropping procedures to solve the problem.

Transfer the plumb cut dimension used on common and jack rafters to the shortest side cut of the hip rafter. See *A*, Fig. 96. Measure down 3

314

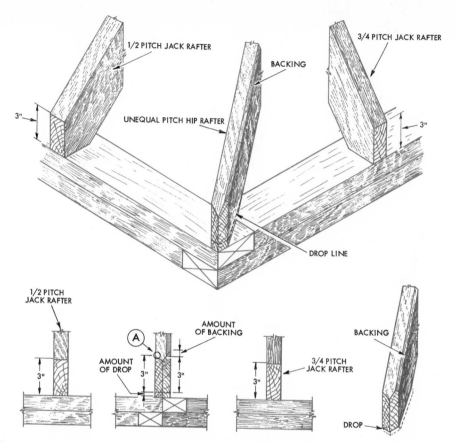

Fig. 96. The hip should be dropped to permit the sheathing to lie flat. If the difference of pitch is very great, the hip may have to be dropped and backed.

inches in this case, and mark a level line which will indicate the cut line for the drop. Measure up from this line on the other side of the rafter, mark a 3 inch point and square a line across the cheek. This is the amount of backing needed to make the sheathing lie flat and permit it to meet the sheathing from the other side of the roof. Draw lines parallel

to the edge of the rafter to its full length to indicate the amount of backing and cut on these lines.

7. **Laying Out the Hip Jacks.** Two types of hip jacks are required, one set having ¾ pitch (18 inch unit rise) and the other ½ pitch (12 inch unit rise). The jacks can be stepped off using the method outlined previously under HIP JACK RAFTER LAY-

315

OUT, or a total run method may be used if the rafters are not too long. The main differences will be in the method of obtaining the common difference, the shortening at the hip, and the location of the side cuts.

Choose one of the boards laid out for a common rafter. The 3 inch plumb cut and seat cut at the plate have been marked and the line representing the intersection of center lines at the ridge has been marked also. See Fig. 97. Measure the total run of the longest ¾ pitch jack rafter

on the layout, Fig. 93. Using the step-off method with a unit run of 12 and a unit rise of 18, lay out the jack on the common rafter, locating the line which represents the center line intersection of the jack and hip. Refer to the layout, Figs. 93 and 95 to note the shortening at the hip. Measure 1 inch back and draw a line to represent the shortening. Square this line over the top of the rafter to intersect the center line. Measure ⁹⁄₁₆ of an inch (½ of 1⅛ inches) in front of the line to establish the side

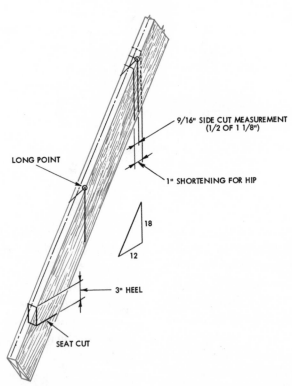

Fig. 97. The hip jacks are laid out using measurements taken from the plan view (Fig. 95).

cut for the long point of the rafter. Extend the side cut to the top edge of the rafter and lay out a line through the center point to establish the side cut on the other side. See Fig. 97.

The common difference can be found by measuring the total run of two adjacent rafters on the layout. See Fig. 93. Subtract one from the other to obtain the run of the common difference (10½ inches). Using a framing square and another board, lay out the common difference as shown in Fig. 98. Set the framing square with 18 inches on the tongue and 12 inches on the blade and mark a line along the blade. Slide the framing square along the line until it reaches the 10½ inch point. Draw a line along the tongue. The distance between the two marks is the "common difference" between jacks.

When a roof is framed with a number of hip jacks in a set, it is advis-able to use a common rafter as a pattern on which to mark the jacks. After the longest jack has been laid out, the "common difference" can be used to lay out the long points of the other jacks. The side cuts can then be laid out quickly.

8. Laying Out the Unequal Pitch Valley Rafter. The problem of laying out the unequal pitch valley rafter is solved by following the same steps used in laying out the unequal pitch hip rafter, as oulined in the preceding pages. In this problem the valley portion of the roof and the hip portion are almost the same. See Fig. 93 and Fig. 99. However, this situation rarely occurs. It is advisable to make a layout of each part of a roof where unequal hips, valleys and jacks develop.

The valley rafter and hip rafter are similar in layout. Deductions and side cuts are obtained in the same way. The detail layout in Fig. 99

Fig. 98. The common difference for unequal pitch jacks is derived by marking the unit rise and run of the common rafter on a board and advancing the square to the run of the common differences.

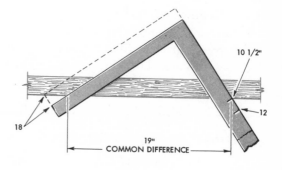

SET SQUARE AT 18" UNIT RISE
12" UNIT RUN–MOVE 12" TO 10 1/2"

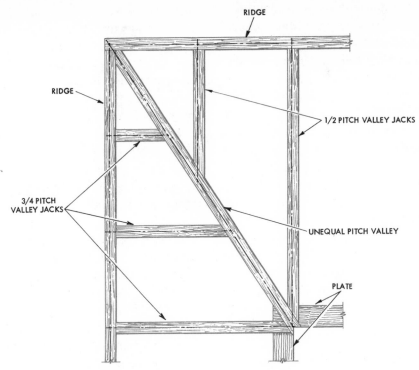

RIDGE

RIDGE

1/2 PITCH VALLEY JACKS

3/4 PITCH
VALLEY JACKS

UNEQUAL PITCH VALLEY

PLATE

Fig. 99. The rafters should be drawn in place to show how the cuts are to be made. This is the valley area.

shows the side cuts at the plate. The valley rafter need not be dropped or backed because it does not extend above the other rafters.

9. Laying Out the Unequal Pitch Valley Jack Rafters. The common rafter pattern can be used to advantage in laying out the valley jack rafters in the same manner as the hip jack rafters. The deduction for the hip, the side cuts, and the common difference are found in the same way. Measurements should be taken from the line representing the center line intersection of the ridge and common rafters.

Unequal Pitch Roof With Overhang

Several new problems arise when a roof with more than one pitch is designed to have an overhang. In- stead of using the plate as the base for measurement, the line represent- ing the top of the fascia, which nails to the ends of the rafters, becomes the base. This line is to be kept level around the house and adjustments become necessary in the line lengths, bird's-mouths and side cuts. If the change of pitch is great between one part of the roof and another, or if the overhang is wide, the rafters on the steep slope may have poor bearing on the plate. It then becomes necessary to raise the plate for this part of the roof until a proper bird's-mouth can be supported.

PROCEDURE

The problem is a typical unequal pitch roof with an overhang with a 1 foot run. See Fig. 100. The house is the same as that for the problem shown in Fig. 92.

1. Laying out the common rafters.
2. Laying out the hip and valley rafters.

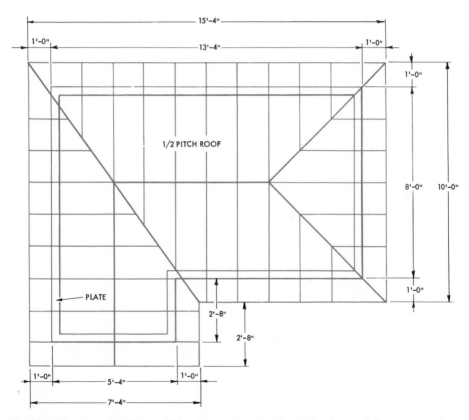

Fig. 100. The same building used for the problem in Fig. 92 is given a 1 foot run overhang on all sides. Note that hip and valley rafters do not cross plate corners.

Fundamentals of Carpentry

3. Laying out the hip jack and valley jack rafters.

1. Laying Out the Common Rafters. When all of the slopes of a roof are equal, the matter of placing an overhang on all sides of the roof is no great problem because the same amount of stock is added to each

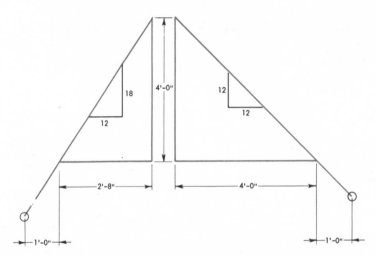

Fig. 101. Extending an overhang on an unequal pitch roof creates a problem in fascia levels.

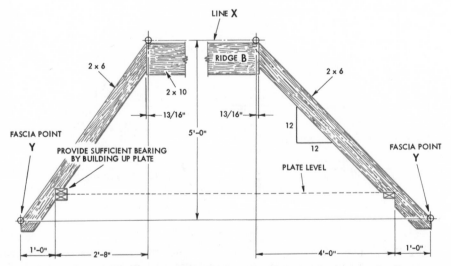

Fig. 102. An unequal pitch uses the fascia level as the basis for the layout of rafters.

common and jack rafter, and the fascia when applied will be level all around the house. This is not true with an unequal pitch roof, because when two rafters of a different pitch use the same unit run and rest on plates which are level, the ends of the rafters will not be level. See Fig. 101. It becomes necessary to work out the details of the roof, using the line of the top of the plumb cut at the ends of the rafters as the base for

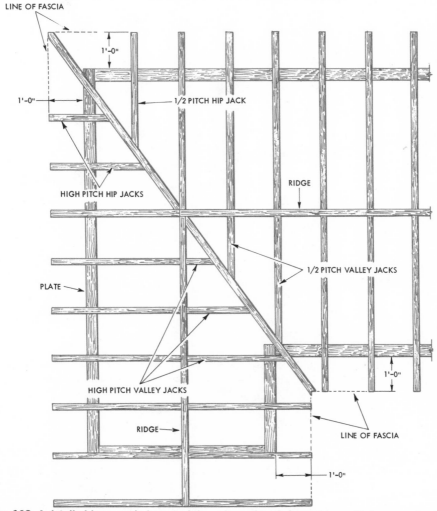

LINE OF FASCIA

1'-0"

1'-0"

1/2 PITCH HIP JACK

HIGH PITCH HIP JACKS

RIDGE

1/2 PITCH VALLEY JACKS

PLATE

1'-0"

HIGH PITCH VALLEY JACKS

LINE OF FASCIA

RIDGE

1'-0"

Fig. 103. A detailed large scale layout of the rafters gives information on their run and cuts.

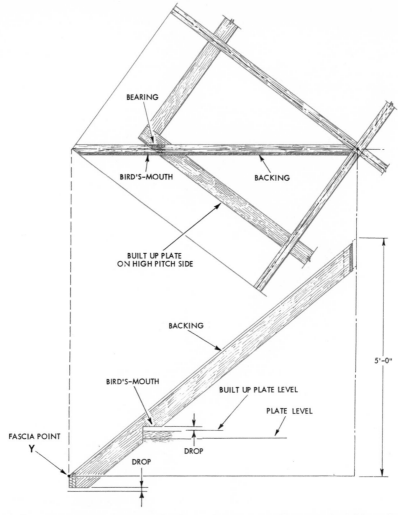

Fig. 104. The hip rafter for an unequal pitch roof with an overhang can be laid out in detail from the plan view. A 2 x 4 is required to raise the plate level to provide adequate bearing.

all measurements, rather than the plate. (Fascia Point Y, Fig. 102).

Lay out a common rafter at ½ pitch (12 inch unit rise and 12 inch unit run, with a total run of 4 feet and an overhang with 1 foot run). Lay out the shortening at the ridge and the bird's-mouth as previously outlined. This rafter will have a total rise of 5 feet from the fascia point

Y to the top of the ridge, line *X*. See Fig. 102. (Line *X* is the theoretical line of the top of ridge using base triangles.)

The common rafter for the steeper slope will no longer be ¾ pitch because it must be brought into a position so that fascia point *Y* is level with point *Y* on the ½ pitch rafter. When the difference in slope between the two rafters is very great or the overhang is wide, the plate must be built up to a greater height. It may be necessary to raise the plate by adding a 1 × 4 or 2 × 4 in order to provide enough bearing for the seat cut of the bird's-mouth. The common rafter patterns will be used for the hip and valley jacks because they have the same upper or lower ends.

2. Laying Out the Hip and Valley Rafters. A layout of the roof (see Fig. 100) will point out the fact that the hip rafter and the valley rafter do not pass over the plate corners. The layout at larger scale, showing the rafters in detail (Fig. 103), will give exact information as to the deductions and side cuts to be made at the

upper ends of the rafters. The layout will also give information regarding the bird's-mouths and the tail cuts. A layout of the side view of the rafter gives more information regarding the seat cut which is related to the fascia point *Y*. See Fig. 104. Backing and dropping of the unequal pitch hip rafter is achieved in the same manner as outlined under *Backing and dropping the hip rafter* for the unequal pitch roof without overhang. The point to remember is that the backing and drop are measured on the cheeks of the tail cut and the drop is transferred to the plumb cut at the plate.

3. Layout of Hip Jacks and Valley Jacks. Refer to Fig. 103 for information on total run, deductions and side cuts. The intersections must be drawn at large scale and measured carefully. The jacks can be laid out on the common rafter pattern in the same manner as outlined for the unequal pitch roof without overhang. See Figs. 95 and 97. The dimensions for cuts will not be exactly the same for the roof without a projection and the roof with a projection.

Roof Trusses and Trussed Rafters

Trusses of wood have been used for hundreds of years and have permitted the covering of large areas with a clear span. It is still found to be practical both as regards cost and construction to support the roofs of

large structures with trusses made with wood members. See Fig. 105. These trusses are spaced at wide intervals ranging from 8 feet to 20 feet apart.

A great surge has taken place in

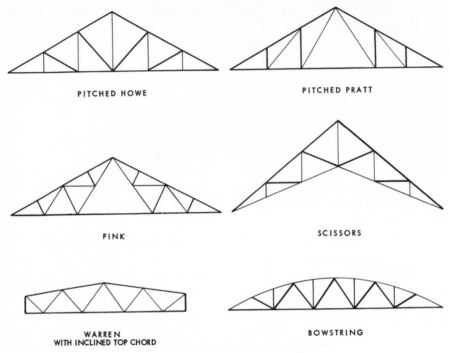

PITCHED HOWE

PITCHED PRATT

FINK

SCISSORS

WARREN
WITH INCLINED TOP CHORD

BOWSTRING

Fig. 105. Heavy trusses using these shapes are made of wood.

the use of wood trusses for small homes within the past twenty years because they have been found to have the following *advantages:*

1. The great speed of erection permits putting the building under roof in a much shorter time than if conventional framing were used.

2. The entire load of the roof is transferred to the outside walls. This means that there is no need for load bearing partitions. Thus the architect has greater freedom in planning.

3. With no partitions required it is possible to lay flooring and install ceilings from outside walls to outside

walls thus creating a saving in these operations.

4. There is usually a saving in material over conventional roof framing.

5. The ease of erection tends to cut labor cost.

6. Trusses may be fabricated at the job or on the job site or be purchased from manufacturers who make this a specialty. They are delivered to the building ready to be placed in position.

There are also a few *disadvantages* to be considered:

1. Three men are required as a

minimum crew to erect and fasten the trusses in place.

2. Appreciable savings can only be made when many trusses of the same type are required and jigs are made to make rapid assembly possible. Transportation may add to the cost.

3. Trusses lend themselves to use on simple gable roofs. When the roof plan is irregular in shape with offsets, change of span, hips or dormers the use of trusses adds considerable complication to the construction and makes their value doubtful.

4. Special care must be used to follow the exact specification as to size and arrangement of members and the manner of fastening them so that the truss may develop the proper strength characteristics.

Trussed Rafter and Truss Design

The carpenter should know about the parts of trusses, how they are assembled and how they are erected. He should know why they are designed as they are so that he can work with them intelligently. The actual design however is a job for an engineer. The size of the members and the manner of connecting them varies with each span, slope and load problem.

A *truss* is a "structural framework composed of a series of members so arranged and fastened together that external loads applied to the joints will cause only direct stress in the members."[3] The loads on a truss are the live loads of wind and snow and the dead loads of roofing, sheathing and the weight of the truss itself. In Fig. 106 the loads are considered as concentrated at the panel points indicated by arrows and are transferred through the members to the supports at the walls. The members

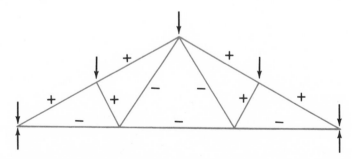

Fig. 106. The load on a truss is considered to be concentrated at panel points. Some members are in tension (−) and some in compression (+).

3. "Minimum Property Standards for One and Two Living Units Federal Housing Authority." F.H.A. No. 300.

marked (+) are in *compression* and the members marked (−) are in *tension*.

A trussed rafter is a "truss where the chord members are also serving as rafters and ceiling joists and are subject to bending stress in addition to direct stress."[4] A simple trussed rafter (Fig. 107) must have members which are sufficiently strong to carry the weight of the sheathing and roofing. The sloped members (top chords) are considered to be rafters. Because the ceiling is hung from the bottom horizontal members (bottom chords), they must be designed to withstand bending stress or deflection within the permissible limit.

Trusses and trussed rafters used in the construction of homes are usually placed on 24 inch centers and

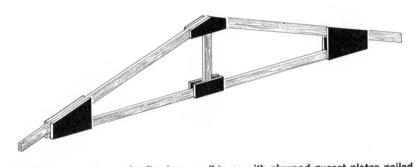

Fig. 107. The king post trussed rafter is a small truss with plywood gusset plates nailed and glued in place.

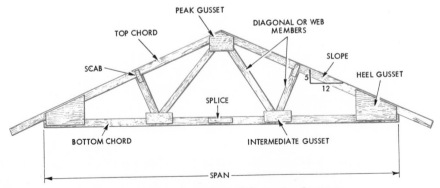

Fig. 108. The carpenter should know the names of the parts of a truss.

4. *Ibid.*

have slopes of 4, 5, 6 or 7 inch rise per foot of run. Fig. 108 gives the names of the various parts of a "W" truss.

Construction. Considering construction, trusses and trussed rafters may be classified into two groups. (1) Assembled trusses using split rings or other devices between the members at connections. See Figs. 109, 110, 111. (2) Single plane assemblies using nailing plates or nailed-glued features. See Figs. 107 and 112.

When the split ring connector is used circular grooves are cut into the two members to be joined. A 2½ inch ring is used for 2 inch lumber. A 4 inch ring is used for heavier trusses using 3 inch or thicker material. The ring is imbedded, half of its depth into each member, and is brought up tight with a bolt which passes through the connection. See Fig. 110. The split ring is designed to transfer the stress at each connection. One advantage of the split ring method of fastening is that the

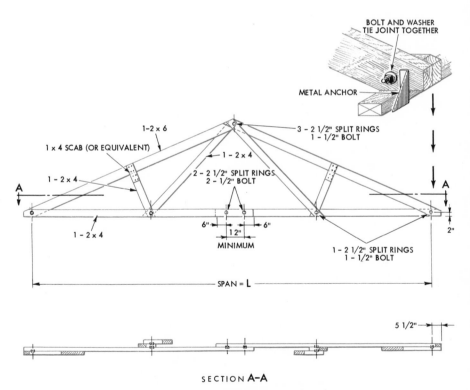

Fig. 109. Split ring connectors are used in the assembly of the truss.

Fig. 110. Split rings fit into grooves cut in the members. The truss may be assembled on the job. (Timber Engineering Co.)

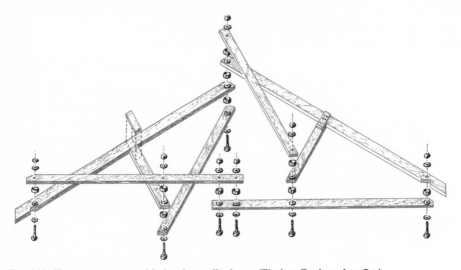

Fig. 111. Trusses are assembled using split rings. (Timber Engineering Co.)

trusses can be made on the job with a minimum of equipment and with greater ease than other systems. The split ring also permits greater shrinkage and swelling of the lumber. This type of truss can be transported knocked-down to be assembled quickly at the job.

The "single plane" type of truss or trussed rafter has all of its members in one plane instead of overlapping. The connections are made either with nailing plates or with plywood gusset plates which are nailed and glued. See Figs. 107 and 112.

Single plane trussed rafters and trusses are usually made on an assembly table in a jig which consists of blocks arranged to position the members correctly. See Fig. 113. The

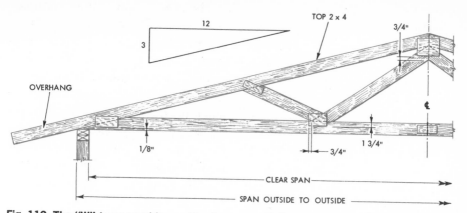

Fig. 112. The "W" truss provides a wide clear span. Nailing plates are used at the joints.

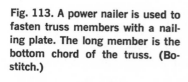

Fig. 113. A power nailer is used to fasten truss members with a nailing plate. The long member is the bottom chord of the truss. (Bostitch.)

nailing plates are pre-punched galvanized metal strips or sheets. The holes are placed in a pattern and spaced so that the nails will develop the necessary strength when driven in place. The number, size and type of nails is specified by the engineer. The important thing to remember is that the strength of the connection is determined by the shear strength of all of the nails. There must be no short cut in following the specifications. Plates are placed on both sides of each connection. A variation of the nail plate with holes, is a one piece type in which the projections are punched out and bent up to remain a part of the plate. See Fig. 114. Special equipment is required to press the joint together. One method is to pass the whole truss between compression rollers to force the projections into the wood.

Much experimentation has been done with a combination of nailing and glueing. Gusset plates of plywood of the size necessary to develop the correct strength are glued to both sides of the truss at each connection. Such trusses require a minimum amount of nailing but the nails must be driven in a prescribed pattern. The glue and plywood should meet certain standards. The temperature should be maintained above 50° and a specified curing time must be provided.

The selection of lumber is important. The strength characteristics are the vital considerations. Stress grade lumber is acceptable.

Manufacture and Erection. Split ring and nailed plate trusses can be made on the job or on the job site efficiently. A large flat surface is required and some form of jig devised particularly for nailed plate trusses. Nailing guns and clamps are useful in the assembly operation.

The most efficient way to manufacture trusses is in a factory where they may be made under controlled conditions of temperature and moisture and where special cutting, nailing and pressing equipment is available. Jigs which are adjustable to various sizes and slopes of trusses are available to hold the members in position.

Trussed rafters and lightweight trusses are usually erected by a crew of three men. The assembled trusses are hung upside down resting on the two walls and then turned up into

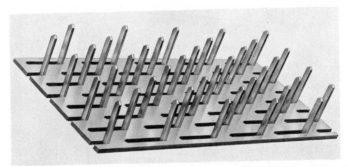

Fig. 114. Nailing plates are made in one piece. (Automatic Building Components, Inc.)

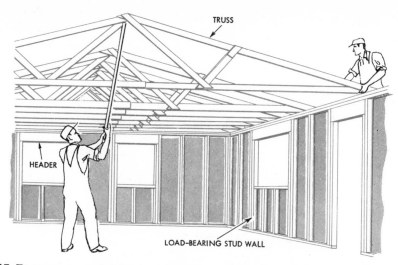

Fig. 115. Trusses are swung into place, lined up and fastened quickly. Each truss is secured in place prior to setting the next one. (University of Illinois, Small Homes Council.)

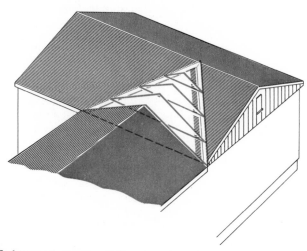

Fig. 116. Modified trusses may be used at the intersection of an ell-shaped building. (University of Illinois, Small Homes Council.)

position. See Fig. 115. The two men on the wall will nail them in place. When the trusses are heavy two men on the ground carry them or a crane is used to move and lift them into place.

Roofs which intersect may be built using trusses. Generally the trusses

331

are used for the straight parts and modified trusses or conventional roof framing is used at the places of intersection. See Fig. 116. The same is true of hip roofs and roofs which are of irregular shape. Trusses are usually quite satisfactory and have many advantages.

Checking On Your Knowledge

The following questions give you the opportunity to check up on yourself. If you have read the chapter carefully, you should be able to answer the questions. If you have any difficulty, read the chapter over once more so that you have the information well in mind before you go on with your reading.

DO YOU KNOW

1. What are the names of the three roofs generally used for houses?
2. What roof is a modified gable roof with two slopes?
3. What roof is a modified hip roof with two slopes?
4. What distinguishes a common rafter from other rafters?
5. What is an overhang? a bird's-mouth?
6. What is the unit run used for common rafters?
7. What is the "cut" of a roof?
8. How do you find the length of a ridge of a hip roof with dimensions 24 x 36 feet? What would the theoretical length be?
9. How much shortening is made on the common rafter at the ridge?
10. How much shortening is made on the jack rafter at the hip?
11. Why is the number 17 so important?
12. What is backing?
13. Why would a hip rafter be dropped? How is this done?
14. What is the function of a supporting valley rafter?
15. What is a cripple jack rafter?
16. Why does a valley rafter need no backing or dropping?
17. What is the common difference of jack rafters?
18. What is the purpose of a saddle?
19. Why does a roof over a bay window usually require a rafter layout?
20. Describe one type of roof which has unequal pitch rafters.
21. Why must some length other than 17 be used as the run for an unequal pitch hip rafter?
22. Why is a large scale layout needed for an unequal pitch roof?
23. What advantage and disadvantages do trusses have over conventional roof framing?
24. What is a trussed rafter?
25. What types of connections are used to hold the members together?

Exterior Finish

The material presented in this chapter deals with the roof and outside wall covering, and with the details of architectural woodwork and metalwork which are a part of the exterior of a house. The installation of window and exterior door frames and the exterior trimming around them is considered a part of exterior finish.

The primary purpose of the covering of the house is to protect the structure and the interior from the elements. Water, dust and wind must be kept out. The transfer of water vapor, heat and cold through the walls must be controlled and kept at a minimum. Some materials will serve these purposes better than others. Some woods are more durable when exposed to weather, and

each type of roofing and siding has some advantage. Aluminum and steel have been introduced and used extensively. The manner in which these materials are installed has a significant bearing on whether they serve their purpose well or not. Instructions are given on how they should be used. Gutters and flashing, although not always a part of the carpenter's responsibility, are studied so that the builder may be familiar with the problem of protecting the building from water damage.

The carpenter should learn how to install window and door frames quickly and efficiently, and also the manner of installing siding and architectural trim such as cornices and special trim at doorways and windows. These details of trim are very important because they add to or detract from the architectural beauty of the house. The carpenter must follow the architect's drawings as closely as possible in order that the results which he and the owner want may be achieved. They must be constructed so that they are weather tight and structurally sound, and they must be fitted with precision because they are visible to anyone approaching the house.

The exterior finish of a building is intended to serve three purposes: (1) to protect the vital parts of the structure—the framework; (2) to seal all cracks and crevices to prevent infiltration and escape of air; and (3) to enhance the appearance of the house. The architect draws the plans with these objectives in mind but the carpenter must be on guard constantly to see that they are achieved.

The principal parts of the outside finish include the *cornice trim*, or *overhang, gutters, roof covering, door* and *window frames, wall covering, corner treatment,* and *water table*. The application of this outside finish follows after the walls and roof have been sheathed. Traditional or regional houses may have porches, canopies, front entrance doorways, unusual treatment at windows and bays, railings, fences and decks. Some of these items are manufactured in a mill and brought to the job for installation, requiring little work on the part of the carpenter. However, some of them are built by the carpenter and require careful study of the details shown on the building plans in order that they may be constructed properly.

The order in which the work is done depends to some extent upon the type and design of the building, the trim used, and the relation of the different members to each other. For example, the roof generally is not covered until some of the cornice work has been done; the application of the water table usually precedes corner boards; the window and door frames must be set before wall covering is applied. However, roof covering is of great importance. Therefore, cornice work is usually the first of the outside trim applied.

Materials

The material used for exterior finish varies with the design of the house, the locality, and other conditions. There are many different materials used for exterior finish, such as wood, brick, stone, metal, stucco, and the various manufactured products. Even though steel, aluminum and plastic materials have grown in use for exterior wall covering, wood and wood products still dominate the field.

Wood for Exterior Finish. In choosing the wood for the exterior finish, several factors must be taken into consideration, such as decay resistance, paint-holding quality, and appearance (lumber grade). This selection will depend to some extent upon the kind of wood available in the area.

Woods commonly used for outside finish and carried in stock by local lumber yards include pine, cypress, western cedars, redwood, and Douglas fir.

When considering the paint-holding quality of wood, not only the species but also the density is important. The paint-holding property of light spring wood is better than that of the heavier summer growths. Edge, or vertical-grain, boards also are found to hold paint better than the flat or plain-sawed boards.

Any defect which mars the appearance of wood makes it undesirable for exterior trim. Also, a defect in wood impairs its durability and paint-holding property. Therefore, it is advisable to select only the high-grade woods for finishing and trimming the exterior of any permanent building.

Building Paper. An important material, which is almost indispensable in connection with outside finish, is *building paper*. This paper serves two useful purposes: (1) waterproofing, and (2) reducing the infiltration of air and dust. Building paper is not considered of much value as a thermal-insulation material. All such paper should be applied carefully around windows and door frames. Special care should be taken when applying building paper over wall sheathing and roof boards for weather tightness. It is not required over plywood, fiber board, or treated gypsum board sheathing. The paper must not be waterproof in the sense that it prevents all vapor penetration. If waterproof paper were used it would prevent the escape of water vapor in the wintertime which would then condense in the wall. Asphalt saturated felt of low vapor resistance serves very well. Asphalt saturated felt, polyethylene film or other plastic film may be used around window openings.

When the walls require building paper it should be applied over the whole area as soon as possible after the sheathing has been nailed in place. There should be at least a 4 inch toplap at each horizontal joint and a 4 inch sidelap at end joints. It should be lapped at least 6 inches from both sides around corners. Sufficient fasteners to hold it in place until siding is applied are needed.

Flashing of metal or other waterproof material is required at points which are particularly susceptible to water damage, such as the drip cap of windows and water tables at the bottom of the siding.

Exterior Wall Covering

Manufacturers of building materials used for the outside surface of homes aim for three qualities: beauty, easy maintenance, and durability. Cost is always a factor. A number of new products have been developed to take their place alongside the time honored wood boards and wood shingles used for wall covering. The age-old problems of resistance to rot, warp, split and the attack of termites; as well as the home owners problem of the need for frequent painting have been overcome to a great extent by the new products. However, they in turn are relatively expensive and have their own shortcomings.

The more common types of wall covering are as follows:

1. Wood siding is still popular because of its workability and economy.

2. Wood shingles are used to create certain architectural effects. They present a beautiful wall. Wood shingles are quite inexpensive. Shakes are hand split wood shingles which present a rugged appearance.

3. Plywood is manufactured in sheets and panels for use as exterior wall coverings. It is also available as siding.

4. Wood fiberboard, hardboard, and particleboard have been developed to be used in several ways as wall covering. This "man made" product is made of wood fiber which has been treated, pressed and cut into sheets and planks.

5. Mineral fiber panels and shingles are generally made of asbestos and cement. They are affected very little by weather or age.

6. Metal siding of aluminum and steel has reached considerable acceptance. The baked-on finish saves the home owner the problem of frequent painting.

7. Plastics have entered the wall covering field also. Wood siding and hardboard is available covered with a laminated vinyl sheet or with a surface coating of vinyl. Solid vinyl siding is also manufactured, providing a material which is extremely durable and which has the maintenance problem practically solved.

Wood Siding

Early in our Colonial history, *bevel siding* came into use and it is still used extensively by builders and contractors. See Fig. 1. Fig. 2 shows a section of bevel siding. The full width of the butt of each piece casts a deep shadow on the wall, emphasizing the horizontal effect. Bevel siding is available in widths varying from 4 to 12 inches, and ranges from $15/_{32}$ to $3/_4$ of an inch on the thick edge. The thin edge is $3/_{16}$ of an inch. The 8 inch or wider bevel siding,

Fig. 1. Bevel siding brings out the horizontal lines. (Western Pine Assoc.)

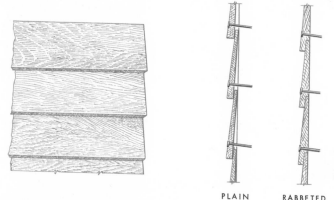

PLAIN   RABBETED

Fig. 2. Bevel siding: A traditional siding pattern. A strong shadow line is produced. (California Redwood Assoc.)

which is thicker, is often called *bungalow* or *Colonial siding*.

Since siding is exposed to the weather, durability of the wood is an important factor to be considered when selecting siding material.

Rabbeted bevel siding (also called Dolly Varden siding) is a popular and economical siding pattern which fits tightly against the wall sheathing. See Fig. 2. *Drop siding*, which is usually thicker than bevel siding,

337

Fundamentals of Carpentry

makes a strong, tight wall that has greater insulation value against wind and cold. See Figs. 3 and 4. Some siding is made with tongue and groove, which makes for a weathertight wall. See Fig. 5. The rustic effect of a real log wall, without the attendant structural difficulties, is produced by the *log cabin siding* illustrated in Fig. 6. This type of siding may be applied either horizontally or vertically with equally good effect. A simple and sturdy wall covering can be made with wide

boards placed vertically and the joints covered with 1 × 2 battens as shown in Figs. 7 and 8. The battens may be molded for added interest. Vertical battens may also be placed behind the joints of wide boards used as vertical siding, as shown in Fig. 9. This type of construction provides a double air space in the wall, thereby improving its insulation value slightly.

Other types of siding used commonly are shown in Figures 10, 11, 12 and 13.

Fig. 5. Drop siding is provided with tongue and groove.

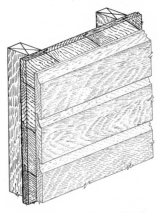

Fig. 3. Drop siding is comparatively weathertight. It fits flush with the sheathing.

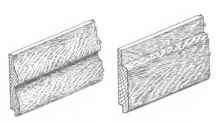

Fig. 4. Drop siding comes in a variety of shapes.

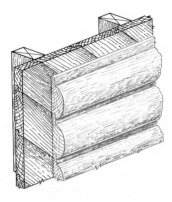

Fig. 6. Siding gives a rustic log cabin effect.

Fig. 7. Board and batten: Apply in vertical courses only for exteriors; it produces bold effects. (California Redwood Assoc.)

Fig. 8. Battens emphasize vertical lines. (Western Red Cedar Lumber Assoc.)

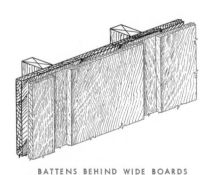

BATTENS BEHIND WIDE BOARDS

Fig. 9. Another method of applying boards and battens (or boards on boards) provides an air space in the wall.

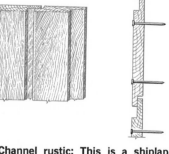

Fig. 10. Channel rustic: This is a shiplap variation that gives a board on board effect with strong patterns of light and shade. It can be applied in vertical or horizontal courses. (California Redwood Assoc.)

339

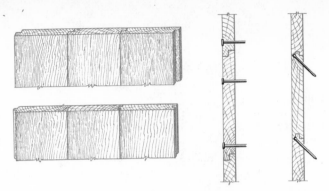

Fig. 11. Flush patterns: Square edge tongue and groove and shiplap give the same flush appearance when installed. It can be applied vertically or horizontally. (California Redwood Assoc.)

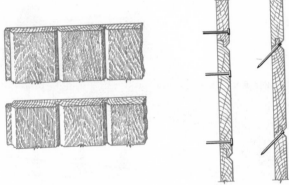

Fig. 12. Vee joint: The same effect is obtained from either tongue and groove or shiplap vee joint. These produce a strong shadow pattern. Can be applied vertically or horizontally. (California Redwood Assoc.)

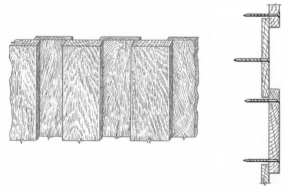

Fig. 13. Santa Rosa siding: The thin under batten makes this a most economical pattern, both in terms of coverage and ease of handling. It is applied in vertical courses. (California Redwood Assoc.)

Wood siding may be purchased pre-primed or completely finished with paint. It also comes covered with a bonding sheath of vinyl plastic.

Siding cannot be applied until the door and window frames are set. Siding must be lapped so it will shed water and make the wall covering windtight and dustproof. The minimum amount of lap which is required for lapped bevel siding is 1 inch. The lap may vary slightly, if necessary, to make the siding line up with the bottom of the window sills and the tops of drip caps at window and door heads. In order that the exposure of the siding may be as nearly uniform as possible, it is advisable to lay out a story pole, for the entire height of the wall showing the exact height of each piece of siding. The square butt joints between adjacent pieces of siding, in successive courses, should be staggered as widely as possible. Rabbeted bevel siding is usually lapped ½ inch.

Applying Wood Siding. Generally siding is applied without the use of a water table. (A water table is shown in Fig. 16.)

Extend the lowest board over the foundation wall at least 1 inch. See Fig. 14. Snap a level chalk line to indicate the top of the first piece and nail it in place. Treat cuts at corners and at joints with paint or preservative. Stagger all joints which occur on the wall.

A clean sharp corner is made when the corner boards are mitered. It is

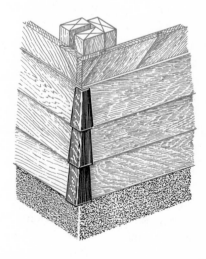

Fig. 14. Metal corners serve to finish the siding application.

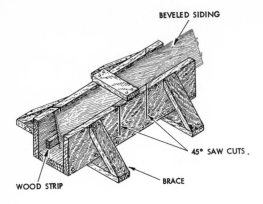

BEVELED SIDING

45° SAW CUTS.

WOOD STRIP

BRACE

Fig. 15. A miter box is fitted to give the correct cut and pitch to siding which is to be mitered at corners.

difficult to make mitered joints that will not open under the influence of changing weather conditions. Plain mitered corners, if they are to look well, must fit closely and stay in place. Properly seasoned lumber, which has been kept dry on the job, as well as good workmanship are important factors. Painting the ends of the joints will prevent absorption of moisture.

Make a simple miter box which is about 1 inch higher than the siding is wide. Place a strip in the miter box to give the siding the right angle if the siding does not have flush application to the sheathing. See Fig. 15.

Metal corners save much time and permits the corners to be sawed with less precision. See Fig. 14.

Water Table and Corners. The lowest piece of siding generally serves as a water table. Some types of architecture require a traditional water table made up of a wide horizontal board covering the line where the sheathing and foundation meet and a drip cap which will throw water away from the foundation. The drip cap should be flashed and the first piece of siding should be cut to fit against it. See Fig. 16. When a water table is used, bevel the first piece of siding on the bottom edge so that it will fit tightly on top of the drip cap. When corner boards are used, cut the siding to fit against them. After cutting the ends of the siding boards, smooth them with a block plane to insure tightly fitted joints that will keep out wind, dust, and water. For accurate cutting of siding, so that it will fit at these important joints, use a simple wood-marking gage made from a 1 × 2 inch piece. While laying out and marking siding pieces for cutting, rest the board on nails set on the line of correct exposure, as shown

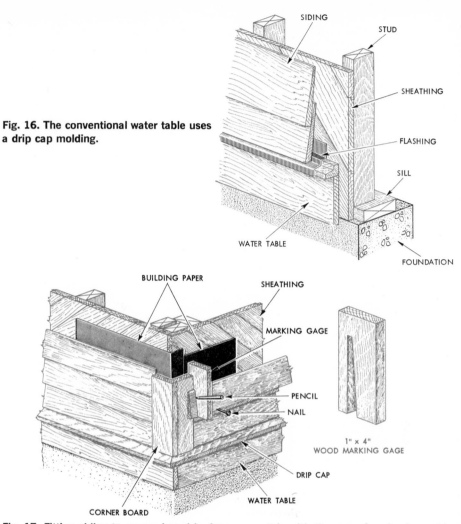

Fig. 16. The conventional water table uses a drip cap molding.

Fig. 17. Fitting siding to corner board is done accurately with the use of a simple marking gage.

in Fig. 17. The pencil indicates the cutting line.

Nailing Siding. The nailing of siding is very important. A regular siding nail should be used: 6*d* nail for ½ inch bevel siding and 8*d* nail for ¾ inch siding. Either zinc coated (galvanized), aluminum, or stainless steel nails should be used because none of these will rust. Use of the

343

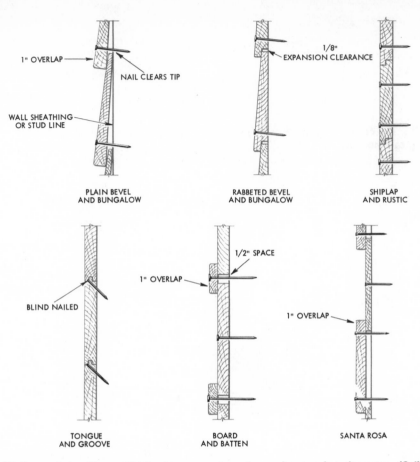

Fig. 18. Suggested nailing methods show correct overlap and expansion clearance. (California Redwood Assoc.)

non-rusting nails not only adds to the life of the wall covering, but also prevents staining of the painted surface of the wood with rust streaks. Nails should not cause splitting even when driven near the edge of the siding. They should not "pop out" after being driven flush with the siding. Fig. 18 shows the manner of nailing some of the typical siding patterns. A clearance is shown to permit expansion. Nails are not generally driven through two pieces.

Wood siding may be obtained preprimed. It is applied in the conventional manner. If prefinished siding is used it must be applied according to manufacturers directions.

Side-wall Shingling

Shingles are used for side-wall covering to achieve special effects. They have a long life, require little upkeep, and there is a saving on paint. Shingles in bundles may be dipped in stain before applying or may be purchased ready to apply.

The specifications and application directions for side-wall shingles are similar to those for roof shingles which are explained later. A greater variety of designs have been developed for side-wall covering and as a rule the amount of exposure is greater than for roof covering.

The customary method used in laying shingles on the side wall is in straight courses. The monotony of the straight course lines can be overcome by staggering the shingles; that is, raising alternate shingles.

Laying the shingles in a double course, as shown in Fig. 19, increases insulation slightly. The deep shadow line secured in this way adds much to the appearance of the house. Hand split shakes add character and a soft, pleasing appearance to a dwelling. A method of applying handsplit shakes on a side wall is illustrated in Fig. 20.

Applying the Shingles. Shingles must be nailed to a solid base, wood sheathing or plywood are recommended. Building paper should be carefully applied to the wall first. Flashing should be applied over the drip cap of the water table. See Fig. 20.

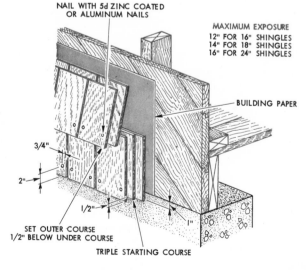

NAIL WITH 5d ZINC COATED OR ALUMINUM NAILS

MAXIMUM EXPOSURE
12" FOR 16" SHINGLES
14" FOR 18" SHINGLES
16" FOR 24" SHINGLES

BUILDING PAPER

3/4"

2"

1/2"

1"

SET OUTER COURSE
1/2" BELOW UNDER COURSE

TRIPLE STARTING COURSE

Fig. 19. Double course shingling increases insulation value of wall and adds deep shadow lines.

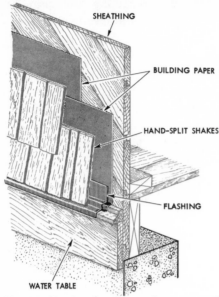

Fig. 20. Hand split shakes give a rugged appearance.

The first course of shingles is doubled or tripled. Following the laying of the first course, a careful study should be made of the wall in relation to its total height, the size and height of windows and other openings. A story pole should then be laid out, with the different courses indicated on it. All the courses should have the same exposure, if possible. It is desirable to have the courses line up with the top and bottom of window and door openings. To make such an alignment possible may require a slight adjustment of the exposure of the courses. The spacing indicated on the story pole should be marked off on each

shingle course at both ends of the wall, then the shingles are laid in accordance with this spacing by using a straightedge or by snapping a chalk line as a guide line.

Sidewall shake panels are manufactured with shakes glued to a backer board in widths of 46¾ inches and in some cases 4 and 8 feet long. They are prefinished in several popular stained colors. Annular threaded nails of matching colors are used. The panels are applied rapidly and are easy to handle.

Plywood Exterior Wall Covering

Plywood has become a versatile material as exterior wall covering because of the introduction and perfection of waterproof glues. It can be applied in full sheets of ⅜, ½, or ⅝ inch thickness and has sufficient strength so that conventional sheathing can be eliminated if the nailing follows basic standards. The application shown in Fig. 21 requires nails to be spaced 6 inches apart on panel edges and 12 inches apart on studs. 6*d* or 8*d* galvanized or aluminum casing nails are recommended. Another novel type of plywood used for siding is shown in Fig. 22. This plywood is ⅝ of an inch thick with 5⁄16 inch grooves on 2 inch or 4 inch centers.

Plywood is also available as lap siding or beveled siding. The width of the pieces are 12, 16 or 24 inches and 8 feet long. The plywood used

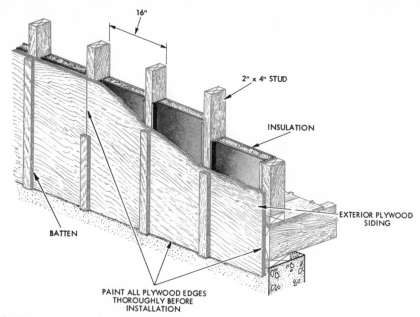

16"

2" x 4" STUD

INSULATION

EXTERIOR PLYWOOD
SIDING

BATTEN

PAINT ALL PLYWOOD EDGES
THOROUGHLY BEFORE
INSTALLATION

Fig. 21. The edges of plywood panels are carefully joined and protected when plywood is used as exterior finish. (Douglas Fir Plywood Assoc.)

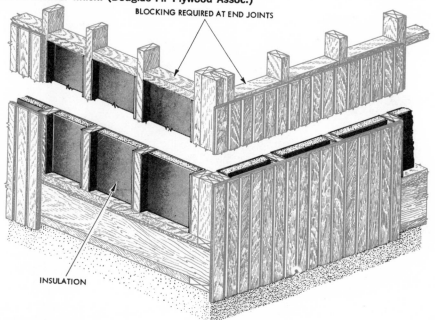

BLOCKING REQUIRED AT END JOINTS

INSULATION

Fig. 22. Grooved plywood sheets make an excellent exterior finish which can be applied quickly. (Douglas Fir Plywood Assoc.)

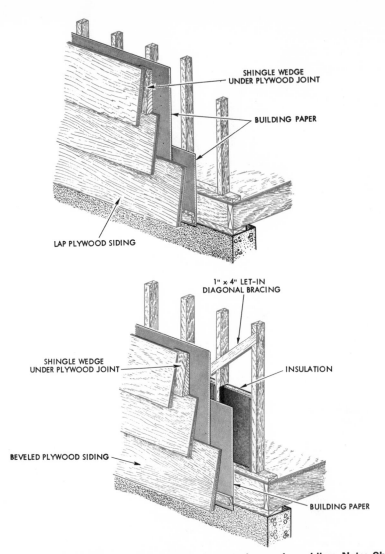

Fig. 23. Plywood is supplied in flat or beveled pieces to be used as siding. Note: Sheathing may be omitted if local building code permits.

for lap siding ranges from ⅜ inches to ¾ inches thickness. See Fig. 23. Plywood beveled siding has ½, ⅝ or ¾ inch thick butts and comes in widths from 12 to 24 inches. A starting strip is used to bring the lowest piece away from the wall and shingle wedges are placed under the joints which are made to occur at studs.

Plywood siding is available with

coatings and plastic films which help overcome the paint problem for many years. Among other surface treatments are channel grooved, striated, embossed and rough surfaced plywood.

Hardboard Siding

Hardboard has proved to be a very popular material for wall covering because it has no knots or imperfections; it is dense, resisting abrasion and denting; and it can be sawed and nailed easily. It is a product made of small wood chips which are "exploded" under high pressure steam, cleaned and refined. The wood fibers and the natural binding agent, lignin, found in the wood is reunited under heat and pressure to form hardboard. This material is sold as wall covering in sheets and siding in a variety of styles, surfaces and finishes.

Panel hardboard siding is available in sheets nominally $7/16$ inch thick 4 feet wide and 8, 9 and 10 feet in length. West of the Rockies it is

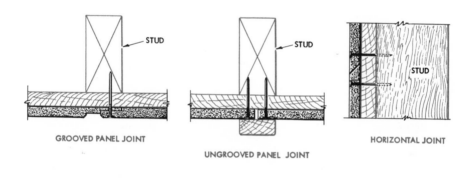

GROOVED PANEL JOINT

UNGROOVED PANEL JOINT

HORIZONTAL JOINT

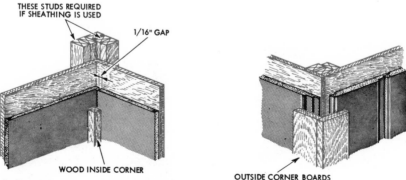

THESE STUDS REQUIRED IF SHEATHING IS USED

1/16" GAP

WOOD INSIDE CORNER

OUTSIDE CORNER BOARDS

Fig. 24. Hardboard panel siding is easily applied. All joints occur at framing members. (Masonite Corp.)

obtainable up to 16 feet in length. It is provided with V grooves, and other grooved patterns, with raised integral ribs which resemble battens or as plain sheets to which battens are applied. See Fig. 24 for nailing suggestions. A $\frac{1}{16}$ inch space is required wherever two sheets join vertically. Battens are placed over ungrooved panel joints. All joints must fall on framing members. Sheets which are prefinished with a vinyl plastic sur-face may be applied in the conventional manner except that nails are concealed in a special way. Backer strips of hardboard are nailed to cover the joints and plastic or metal snap-on batten covers fit over the batten backer strips. See Fig. 25. The batten covers are color keyed to match the finish on the panels. When nails must be exposed touch-up paint of the same color is applied or special pre-coated nails of the same color

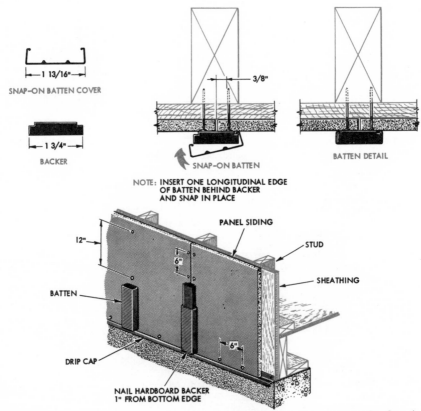

Fig. 25. Prefinished hardboard requires the use of snap on battens. (Masonite Corp.)

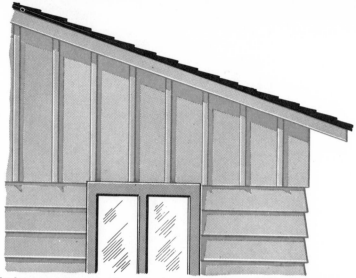

Fig. 26. Vinyl covered panels with snap on battens are shown in the gable end and vinyl covered siding on the lower wall. Note the window using an extended jamb instead of an external casing. Calking provides a weather seal. **(Boise Cascade Building Products)**

are used. Caulking with the same color is obtainable to cover end joints at windows or other exposed places. See Fig. 26.

Lap siding of hardboard is available in widths of 6, 9 and 12 inches and in lengths of 12 and 16 feet. It is generally ⅜ or ⁷⁄₁₆ inch thick. The common type has a smooth grainless surface but it may be purchased also with a simulated textured pattern with a rough sawn appearance. Fig. 27 gives details of application. Prefinished hardboard lap siding is fastened in several ways. One way is to place nails along the top edge which will be concealed by the next piece. The adhesive is applied at

intervals along this top edge to hold the bottom of the next piece and to permit water vapor to escape. See Fig. 28. Another ingenious method is to use a mounting strip which is part of the siding. It presses against the angled top of the lower piece of siding in a wedge action. See Fig. 29.

Mineral Fiber Wall Covering

Mineral fiber material used for wall and roof covering is made of asbestos fiber and Portland cement. It is fireproof, termite proof, will not warp or shrink and is very long lasting. It is generally used in the form of siding (shingles) in pieces 12 × 24 by ³⁄₁₆ inch thick. One style is 9

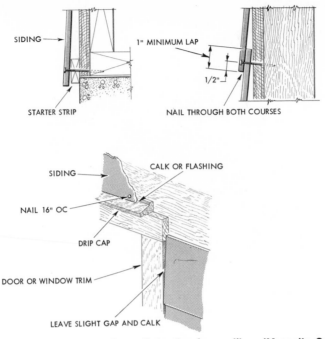

SIDING

1" MINIMUM LAP

1/2"

STARTER STRIP

NAIL THROUGH BOTH COURSES

SIDING

CALK OR FLASHING

NAIL 16" OC

DRIP CAP

DOOR OR WINDOW TRIM

LEAVE SLIGHT GAP AND CALK

Fig. 27. Hardboard lap siding is easily applied using face nailing. (Masonite Corp.)

× 32 × ³⁄₁₆ inch thick. It is also available in panels 4 feet wide by 8, 9, 10 or 12 feet long by ⅛ inch thick. Asbestos cement siding is provided with pre-drilled holes. It cannot be nailed without using these holes or making other holes first because the dense material would break if nails were driven through it. Each bundle of siding is provided with half pieces so that every other course may be staggered from the starting corner. An asbestos board shear tool is used to cut odd lengths. One type of material made of asbestos fiber, wood fiber and Portland cement, however, may be cut with carpenter's tools and nailed without being pre-drilled. Power hand saws should have carboloy tipped blades. This material is supplied in the form of siding 9½ and 12 inches wide, ⅜ inch thick and 12 feet long.

Mineral fiber (asbestos cement) siding is generally made with a grooved or striated surface to resemble shingles. It comes in a variety of colors. A pigmented veneer of Portland cement is applied to the siding prior to final application of acrylic coating before it is oven baked. Asphalt backer strips (which

Fig. 28. Prefinished hardwood lap siding is applied with nails and adhesive. Nails are driven along the top edge. Adhesive is placed at intervals to hold the bottom of the next piece. (Boise Cascade Building Products)

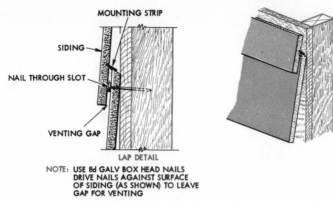

NOTE: USE 8d GALV BOX HEAD NAILS
DRIVE NAILS AGAINST SURFACE
OF SIDING (AS SHOWN) TO LEAVE
GAP FOR VENTING

Fig. 29. Vinyl covered siding is applied with the use of mounting strips so that all nails are concealed. (Masonite Corp.)

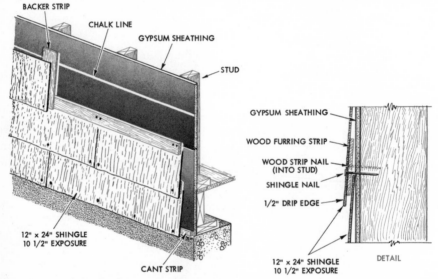

Fig. 30. A typical asbestos cement siding shingle application shows cant strip, furring strip and backer strip. (National Gypsum Co.)

help to waterproof the wall) and aluminum nails are furnished with the siding. Nails as well as inside and outside corners and cap strips are available in the same color as the siding.

A typical installation procedure is shown in Fig. 30. A cant strip which can be a wood lath or other piece approximately ½ by 1 inch is nailed to the wall in a level position at the bottom of the siding. A level line is

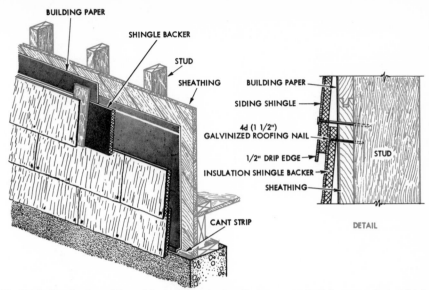

Fig. 31. Asphalt asbestos siding shingles may be applied over asphalt impregnated shingle backers. (National Gypsum Co.)

snapped 11½ inches above the bottom of the cant strip to serve as a guide to line up the top of the first row of siding. (Other lines should be snapped 10½ inches apart vertically.) Using the 12 inch material permits a ½ inch overlap at the bottom of the lowest piece to serve as a drip. The siding is nailed through the prepared holes at the lower edge with 1⅛ inch aluminum nails. Backer strips are placed behind each vertical joint. A wood furring strip is then nailed in place at the top edge of the shingle. The nails for the furring strips may be a common galvanized shingle nail and should be driven so as not to touch the siding. The next row of shingles is then nailed in place

using a half piece to start from the corner. Fig. 31 shows the use of a shingle backer in an application over wood sheathing. The shingle backer provided additional insulation plus a shadow line.

Mineral fiber, prefinished sheets are applied with the use of extruded aluminum joint strips, inside and outside corners and cap strips of the same color.

Metal Siding

Metal siding is provided in both steel and aluminum as bevel siding or to simulate vertical boards, or boards and battens. The surface is either smooth or is made to look like wood grain. The protective plastic

Fig. 32. Metal siding may be obtained with an insulating backing. (Alcoa Building Products, Inc.)

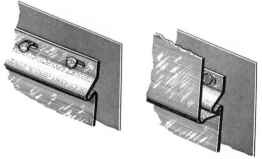

Fig. 33. Metal siding is fastened with nails through elongated holes which permit thermal expansion. The pieces interlock to form a firm seal. (Alcoa Building Products, Inc.)

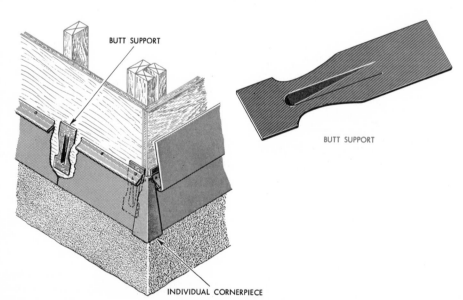

BUTT SUPPORT

BUTT SUPPORT

INDIVIDUAL CORNERPIECE

Fig. 34. A butt support or backer is placed under each horizontal joint. (Aluminum Assoc.)

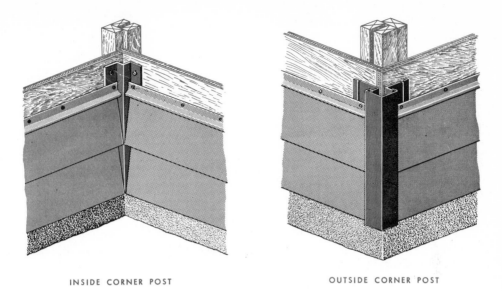

INSIDE CORNER POST OUTSIDE CORNER POST

DOOR AND WINDOW TRIM

Fig. 35. Inside and outside corner posts and trim at doors and windows are special shapes. (Aluminum Assoc.)

and baked on finishes are guaranteed to last for many years. The metal siding may be purchased with an insulation backing board which helps to stiffen it as well as to add to the insulation value. The material is installed easily with carpenter's tools plus a hacksaw and tin snips. The low maintenance cost and excellent appearance makes it attractive. To eliminate static electricity, and thus to reduce the hazard of lightning, it is suggested that lowest course of siding be satisfactorily grounded.

Fig. 32 shows how the siding is provided with an insulating backing and Fig. 33 shows how the siding is nailed and how the pieces interlock.

A metal piece called a butt support or back up tab is placed under each horizontal joint. See Fig. 34. Special shapes are provided for starter strip, outside and inside corners (Fig. 35) and window head flashing. One shape is designed to be fastened at the sides of windows and doors to receive the ends of the pieces of siding. See Fig. 35.

Plastic Siding

Plastic is often used as a protective coating for other siding material. However, it is also now available in the form of solid siding designed to resemble other bevel siding and vertical board exterior wall coverings. It is stamped or extruded to a $\frac{1}{20}$

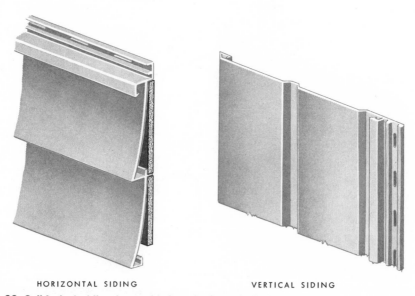

HORIZONTAL SIDING   VERTICAL SIDING

Fig. 36. Solid vinyl siding is provided as horizontal clapboards or vertical units. (Bird & Son, Inc.)

inch thickness and made into boards 12 foot 6 inches long with slots for nailing and interlocking lips as integral parts. See Fig. 36. All of the necessary accessories in the form of corners, starter strips, flashing and window and door trim members are available of the same material. The siding is supplied with or without insulation backing. The relatively high cost is offset by the fact that the material is virtually indestructible. It will not dent or corrode, has a color which goes through the material and never needs painting. It is worked with tools of the trade.

Roof Covering

The main purpose of any type of roof covering is to keep out rain and snow, and to provide protection against wind and dust. In addition, the roof acts as a thermal insulator and, if chosen carefully, it can add materially to the architectural beauty of the building.

Many different kinds of roof-covering materials are available, including tile, slate, built-up roofing, asphalt shingles, mineral fiber (asbestos-cement) shingles, and wood shingles. Carpenters are concerned chiefly with the last three.

The slope of the roof determines the type of roofing which can be used. A flat roof or one with a slope of less than 2 inches per foot requires a built-up roof. A roof with a slope of from 2 to 4 inches per foot may use asphalt shingles with certain precautions used for sealing the shingles. A roof with a slope greater than 4 inches per foot can use asphalt shingles without any problem.

The length of life of any type of roof covering depends primarily on the material itself, but also to a great extent on the way in which it is laid. The best material, if poorly applied, will give unsatisfactory service.

A few important terms should be understood.

Square. Roofing is estimated and sold by the square. This is the amount required to cover 100 square feet of roof surface.

Coverage. Shingles overlap and, depending on the manner in which they are laid, one, two or three thicknesses are over the roof at any one place. Thus the roofing is termed single coverage, double coverage, etc.

Shingle Butt. The lower exposed edge of the shingle. This end is thicker on wood shingles.

Exposure. Exposure "to the weather" is the distance from the butt of one shingle to the butt of the one above it.

Underlayment. An application of saturated felt over the roof surface to protect the roof sheathing until shingles are applied and to provide additional weather protection after the shingles are in place.

Flashing. Additional protection in the form of sheet metal or mineral surfaced roofing is placed in the valley intersection of two roofs and around the base of a chimney to provide a means to carry off water.

Toplap. The width of the shingle minus the exposure.

Asphalt Shingles

Asphalt shingles are made of asphalt saturated felt coated with mineral granules which give them their color. Light colors are preferred in warm climates because they tend to reflect rather than absorb heat rays. The shingles come in several sizes and shapes. Some common types are shown in Table I. Three tab square butt shingles, 12 inches wide by 36 inches long, are the most popular. They can be applied quickly,

are relatively inexpensive, are approved for use by most local fire codes, and are attractive.

The weight of the shingles is important because it is related to the ability of the material to stand up under long use. It is also a consideration in calculating the dead load on the structure and has a bearing on the size of the rafters. Heavier roofing material is generally considered to be superior.

Asphalt saturated felt used for underlayment and for built-up roofs comes in 36 inch wide rolls of 144 feet length; 15 and 30 pounds per square are the usual weights used depending on the requirements of the application.

The underlayment is commonly 15 pound felt, and is laid with the proper sidelap and top lap. See Fig. 37. A drip edge made of galvanized steel is recommended for application to the edge of the roof sheathing both

	SHINGLE TYPE	SHIPPING WEIGHT PER SQUARE	PACKAGES PER SQUARE	LENGTH	WIDTH	UNITS PER SQUARE	HEADLAP	EXPOSURE
STRIP SHINGLES	2 AND 3 TAB SQUARE BUTT	235 LB	3	36"	12"	80	2"	5"
	2 AND 3 TAB HEXAGONAL	195 LB	3	36"	11 1/3"	86	2"	5"

Table I   Asphalt Roof Shingles

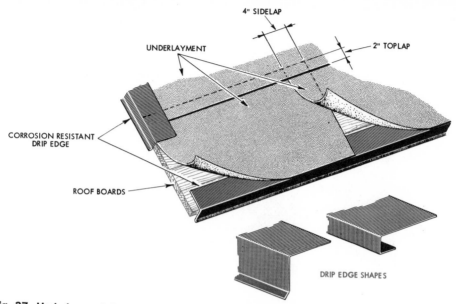

Fig. 37. Underlayment for asphalt shingle application must have proper sidelap and top-lap. Note drip edge on eave and rake sides of roof.

at the eaves and on the rake end (the sloped roof end). The underlayment is placed over the drip edge.

In cold climate where the temperature may drop to 0° or lower ice often forms along the eaves and as it thaws and freezes again water backs up under the shingles. To prevent this condition from causing damage, eaves flashing, consisting of a starter strip of 15 pound felt, is placed over the roof boards and the drip edge. It is extended back with additional strips if necessary to a line at least 12 inches inside the interior wall line (24 inches for low sloped roofs). The regular underlayment strips are then

laid and cemented with plastic asphalt cement to the starter strip. See Fig. 38.

Valleys may be flashed by using an open or closed method. The open valley method, see Fig. 39, requires the use of a strip of mineral surfaced roofing fastened face down to the roof. A second piece which has the same color as the roof shingles is then cemented in place face up. The shingles are cut parallel to the valley line and cemented to the valley flashing strip. Closed valley flashing is accomplished by using a piece of mineral surface roofing nailed in place in the valley and then weaving

361

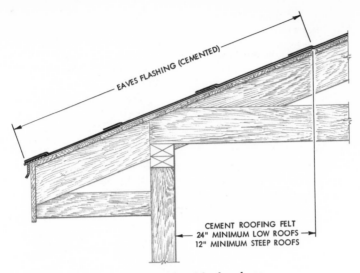

EAVES FLASHING (CEMENTED)

CEMENT ROOFING FELT
24" MINIMUM LOW ROOFS
12" MINIMUM STEEP ROOFS

Fig. 38. Eaves flashing prevents damage caused by ice dams.

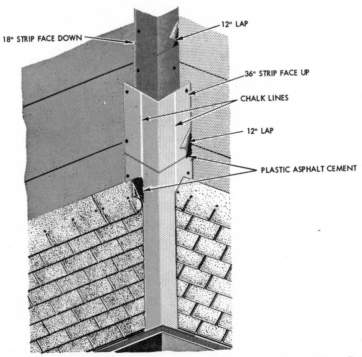

18" STRIP FACE DOWN

12" LAP

36" STRIP FACE UP

CHALK LINES

12" LAP

PLASTIC ASPHALT CEMENT

Fig. 39. Valley flashing may be done using strips of mineral surfaced roll roofing.

362

the strip shingles alternately. See Fig. 40.

Flashing at chimney's requires the use of 90 pound roll roofing or metal flashing. See Figs. 41 and 42. When roll roofing is used for flashing the shingles are laid up to the chimney.

The roofing is cut to fit with overlapping corners and applied in a bed of asphalt plastic cement. The cement is used to make the upper surface against the chimney waterproof. Metal flashing is a more effective way. The underlayment is laid

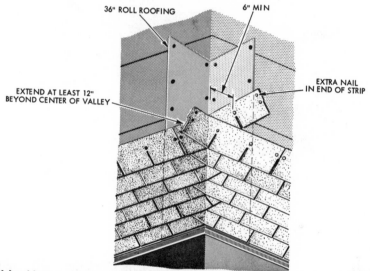

36" ROLL ROOFING

6" MIN

EXTEND AT LEAST 12"
BEYOND CENTER OF VALLEY

EXTRA NAIL
IN END OF STRIP

Fig. 40. Strip shingles may be crossed to provide a tight valley.

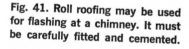

Fig. 41. Roll roofing may be used for flashing at a chimney. It must be carefully fitted and cemented.

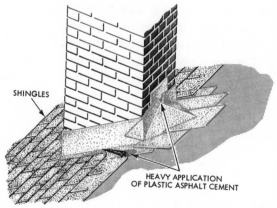

SHINGLES

HEAVY APPLICATION
OF PLASTIC ASPHALT CEMENT

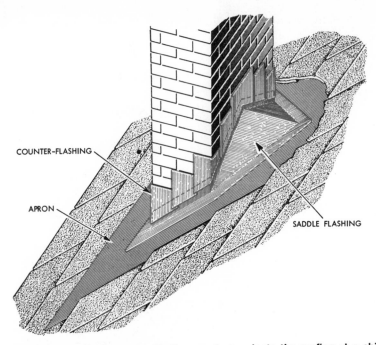

COUNTER-FLASHING

APRON

SADDLE FLASHING

Fig. 42. Metal step flashing is the most effective way to terminate the roofing at a chimney.

up to the faces of the chimney. Pieces of non corrosive metal are bent to the contour of the roof extending two inches over the underlayment and extending up along the chimney face. Each piece of flashing is placed so that it is underneath the shingles and laps the next piece of flashing. A cap flashing is bent at the top to be inserted in the brick joints and is extended down to cover the base flashing.

The nails used for applying asphalt shingles should be corrosive resistant, such as galvanized steel or aluminum with flat heads. Shanks may be smooth or threaded. Threaded nails have greater holding power. Galvanized threaded nails should have annular grooves, aluminum nails should have screw threads.

Applying Asphalt Shingles. Following the application of the metal drip edge, the underlayment, the application of eaves flashing when considered necessary, and the preliminary steps in valley flashing, the roofing operation is begun with the application of a starter course. This

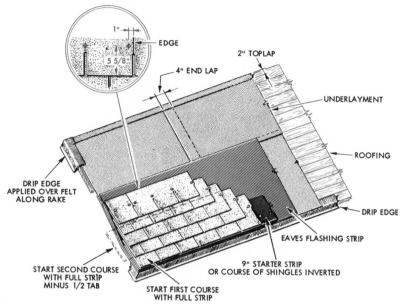

DRIP EDGE
APPLIED OVER FELT
ALONG RAKE

EDGE

2" TOPLAP

4" END LAP

UNDERLAYMENT

ROOFING

DRIP EDGE

EAVES FLASHING STRIP

9" STARTER STRIP
OR COURSE OF SHINGLES INVERTED

START SECOND COURSE
WITH FULL STRIP
MINUS 1/2 TAB

START FIRST COURSE
WITH FULL STRIP

Fig. 43. An asphalt shingle roof begins with the application of a drip edge followed by underlayment, eaves flashing strip, or starter strips. Then the first full strip is nailed in place.

consists of a 9 inch or wider strip of mineral surface roll roofing of the same color or strip shingles turned around so that the tabs point up the roof. This provides a roofing edge without slots. The first regular course is then nailed in place ¼ or ⅜ inch over the drip edge on the eaves as well as on the rake (at the gable end). The first shingle should be a whole strip. The second course can be cut so that the lap will occur at the half tab point if so desired. See Fig. 43. It can also be cut less than a half tab to give a different effect. Four nails are used in each shingle. A nail is placed 1 inch in from each edge and two other nails are placed near the tab slots. Each nail passes through two thicknesses of shingles and is concealed by the next course when it is applied. Lines are snapped on the underlayment to indicate the location of each course. Some felt comes with lines on it. Lines may be used as guidelines on shingle aplication. The sheets must be started accurately.

Ridges and hips are finished in Boston style. Strips are cut into pieces and are applied over the hip or ridge with each piece lapping over the next piece. See Fig. 44.

Roofs with a slope of 2 inches per

Fig. 44. Boston hip and ridge requires overlapping strips for asphalt shingled roof.

foot to 4 inches per foot may be roofed with shingles in which the tabs are sealed to prevent rain from driving underneath and wind from ripping them up. A starter strip mopped with adhesive to prevent moisture penetration is required. Hexagonal strip shingles, See Table I, present no particular problems. When they are applied in windy locations, shingles with factory applied adhesive may be used or the tabs may be cemented down with a dab of quick setting cement.

Built-Up Roofing

Built-up roofs are made with 3, 4 or 5 plys of felt. Usually 15 pound felt is used. The first layer is laid dry and nailed in place with galvanized roofing nails. This is mopped with a hot asphalt or hot coal-tar pitch which is spread to meet a cer-

tain specification, for example, 25 pounds per 100 square feet. Each succeeding layer of felt is mopped with the same coating. The top layer is covered with a thin layer of marble chips, pea gravel or fine slag: 400 pounds of gravel or crushed rock or 300 pounds of slag per 100 square feet are typical amounts required. See Fig. 45. The aggregate put on the surface serves to protect the felt and to reflect heat. When the roof slope is greater than 2 inches per foot it is difficult to retain the gravel on the roof. The edge of the roof all around is protected by a metal strip (galvanized steel) called gravel stop. It is nailed in place prior to the roofing operation. See Fig. 46.

Mineral Fiber Shingles

Mineral fiber shingles are made of asbestos fiber and Portland cement.

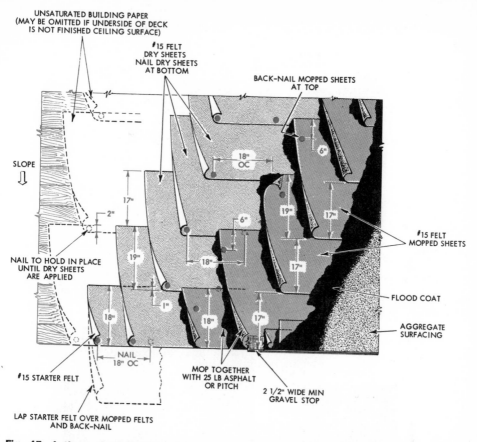

UNSATURATED BUILDING PAPER
(MAY BE OMITTED IF UNDERSIDE OF DECK
IS NOT FINISHED CEILING SURFACE)

#15 FELT
DRY SHEETS
NAIL DRY SHEETS
AT BOTTOM

BACK-NAIL MOPPED SHEETS
AT TOP

SLOPE

18"
OC

6"

17"

2"

19"

17"

6"

19"

17"

NAIL TO HOLD IN PLACE
UNTIL DRY SHEETS
ARE APPLIED

#15 FELT
MOPPED SHEETS

18"

1"

17"

FLOOD COAT

AGGREGATE
SURFACING

18"

18"

17"

NAIL
18" OC

#15 STARTER FELT

MOP TOGETHER
WITH 25 LB ASPHALT
OR PITCH

2 1/2" WIDE MIN
GRAVEL STOP

LAP STARTER FELT OVER MOPPED FELTS
AND BACK-NAIL

Fig. 45. A three ply built-up roof is made of three thicknesses of overlapping asphalt-saturated felt mopped with asphalt or pitch. (FHA Minimum Property Standards)

Because of their mineral content they are considered highly fire resistant. Care must be taken in handling and installing them and care must be used if workmen find it necessary to walk on them because of their brittle nature. The most popular styles are Dutch lap and the so called hexagonal. Both are $16 \times 16 \times \frac{5}{32}$ inch. They come in several colors. The Dutch lap shingles have a wood grain or striated surface. See Fig. 47. A slope of 5 inches per foot or greater is suggested for mineral fiber shingled roofs.

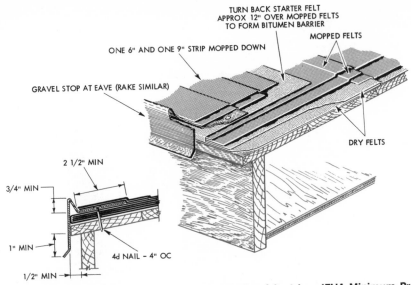

TURN BACK STARTER FELT
APPROX 12" OVER MOPPED FELTS
TO FORM BITUMEN BARRIER

MOPPED FELTS

ONE 6" AND ONE 9" STRIP MOPPED DOWN

GRAVEL STOP AT EAVE (RAKE SIMILAR)

DRY FELTS

2 1/2" MIN

3/4" MIN

1" MIN

4d NAIL – 4" OC

1/2" MIN

Fig. 46. Detail shows gravel stop and manner of placing felt strips. (FHA Minimum Property Standards)

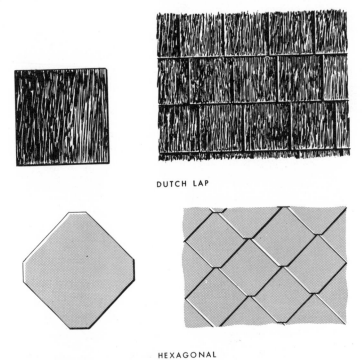

DUTCH LAP

HEXAGONAL

Fig. 47. Asbestos cement shingles are fireproof and have long life.

Holes are pre-punched for nails. Galvanized aluminum and stainless steel nails are recommended. They should have threaded shanks particularly if the roofing is to be applied over plywood sheathing.

Dutch lap shingles are nailed so that there is concealed nailing for two corners with the third corner held by a storm anchor. See Figs. 48 and 49. The storm anchor is placed through the shingle from

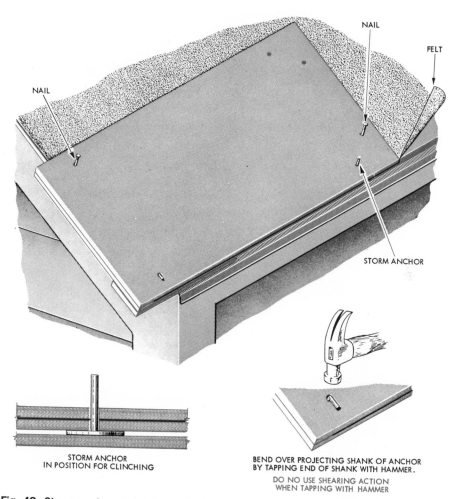

NAIL

FELT

NAIL

STORM ANCHOR

STORM ANCHOR
IN POSITION FOR CLINCHING

BEND OVER PROJECTING SHANK OF ANCHOR
BY TAPPING END OF SHANK WITH HAMMER.

DO NO USE SHEARING ACTION
WHEN TAPPING WITH HAMMER

Fig. 48. Storm anchors hold down the lower corners of mineral fiber (asbestos cement) shingles when laid with Dutch lap.

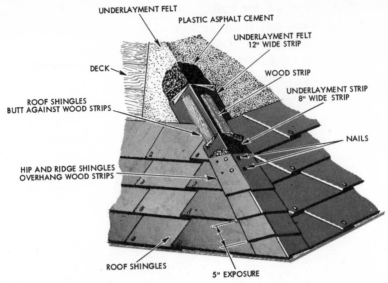

UNDERLAYMENT FELT

PLASTIC ASPHALT CEMENT

UNDERLAYMENT FELT
12" WIDE STRIP

DECK

WOOD STRIP

UNDERLAYMENT STRIP
8" WIDE STRIP

ROOF SHINGLES
BUTT AGAINST WOOD STRIPS

NAILS

HIP AND RIDGE SHINGLES
OVERHANG WOOD STRIPS

ROOF SHINGLES

5" EXPOSURE

Fig. 49. Mineral fiber (asbestos cement) shingles are overlapped to form a Boston hip.

below before it is put in place. Then the next shingle is applied. The storm anchor is bent over to hold the two shingles together.

Wood strips must be applied to hips and ridges to provide level nailing surfaces. Fig. 49 shows the application of a Boston hip using overlapping pieces at the corner. (It also shows a Dutch lap application). When the pieces have been nailed in place at the ridge or hip the joints are pointed up with plastic asphalt roofing cement. Valleys are flashed with metal using an open or closed method. In the closed method individual sheets of flashing are bent to fit the valley and made to rest on

top of each pair of shingles meeting at the valley and under the next pair to be applied.

Hexagonal shingles are actually square with the corners cut off. When laid on the roof they give an effect which is called "hexagonal". Three edges are covered and nailed with two nails. The front exposed corner is fastened with a copper storm anchor. See Fig. 47.

Wood Shingles

Wood shingles have been used for roofing for centuries and even though they have been replaced by material which can be applied with greater ease they are still used to create a rustic architectural effect. Fire codes in some communities will not permit their use. They are generally made of red cedar, redwood or cypress because these woods have excellent decay resistance. Two types are available: machine sawed shingles and hand split shingles called "shakes".

Machine sawed shingles are made in 16, 18 and 24 inch lengths and in random width. The shingles are tapered with a thickness at the butt of ⅜ to ½ inch.

Sheathing for wood shingle roofs may be plywood, boards laid without spaces, or boards which are laid with a one or two inch space between them. The attic space should be well ventilated. Building paper is not required except in severe climates. Nails should be galvanized or alu-

minum. Exposure of the shingles varies with their length, 5 inches for 16 inch shingles, 5½ inches for 18 inch shingles, and 7½ inches for 24 inch shingles.

Starting at the eaves the first course should be doubled or tripled in order to cover the spaces between shingles. See Fig. 50. Butts shall be made to extend 1½ inches beyond the first sheathing board at the eaves and be given a 1 inch projection at the rake. A space of ¼ inch should be allowed at each shingle joint to permit them to expand. Joints should be arranged so that there is an offset of at least 1½ inches between the joints on one course and those in the course above. Only two nails should be used in each shingle. Nails should be placed far enough away from the edge to prevent splitting of the shin-

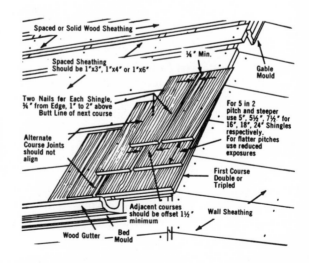

Fig. 50. Wood machine sawed shingles are applied in random widths so that joints between shingles are well covered. Note the wood gutter. (Red Cedar Shingle and Handsplit Shake Bureau)

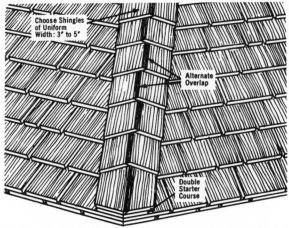

Choose Shingles of Uniform Width: 3″ to 5″

Alternate Overlap

Double Starter Course

Fig. 51. Wood shingles are carefully fitted to make a Boston hip. (Red Cedar Shingle and Handsplit Shake Bureau)

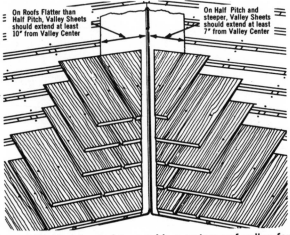

On Roofs Flatter than Half Pitch, Valley Sheets should extend at least 10″ from Valley Center

On Half Pitch and steeper, Valley Sheets should extend at least 7″ from Valley Center

Fig. 52. Crimped metal flashing is used to provide a waterproof valley for a wood shingle roof. (Red Cedar Shingle and Handsplit Shake Bureau)

gle (¾ inch minimum) and 1 or 2 inches above the butt line of the next course so that they are concealed.

Hips and ridges should be made using the "Boston" method. Shingles should be cut and fitted to alternately overlap. Nailing is concealed by the pair above. See Fig. 51. Valleys are flashed with galvanized or aluminum metal extending up on each side of the valley a distance of 10 inches on roofs with a slope of 12 inches per foot or less, and a distance of 7 inches on roofs with a slope of more than 12 inches per foot. See Fig. 52. The flashing should be crimped (raised) in the center to prevent water running down one slope from crossing and going under the shingles on the other slope.

Shingles used at the sides of the valley should be full shingles with the valley corner cut off rather than broken. See Fig. 52.

Handsplit shingles are split rather than cut from a log and show the natural, rough wood grain. They are 18, 24 and 32 inches long and from 5 to 18 inches wide. They are split from the log in two ways. They are *straight split*, which means that the

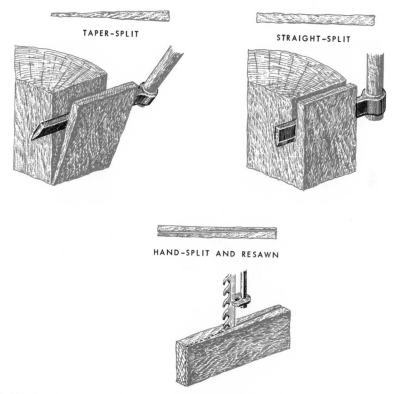

Fig. 53. Hand split shingles called shakes are split from a log. Taper split are cut from alternate ends of the log to give a taper to the shingle. (Red Cedar Shingle and Handsplit Shake Bureau)

two sides are roughly parallel, or *taper split*, which means they are split so as to have a slight taper. See Fig. 53. A term handsplit and resawn means that a straight split shingle is sawed to make two tapered shingles. Thickness at the butt of handsplit shingles ranges roughly from ⅝ to 1¼ inch.

Procedure for applying handsplit shingles is similar to that of applying other wood shingles. A 36 inch wide strip of 30 pound roofing felt should be laid over the sheathing at the eave line. The first course is doubled or tripled; 15 inch shakes can be used to advantage for this starter course. After applying each course of shakes, an 18 inch wide strip of 30 pound roofing felt should be laid over the top portion of the shake and extending out over the sheathing. See Fig. 54. The following shake exposures are recommended: 7¼ inches for 18 inch shakes, 10 inch exposure for 24 inch shakes, and 13 inch exposure for 32 inch shakes.

Hips and valleys are treated in the same manner as for machine-made wood shingles. See Fig. 54.

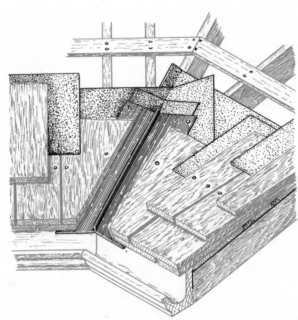

Fig. 54. Hand split shakes provide a rustic appearance. A sheet metal valley which is crimped to provide a water barrier and roofing felt between each course of shingles is shown. (Red Cedar Shingle and Handsplit Shake Bureau)

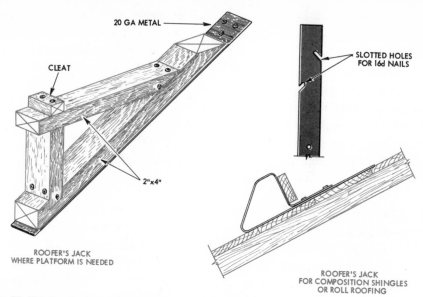

20 GA METAL

CLEAT

2"x4"

SLOTTED HOLES
FOR 16d NAILS

ROOFER'S JACK
WHERE PLATFORM IS NEEDED

ROOFER'S JACK
FOR COMPOSITION SHINGLES
OR ROLL ROOFING

Fig. 55. Roofing jacks are necessary on sloped roofs.

Roof Safety

During roofing operations acceptable provisions shall be made for protection of workmen from falling off roofs. Special provisions shall be taken when working on steep roofs with a slope of 7 inches per foot or greater. This may include one or more of the following methods:

1. Use of a scaffold platform.
2. Use of metal roof jacks.
3. Use of a substantial toeboard at least 10 inches high.

Fig. 55 illustrates a scaffold platform which might be used at a chimney and a metal roof jack.

When working on roofs of ⅓ pitch (slope of 8 inch vertical to 12 inch horizontal) and steeper, workmen should wear a safety belt with a lifeline securely fastened to a substantial anchorage.

Local and state building codes should be consulted for the requirements of roof scaffolding and roof jacks. The *USA Standard Code for Building Construction* also gives requirements for steep roofs.

The Cornice

The exterior finish on a building at the line where the sloping roof meets the vertical wall is known as the *cornice*. In addition to its practical value, the cornice may add materially to the architectural beauty of a building. There are various ways of constructing the cornice, and each has its own particular advantage. The trend is toward wide cornices. The wide cornice gives greater protection to the building, not only from rain and snow but also from the hot summer sun. The cornice provides a means for fastening gutters that carry away water as it runs off the roof.

Fig. 56 is shown in order to describe the various members and their use. It is a classic cornice which would be used today on Colonial buildings or those with traditional architecture. Buildings of contemporary architecture have cornices which are much simplified, although some of the members have been eliminated. Other basic members have been greatly modified. The main members of a cornice, excluding the structural members, are the *frieze, plancier, fascia, crown* and *bed moldings.*

The *frieze* is the finishing member at the top of the siding on the wall. The *plancier* is the horizontal member under the cornice. It is often called the *soffit.* The *fascia* is the face member at the end of the rafter.

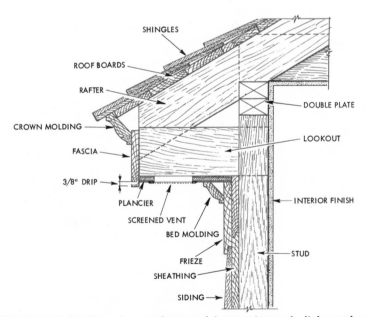

SHINGLES

ROOF BOARDS

RAFTER

CROWN MOLDING

FASCIA

3/8" DRIP

PLANCIER

SCREENED VENT

BED MOLDING

FRIEZE

SHEATHING

SIDING

DOUBLE PLATE

LOOKOUT

INTERIOR FINISH

STUD

Fig. 56. This type of closed cornice requires careful carpenter work. It is used mainly on colonial or traditional buildings.

376

The *bed molding* is used at the junction of the frieze and plancier. The *crown molding* is used to close the gap between the fascia and the shingles.

In a broad sense cornices may be divided into two common types: the *closed* or *boxed cornice*, and the *open cornice*. The cornice may be made of very few members or may be elaborate and ornamental. Regardless of the type used, the cornice should be made to harmonize with the architectural design of the building.

Closed Cornice. A simplified closed cornice for use on a contemporary building is shown in Fig. 57. The plancier is shown as a piece of

plywood supported by the rafter end and a block nailed to the wall. Screened vents are provided at intervals to ventilate the cornice. In some cases the cornice is open to the attic space and helps to ventilate the whole area under the roof. The frieze is a 1×6 inch board. The fascia is another 1×6 inch board fastened to the rafter ends canted for architectural effect. It extends ½ inch below the plancier so that the lower corner serves as a drip. The fascia is often plowed to receive the plancier. The bed molding has been eliminated and the crown mold molding has been replaced by a 1×2 inch strip to support the shingles.

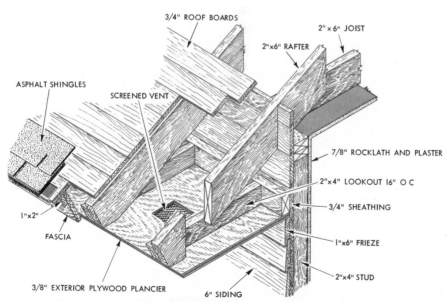

3/4" ROOF BOARDS

2" x 6" JOIST

2"x6" RAFTER

ASPHALT SHINGLES

SCREENED VENT

7/8" ROCKLATH AND PLASTER

2"x4" LOOKOUT 16" O C

3/4" SHEATHING

1"x2"

FASCIA

1"x6" FRIEZE

2"x4" STUD

3/8" EXTERIOR PLYWOOD PLANCIER

6" SIDING

Fig. 57. The closed cornice used on a modern ranch house is simple in design.

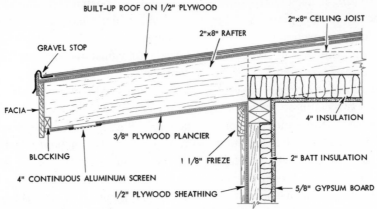

BUILT-UP ROOF ON 1/2" PLYWOOD

2"x8" CEILING JOIST

2"x8" RAFTER

GRAVEL STOP

FACIA→

4" INSULATION

BLOCKING

3/8" PLYWOOD PLANCIER

1 1/8" FRIEZE

2" BATT INSULATION

4" CONTINUOUS ALUMINUM SCREEN

5/8" GYPSUM BOARD

1/2" PLYWOOD SHEATHING

Fig. 58. A cornice for a low pitch roof may be designed in several ways. Adequate ventilation must be provided for the space over ceiling.

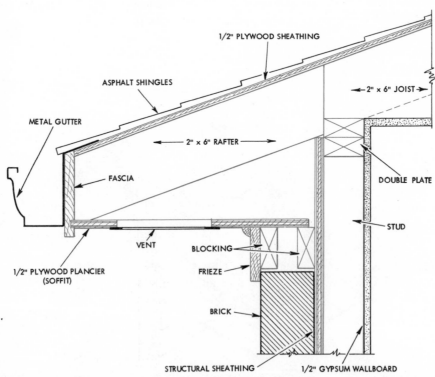

1/2" PLYWOOD SHEATHING

ASPHALT SHINGLES

2" x 6" JOIST

METAL GUTTER

2" x 6" RAFTER

FASCIA

DOUBLE PLATE

STUD

VENT

BLOCKING

1/2" PLYWOOD PLANCIER
(SOFFIT)

FRIEZE

BRICK

STRUCTURAL SHEATHING

1/2" GYPSUM WALLBOARD

Fig. 59. A closed cornice for a brick veneer building is made with basic members. The formed metal gutter adds the finishing touch.

378

Many variations of the closed cornice are used to suit particular requirements. A low pitched roof may have a closed cornice in which the plancier is nailed to the rafters. See Fig. 58. A gravel stop is necessary because the low slope requires a built-up roof. In this case, ventilation is achieved by a continuous opening in the plancier. The air passes freely under the roof in the attic space. Fig. 59 shows the details of a cornice for a masonry veneer wall. Blocking is necessary to provide nailing for the freize. The formed metal gutter, resembling a crown molding in shape, provides a finishing detail to the cornice.

Open Cornice. The rafter overhang is exposed on the open cornice illustrated in Fig. 60. Since the under side of the roof boards on an open cornice are exposed, it becomes necessary to use boards of a good finished quality. The frieze and bed molding, when used, must be cut to fit between rafters. A fascia may be applied over the rafter ends. This type of cornice requires careful cutting and fitting of the members and is difficult to paint. There are several ways in which it may be simplified and also produce unusual effects. See Fig. 61.

Gable Trim

The edge of the roof at the corners and at the gable end must be treated in keeping with the cornice. The classical treatment used for traditional houses requires that the cornice be continued around the corner

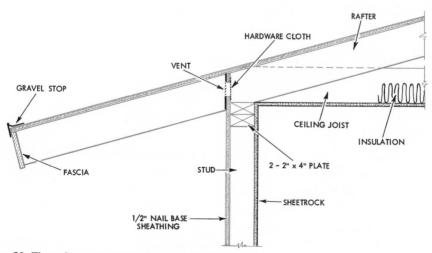

Fig. 60. The rafters are exposed on an open cornice.

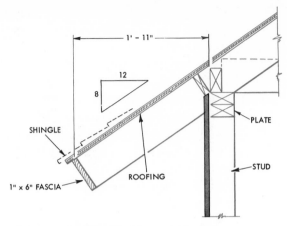

Fig. 61. An open cornice may be simplified in several ways.

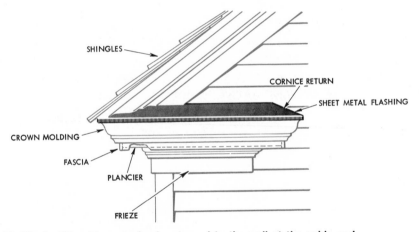

Fig. 62. The traditional box cornice is returned to the wall at the gable end.

of the house and returned to die against the building. Some of the moldings continue up the rake of the roof. See Fig. 62. This involves a great deal of careful work. Generally the end treatment is simplified by ending the siding on a board (called a verge board) equivalent to a fascia. The outside rafter is often terminated with a simple but decorative treatment. See Fig. 63. A 1 × 2 or other size strip is used to support the sides of the last shingles on the rake.

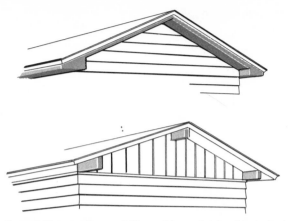

Fig. 63. The junction of the cornice and the gable end trim is made to be simple and attractive.

Attached Gutters

The gutter used in most residential work is the formed metal gutter. It is made of sheet metal and formed so that the front surface takes the shape of a molding. The back lip of the gutter extends up over the sheathing and under the shingles to form waterproof flashing. See Fig. 59.

Metal and Fiberboard Soffits and Cornice Trim

Aluminum, steel and fiberboard manufacturers have developed soffit (plancier) and other cornice trim members which may be assembled quickly and are adaptable to different roof slopes and widths of roof overhang. Baked enamel or other factory finishes resist chipping, blistering and peeling and provide long life. The periodic maintenance cost is almost eliminated. Attic and cornice ventilation is provided through perforated areas in the material.

Metal soffits are made of ribbed material in lengths to cover 8 feet and in several widths from 12 to 48 inches. The sheets of metal forming the soffit slip into place between a metal fascia and a metal channel at the wall. See Fig. 64. Ends of panels interlock so that there is an appearance of a continuous piece. The fascia is supplied to cover the ends of rafters from 4 to 10 inches in width as well as verge boards on gable ends. See Fig. 65. The carpenter must provide blocking, nailing strips and a sub-fascia of wood so that the metal parts may have a sound base.

Manufacturers of fiberboard pan-

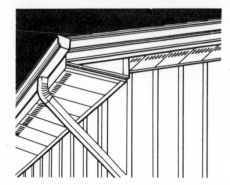

Fig. 64. A metal soffit system provides ventilation for the attic space. (United States Steel Corp.)

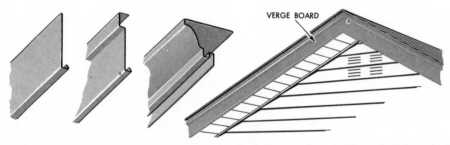

Fig. 65. Metal trim is provided to serve as fascia and verge board. (Alcoa Building Products, Inc.)

els have developed soffit systems also. The material is pre-finished with a long lasting factory finish. It is adjustable to roofs of various slopes and provides a means for ventilation. The fiberboard products may be cut and installed with ordinary carpenters tools.

Door and Window Frames

Door and window frames are usually manufactured at a factory or mill. They are then brought to the job ready for placing in the rough openings provided for them. Doors, windows and frames are often purchased as "packaged" units and are prehung and prefinished. Metal doors and frames are often purchased as a unit. The frames are assembled as they are installed.

After the walls have been framed

and sheathed, the frames for the doors and windows are put in place before the exterior wall finish is applied. The rough openings should be of the correct size and ready to receive the frames. Framing the rough openings has been discussed previously in Chapter IV. Frames designed and made for the various openings should be selected, distributed, and prepared for setting in place.

Wood Exterior Door Frames

The details of door frames may vary, but the construction in general is the same. A typical door frame for both wood and masonry construction is shown in Fig. 66. The jambs, head, and side are rabbeted ½ inch to receive the door. The outside doors of residences swing inward. Therefore, the rabbet must be on the inside. The outside doors of most public buildings must swing outward as a safety measure.

The jambs and casings of doors are usually made of durable soft woods. The sills of the better frames are made of white oak to withstand wear. Where durability is especially desirable, cut stone or concrete is frequently used for door sills. A metal threshold with weatherstrip is usually used.

Setting Door Frames. Before setting a door frame, it should be squared and braced. The bracing is important if the frame is to be handled a great deal before setting. Proceed with the placing of frames as follows:

PROCEDURE

1. As soon as the door frames are delivered to the job they should be treated with a coat of priming paint. It will protect the wood from weathering if there should be a delay in installation and will tend to prevent the evaporation of moisture which may bring about shrinkage and warping of the members of the frames.

2. Before placing a frame in the rough opening, check the various dimensions of the frame and compare them with the corresponding dimensions of the rough opening. This procedure will insure the fit of the frame when you are ready to set it in place.

3. Place the frame on a pair of sawhorses and cut off that part of the sill which projects beyond the casing, so that it is equal to the distance from the face of the casing to the face of the sill. See Fig. 67. The side jambs should not project more than ¾ of an inch below the sill or above the head jamb.

4. Tack a strip of heavy building paper 10 or 12 inches wide against the sheathing around the rough wall opening. Tack a second piece to go around the corner into the opening. See Fig. 68.

5. After placing the frame in the rough opening, brace the frame to

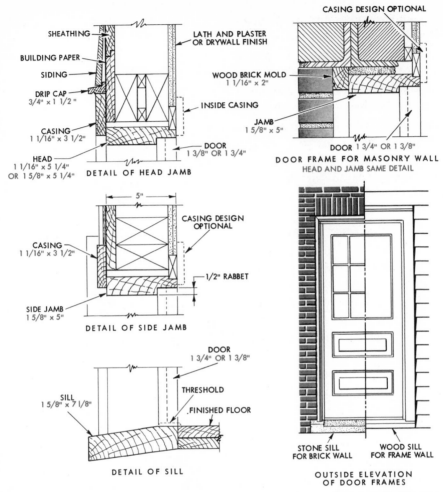

SHEATHING

BUILDING PAPER

SIDING

DRIP CAP
3/4" x 1 1/2"

CASING
1 1/16" x 3 1/2"

HEAD
1 1/16" x 5 1/4"
OR 1 5/8" x 5 1/4"

LATH AND PLASTER
OR DRYWALL FINISH

WOOD BRICK MOLD
1 1/16" x 2"

INSIDE CASING

JAMB
1 5/8" x 5"

DOOR
1 3/8" OR 1 3/4"

CASING DESIGN OPTIONAL

DOOR 1 3/4" OR 1 3/8"

DOOR FRAME FOR MASONRY WALL
HEAD AND JAMB SAME DETAIL

DETAIL OF HEAD JAMB

5"

CASING
1 1/16" x 3 1/2"

CASING DESIGN
OPTIONAL

1/2" RABBET

SIDE JAMB
1 5/8" x 5"

DETAIL OF SIDE JAMB

SILL
1 5/8" x 7 1/8"

DOOR
1 3/4" OR 1 3/8"

THRESHOLD

FINISHED FLOOR

DETAIL OF SILL

STONE SILL
FOR BRICK WALL

WOOD SILL
FOR FRAME WALL

**OUTSIDE ELEVATION
OF DOOR FRAMES**

Fig. 66. Sectional views taken through an exterior door frame show how it fits into the structure and how the trim is applied.

prevent it from falling out while you are adjusting it.

6. The door sill must be level. After the frame is set in place, adjust the sill by using wedge-shaped blocks and cleat, as shown in Fig.

69. The tip of the sill on the inside must be flush with the line of the finished floor.

7. The frame should be adjusted at the bottom and end so the spacing between the frame and the rough

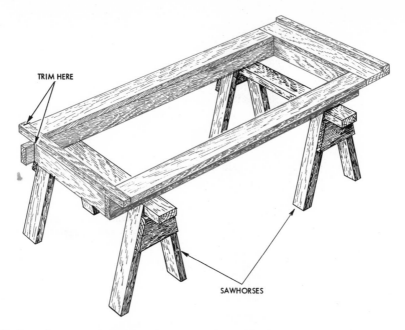

TRIM HERE

SAWHORSES

Fig. 67. Complete door frame is delivered to the job with exterior trim applied. Some carpenters cut off sill flush with exterior casing.

opening is the same on both sides. Drive a nail through the casing into the wall at the bottom on each side to hold the frame in place. When fastening a frame in position, never drive any of the nails completely into the wood until all nails have been placed and a final check has been made to determine if any readjustment is necessary.

8. The jambs must be made plumb and blocked up solid against the rough opening studs. Insert a pair of shingles, one from each side, so that they can be driven up tight near the top of the frame. Place the shin-

gles so that they bear against the head jamb. Using a level and straightedge, plumb the side jambs. See *1*, Fig. 70. Wedge the top opposite side. See *2*, Fig. 70. Place additional wedges at butt and at strike plate locations, and at additional points to stiffen the frame. See *3*, Fig. 70. Check to see that the jambs remain plumb and square.

9. Nail jambs to studs and fasten outside casing to studs with 16d casing nails. Place nails ¾ of an inch from outer edge of casing and spaced about 16 inches apart.

When nailing any trim, whether

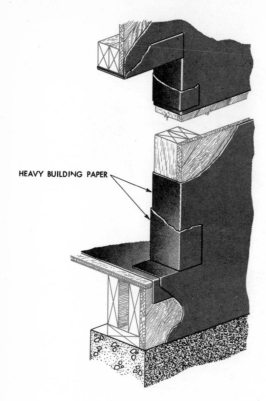

HEAVY BUILDING PAPER

Fig. 68. Building paper is placed around opening before door frame is installed. A second sheet is turned into opening.

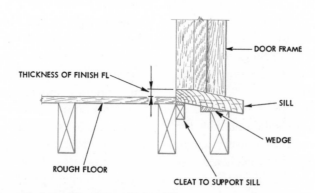

THICKNESS OF FINISH FL

DOOR FRAME

SILL

WEDGE

ROUGH FLOOR

CLEAT TO SUPPORT SILL

Fig. 69. Wedges and cleat are used to support sill.

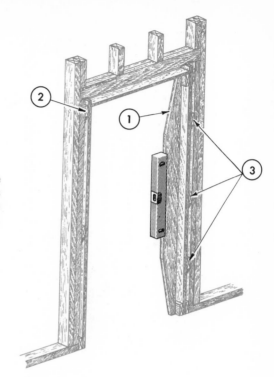

Fig. 70. A level and straightedge are used to plumb door frame. Shingles are used to hold it in place and give solid backing at butts and strike plate.

outside or inside, the nails should never be driven so far that the hammer will touch the surface of the wood. To prevent marring the finished surface of the wood, the final drive and setting of the nails should always be done with a nail set.

Setting a Door Frame in an Exterior Brick Wall. The carpenter is required to be on hand to set door and window frames in a brick building. He is responsible for their location according to plan. See Fig. 71.

He calculates the height of the head jamb above the finished floor and then cuts off the side jambs at the proper angle and measurement to make the door height come out correctly in relation to the floor. He cuts a spreader, which fits over the threshold, to hold the side jambs at the proper dimension and to protect the stone sill. He then checks the frame to see whether it is square or not, and makes minor adjustments in the corner braces. When the frame

387

Fig. 71. The carpenter sets the frames in a brick wall to make sure that they are plumb and located according to plan.

is raised into position, it is lined up so that it will be in the right relationship with the face of the wall. Short angle braces are nailed to the jamb and to the floor. A brace long enough to reach to the floor on an angle is fastened to a top corner of the frame. When the frame is plumb in two directions, the carpenter nails the lower end to the floor. A second brace is fastened to the other top corner of the frame and to the midpoint of the first brace.

Windows

The carpenter should be familiar with all of the different types of windows, and know the advantages of each type. He must make provisions for their installation as he builds the rough frame of the building. The working drawings of the HOUSE PLAN

A in Chapter 1 show almost every type of wood window used in a modern residence, with the exception of a hopper window.

Windows serve several important functions. Some of them are: distribution and control of light; view of the outdoors; privacy; ventilation control; cutting down heat loss and, in some cases, providing heat gain; weather resistance; and providing maximum use of the room and wall space. The amount of light and ventilation in relation to the floor area in each room is generally determined in the building code. In addition to these considerations, the designer carefully plans the size and placement of the windows to create the best architectural effect.

There are three basic types of windows, depending on how they operate. In some windows the sash is held in a fixed position; in others the sash slides vertically or horizontally; and in still others the sash is hinged to swing in or out.

The introduction of large insulating glass units has made the so-called picture window possible, and the desire on the part of owners to have an unobstructed view from inside the building has made it very popular. It is often used in combination with other types of sash, or with louvered ventilators within the same frame; sliding glass doors provide ventilation as well as a wide expanse of glass.

The double hung window is considered most practical in cold climates although every other type is used also. The two sash are arranged in grooves so as to slide past one another in a vertical direction. The horizontal sliding window uses the same principle, except that the grooves or tracks are horizontal; it is the most popular in warm and dry climates. This window is used to advantage in bedrooms, where it is placed high enough on the wall to insure privacy and also to provide wall space below the window. Both types can be provided with spring channels which permit the easy removal of the sash for cleaning and painting.

The most common windows that swing on hinges are the casement windows. Generally they swing out and are operated by a crank device. Screens and storm sash are on the room side. One advantage of casement windows is that they provide 100 percent ventilation. Another type of window that is hinged is the awning window. The hinges are on the top and sash swings out. Several awning windows may be stacked one above the other, or placed side by side to create special effects. A third type of hinged window is the hopper window. It is hinged at the bottom and swings into the room. See Fig. 72. Hopper windows often make up the bottom portion of large combination frames.

389

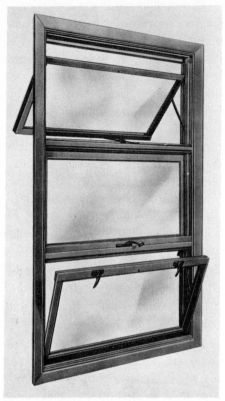

Fig. 72. A window frame is often made with different kinds of sash. The awning window swings out; the hopper window is hinged at bottom and swings into the room. (Andersen Corporation)

Jalousie windows are very popular in warm climates. This window consists of a series of glass slats, 3 to 8 inches wide, which are held horizontally in a metal frame. The slats all operate simultaneously with a cranking device. A jalousie window is not as airtight as other windows, but it permits maximum ventilation without wood sash or frame parts obstructing the view.

Window Frames

Double-Hung Frames. The basic construction of the double-hung window frame is shown in Fig. 73. (Note: It will help to understand how the section views are drawn by looking at the elevation view, Fig. 73, and an isometric view of another type of window, Fig. 78.) The jambs are ¾ of an inch in thickness. They have a parting stop to separate the top from the bottom sash and also a blind stop which produces a groove in the frame in which the window slides. The outside casings are of the same width and thickness as those of the other openings in the building. The joints between frame parts are usually butt joints. On the better-built frames, tongue-and-groove joints are used.

Windows in pairs or multiples are separated by mullions which may be a box construction or a single 1½ inch structural member with jambs fastened to each side. (A box construction would require two jamb pieces and an exterior or an interior casing built to form a box.)

Manufacturers of windows have developed features which make them more weathertight, easier to install and maintain, and interchangeable so that the same window frame can be used in frame construction, with brick veneer, or in a masonry wall

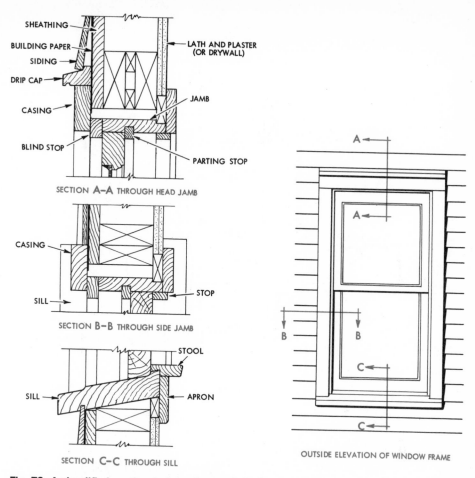

SHEATHING

BUILDING PAPER

SIDING

DRIP CAP

CASING

BLIND STOP

LATH AND PLASTER
(OR DRYWALL)

JAMB

PARTING STOP

SECTION **A–A** THROUGH HEAD JAMB

CASING

SILL

STOP

SECTION **B–B** THROUGH SIDE JAMB

STOOL

SILL

APRON

SECTION **C–C** THROUGH SILL

A

A

B   B

C

C

OUTSIDE ELEVATION OF WINDOW FRAME

Fig. 73. A simplified sectional view of a wood double hung window gives the names of the parts and shows how the parts are related.

with only minor modifications. Fig. 74 shows a typical package window for use in a frame wall. Instead of a outside casing a brick mold (molding) is used. (A brick mold is used to finish the exterior of a wood window in a masonry opening. See Fig. 75.) A spring-type sash balance is shown in the section through the jamb. The window can be ordered for dry wall (gypsum board) or lath and plaster application. (Dry wall is usually ½ inch thick whereas lath and plaster is ¾ inch thick.)

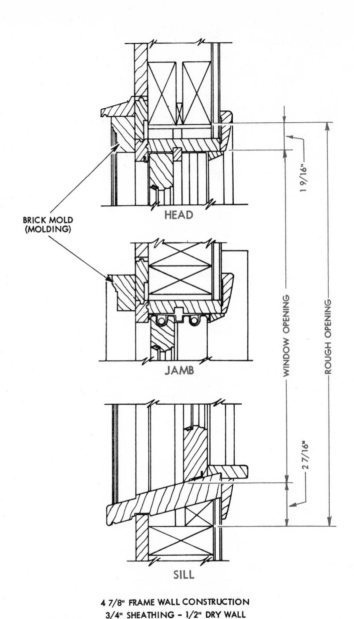

Fig. 74. A wood double hung window and wood frame is designed for use in frame or masonry construction. (Rock Island Millwork Co.)

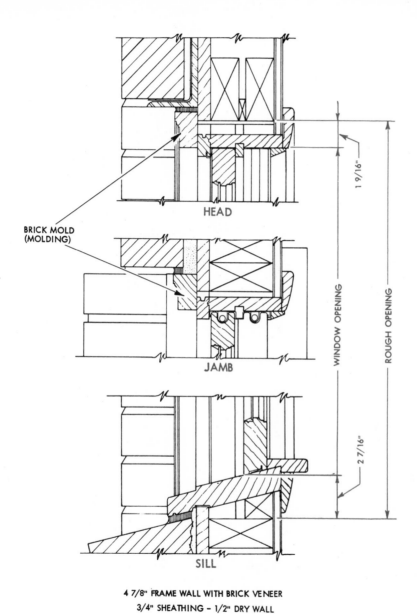

BRICK MOLD
(MOLDING)

HEAD

JAMB

SILL

WINDOW OPENING

ROUGH OPENING

1 9/16"

2 7/16"

4 7/8" FRAME WALL WITH BRICK VENEER
3/4" SHEATHING – 1/2" DRY WALL

Fig. 75. The wood window and frame shown in Fig. 74 is used in a brick veneer wall with only slight modifications. (Rock Island Millwork Co.)

393

Fig. 75 shows the same basic frame used in a brick veneer wall. The brick mold (molding) is placed away from the masonry a short space to provide for calking. The window frame in a brick veneer wall is fastened to the frame part of the wall. Fig. 76 shows a wood window made

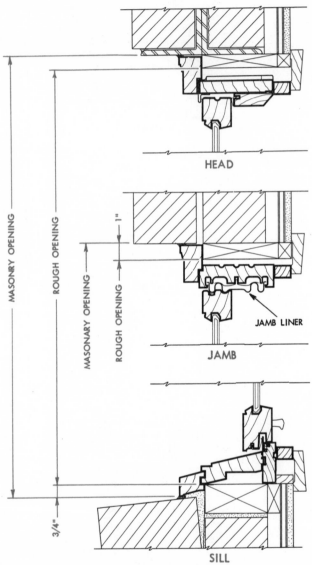

Fig. 76. A package wood window frame which can be used on either a masonry or frame wall. Note absence of blind stops, stool and apron. (Rolscreen Co.)

by another manufacturer which is also universal in application. In this case it is applied in a brick wall. The section through the head shows steel lintels supporting the masonry above the window. The window is designed to eliminate the blind stop entirely. (See Figs. 73 and 75 for a blind stop.) When drywall is used instead of lath and plaster the block at the inside of the jamb is cut to the proper width. The section through the jamb shows a combined jamb and vinyl-spring jamb liner which serves (1) to hold the window in position as it is raised and lowered to any height, (2) to permit the window to be removed for washing, and (3) to provide a weather seal. The section through the sill shows the weatherstripping arrangement and the absence of the usual stool and apron.

Casement Window Frames. The construction and thickness of materials used in casement window frames made in a local mill is often similar to that used in exterior door frames with rabbeted jambs. If the same jambs are used as those of the double-hung windows, the allowances for fitting will be the same as for a double-hung window with sash balances.

Many innovations have been introduced, by large manufacturers who specialize in windows, which should be appreciated by the carpenter and home owner. Fig. 77 shows a

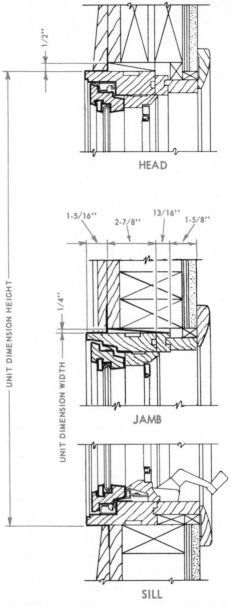

HEAD

JAMB

SILL

Fig. 77. A package casement window sealed in rigid vinyl plastic. Note the absence of exterior casings. The window is operated by a roto-operator through a gear arrangement so as not to interfere with the inside screen. (Andersen Corp.)

package outswinging casement window with many such features. It is glazed with welded insulating window glass. The sash has a wood core completely sealed in rigid vinyl plastic. The frame parts exposed to the weather are covered with rigid plastic which extends behind the siding to form flashing on all four sides of the window, including the sill. There is no exterior casing. The jamb extends beyond the face of the wall to form a thin projection. The siding is cut to fit against it and is calked. Spring-tension vinyl weatherstripping provides a weather seal. The window is operated by a roto-operator through a gear arrangement so as not to interfere with the screen which is on the inside of the window. The stool and apron on the inside of the window have been omitted.

The rough opening for this window must be provided with some accuracy. Only ½ inch is allowed vertically and horizontally for fitting.

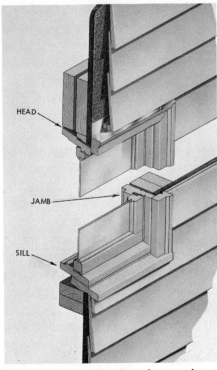

Fig. 78. An isometric view of an awning type window shows how the section through the head, jamb and sill are taken. (Andersen Corp.)

Awning and Hopper Windows. These resemble casement windows in most details. See Fig. 78. The hinges are located at the top of awning windows and roto-operators or bar lock devices are arranged so that the windows can be opened without interfering with the screens. Hopper windows do not need roto-operators because they swing in and the screen is on the outside.

Horizontal Sliding Windows. They are similar in many ways to double-hung windows. The tracks on which the sash slides are often made of aluminum or vinyl and may be compressed so that the sash can be removed for washing.

Setting Window Frames. Note: Due to the fact that many window frames are manufactured locally and are made using basic construction the following detailed instructions are included. Similar methods are used in setting window frames as are used for setting door frames. When the window frames first arrive on the job from the factory, they should be treated with a coat of priming paint. When the paint is dry, the frame should be placed in position and braced. To set the frames, proceed as follows:

PROCEDURE

1. Check the dimensions of the window frame with the corresponding dimensions of the rough opening. A space of at least ½ inch must

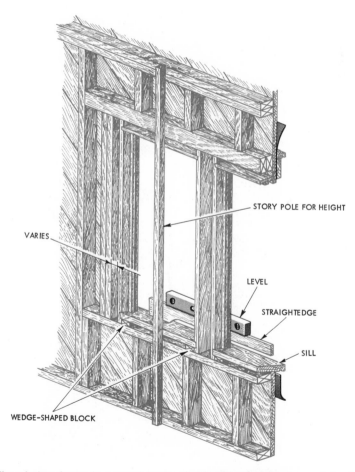

Fig. 79. The window frame is set and made plumb with straightedge and level. The story pole determines the height.

be left on each side of the frame between the casement side jamb and the stud of the rough opening, to make room for adjusting the frame. (The space varies as required.)

2. Place the frame, casing up, on a pair of sawhorses or on the floor. Trim the ends of the sill flush with the outside of the casing. Turn the frame over, with the casings down, and trim the ends of the side jambs to within ¾ of an inch from the sill and head jamb, just the same as when preparing a door frame, as shown in Fig. 67.

3. Tack 10 or 12 inch strips of heavy paper over the sheathing around the rough wall opening. See Fig. 68.

4. The exact height between the

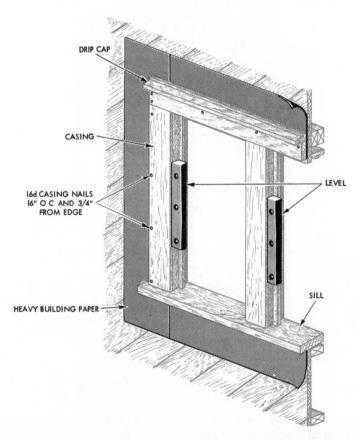

Fig. 80. The jambs are made plumb with a level before casings are nailed.

head jamb and the rough floor can be determined by using a story pole. The story pole is also used to make sure all windows are the same height and are placed according to the drawings. See Fig. 79.

5. A nail may be driven through the casing near the bottom to hold the window frame temporarily in place.

6. Place wedge-shaped blocks under the sill and adjust the frame to the correct height indicated by the story pole; at the same time use blocks to level the sill. See Fig. 79.

The leveling of the sill must be accomplished by placing blocks at points near the outside jambs. On narrow windows, the sill can usually be relied upon to be straight, but the center will usually sag on multiple windows or very wide windows. A straightedge for leveling is necessary to prevent sagging.

7. After leveling, the frame can be held in position by nails placed near the bottom on each side. Drive the nails through the outside casing and into the sheathing or studs. Block the window along the center until the sill is perfectly straight and level.

8. Plumb both side jambs by testing them with a carpenter's level. To hold the frame in position, drive nails through the side casing into the sheathing or framing members near the top of the window, as shown in Fig. 80.

9. Then check the entire frame again with a carpenter's level to make sure all sides of the window are plumb, and the sill straight and level.

10. When you are certain the frame is plumb, nail it securely in place against the wall, using 16d nails. Space the nails 16 inches apart, on center (o.c.), and ¾ of an inch from the outside edge of the casings. Use a nail set for a final setting of the nails. Lastly, apply a strip of heavy building paper under the sill and into the groove of the sill.

Metal Doors, Windows and Frames

Metal doors, windows and frames and metal frames for wood doors have been used successfully in residential construction for many years. Aluminum and steel have been extruded or hot rolled into shapes which provide sturdy structural parts with narrow profiles. Metal doors and metal frames will be discussed in Chapter VII, "Interior Finish."

Metal Windows

Metal is particularly adaptable to the west and south where the climate is relatively warm and dry. The condensation problem in areas where temperatures drop to low levels is compensated for by design features in the windows, careful installation practices, and the use of ceramic or other non-wood window sills. The windows are pre-hung and adjusted before they leave the factory. They are installed rapidly and easily. Because of the narrow frame and sash parts, the glass area of metal windows is greater than that of wood windows.

Aluminum windows are finished

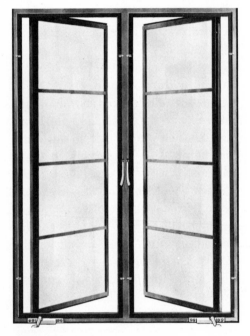

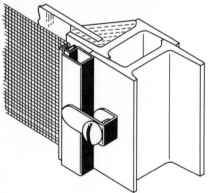

Fig. 81. Metal Casements provide maximum ventilation and light. (Republic Steel Corp.)

in the natural color of the metal. Steel windows are coated with a baked-on primer. They may be ordered pre-finished with a variety of colors in vinyl coatings which will last almost indefinitely.

Windows of several types are available for residential applications. Commercial and industrial windows include many special types and combinations.

A typical residential casement, Fig. 81, is made of hot rolled metal in two members: one the frame and the other the sash. The screen (and storm sash) is mounted on the inside with simple screwed-on clips. Roto-operators extend the sash and hold it in place at the desired position.

Awning windows of metal are very attractive and practical. See Fig. 82. A roto-operator adjusts all the sash to the same opening through a torque bar in the jambs, permitting maximum ventilation and window washing from the inside of the building. The window is installed by nailing the flange into the siding.

One other type of metal window

Fig. 82. Metal awning type windows are designed to open simultaneously. (Reynolds Aluminum Co.)

Fig. 83. Sliding windows are popular in the modern home. (Reynolds Aluminum Co.)

which is quite popular is the sliding window. See Fig. 83. The narrow lines of frame and sash and the ease of movement as the sash glides on nylon rollers are attractive features. Fig. 84 shows the simple installation details. Nails are driven through the flange of the frame into the structural members around the windows. Exterior wood casings are eliminated. The siding is brought up to about ¼ inch of the frame and the space is calked in between.

Double-hung metal windows provide the advantages of ease of operation, and good ventilation and light. The sash is suspended by metal tapes which wind up into motor, spring-type balances in the head. See Fig. 85.

Installing Metal Windows. Certain precautions must be followed in working with metal windows and frames. Openings must be made to manufacturers specifications. They must be square, plumb, level and

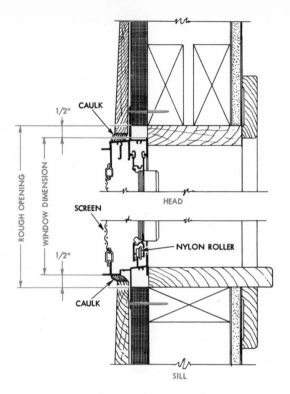

ROUGH OPENING

WINDOW DIMENSION

1/2" CAULK

CAULK

SCREEN

NYLON ROLLER

1/2"

CAULK

HEAD

SILL

Fig. 84. Aluminum sliding window is fastened to wood wall with nails through flanges.

provide sufficient clearance to install the window. Frames must not be distorted, twisted or crowded in the erection process. The sash should be closed and locked at all times during installation. The window frame members should be calked where they join siding, masonry or lintels. Precautions must be taken to keep moving parts, roto-operators, tracks and runways clear of refuse and trash. Holes intended for drainage must not become plugged. Alumi-

num windows and frame surfaces must be kept clean. Plaster and cement, if permitted to harden on the surface, will cause stains. Prefinished vinyl windows and frames should be handled carefully so that the surface is not marred.

Screws or nails are driven through the flange holes to fasten the frame in place. See Fig. 84. Anchors embedded in masonry joints are used for some installations to install the windows in brick walls.

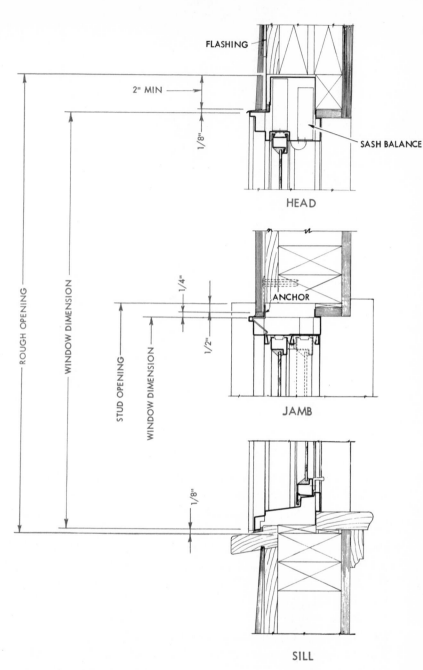

Fig. 85. Metal double hung window sash are suspended from sash balances in the head. (Republic Steel Corp.)

Entrances, Porches and Other Exterior Finish Details

The carpenter is required to build a number of exterior functional and decorative parts of the house other than those described in this chapter. They are generally very specifically covered by details included by the architect in the working drawings. They may include front entrances, special ornamental treatment at windows, decks, porches, railings, columns, posts, fences, shutters and roof ventilators. Some of

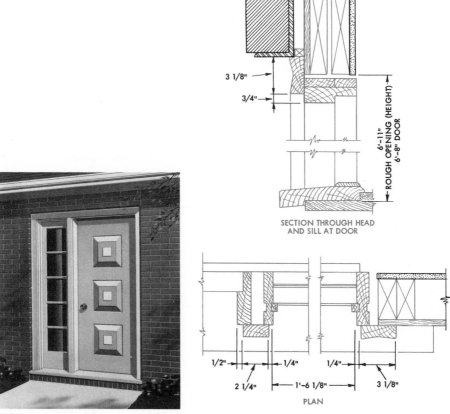

Fig. 86. Many different door styles are used for the front entrance. This shows a door in a masonry wall. (Morgan Co.)

405

these items will be made in a mill and will be shipped to the job. A front entrance frame, see Fig. 86, would arrive on the job with the frame assembled and the door ready to be hung. The problem the carpenter must solve is to set the frame properly for the mason. If the door frame was to be installed in a frame wall he would have to provide the proper size opening, header, and whatever blocking was necessary. Porches, railings and decks require solid rough framing for structural value. Installing posts, columns, railings for porches, and stairs may require considerable skill. The carpenter must know how to build them so that they will not rot out because of years of exposure to water. Stairs will be discussed in Chapter VII.

Checking On Your Knowledge

The following questions give you the opportunity to check up on yourself. If you have read the chapter carefully, you should be able to answer the questions. If you have any difficulty, read the chapter over once more so that you have the information well in mind before you go on with your reading.

DO YOU KNOW

1. What factors are important in choosing wood for exterior covering?
2. What woods are generally used for siding?
3. Why is building paper used over wood siding?
4. What are the different classes of material used for siding?
5. What kinds of nails are suggested for applying wood siding?
6. What is drop siding, beveled siding, boards and battens?
7. How are the corners finished when wood bevel siding is used?
8. What is hardboard? What are its advantages as exterior wall covering?
9. What is mineral fiberboard? What shapes are generally used for siding?
10. Describe insulated metal siding.
11. How is insulated metal siding applied?
12. What is the main advantage of solid vinyl siding?
13. What is the most popular size and shape of asphalt shingles?
14. What is a built-up roof?
15. What roof slopes are suggested for built-up roofs and asphalt shingled roofs?
16. What is step flashing? Counter flashing?
17. What is a Boston hip?
18. What is the difference between shingles and shakes?
19. What is a roof jack?
20. Describe the cornice parts: frieze, plancier and fascia.
21. What is a closed cornice?
22. Why should a cornice be vented?
23. How is a metal soffit installed?
24. What is a packaged window?
25. How are shingles used in fitting a door frame in a rough opening?
26. How is a window in a frame wall fastened in place?
27. What are the advantages of metal windows?

Interior Finish

The carpenter is responsible for putting all of the finishing touches on the interior of the building prior to the work of the painter and decorator. When his work is done with care, the beauty and value of the house are enhanced greatly. The construction items included under the topic of interior finish are: the wall, ceiling, and floor covering; the installation of windows and doors; window and door trim; other trim such as base and cornice; the stairs; cabinets, including kitchen and built-in cabinets; and the installation of hardware. Special architectural features such as mantels and room dividers are also included.

Some of the wood trim used fifty years ago has been eliminated because it was costly to install, and because styles have changed. However,

wood has maintained its favor as an interior finish material because it is easy to work with and is attractive in its own right. The use of wood for wall covering has increased greatly. Both board paneling and veneer plywood sheets are used frequently in finishing interiors because they are very durable and beautiful. Floors of wood will always be the accepted standard in most fine homes.

Many non-wood materials are commonly used today for interior finish. The adoption of "dry wall" gypsum board for wall and ceiling covering has brought about vast changes in the carpenter's work. Also, prefinished wall surfaces simulating wood or other materials have been developed on base sheets of hardboard.

Great changes have resulted from

the introduction of ready-made cabinets, built-in wardrobes, and built-in cases. Years ago the carpenter would make all of these on the job. Some carpenters still make special cabinets which are quite satisfactory, but most of this work is done in mill or cabinet shops today. The carpenter has the job of locating and installing the pieces.

Fitting and hanging doors, fitting trim, and installing hardware requires skill and precision. Although many of the doors and windows come to the jobs prefitted and prehung the carpenter in many parts of the country still has the job of installing doors and sash. Careless work in fitting and hanging doors or installing sash will make it necessary for the carpenter to return to correct his work later. When the trimming of a house has been done by a competent craftsman, it is a pleasure to see the result.

The carpenter who can do good stair work is worthy of respect as a tradesman. He has the technical problem of interpreting the architectural drawings so that the stairs work out as shown on the plans. He often is given some important choices about the actual details of construction, and must use good judgment in providing proper headroom and supports for stringers. On occasion the main stairway of a residence may be made in a mill, but the carpenter has the responsibility of providing the proper stairwell, and may be expected to assemble the parts.

Procedure for Interior Finishing

The work of applying interior finish should not be attempted until the building is closed in and a satisfactory waterproof roof has been laid. Windows and doors should be installed, or the openings closed at least temporarily, so that there can be some control of temperature and humidity. Wood members used for trim must not be permitted to absorb too much moisture. They should be delivered to the job shortly before they are to be used. Some of them may be prefinished and must be given special care in order to protect the finish. Some items have fine moldings which must not be nicked or marred.

The interior finishing of a building consists chiefly in covering the framework of the walls and ceiling with lath and plaster, or with any of the various materials on the market today that are suitable for finishing walls and ceilings. These materials include gypsum wallboard, plywood, wood paneling, hardboard paneling, and other materials designed for this purpose. Included in the interior finish is the floor covering, which must not only give a finished appearance to the floor but must also provide a durable wearing surface. This two-fold purpose is accomplished by applying finished wood flooring, linoleum, ceramic, asphalt, vinyl, or rubber tile over the subfloor. In addition to the wall, ceiling, and floor covering, the interior finish includes stairs, cabinets, windows and doors, together with the trim around the windows and doors. Other trim members include the base, cornice, dado, chair rail, and various special interior appointments indicated on the drawings or required by the building specifications.

Most of the interior finish work mentioned in the foregoing paragraph is done by the carpenter except plastering and ceramic work. The order of procedure in finishing the interior of a building may vary according to the design, specified materials, the relation of these materials to each other, and established practice. However, wall finish is usually applied before other interior work can be done. Window fitting and trimming, the applying of cornice molding, stair rail, and the installing of the stairs is usually done before the floor covering is laid. If the application of floor finish is delayed until this work is done, the finished surface is less likely to be damaged. The setting of cabinets, installing door trim, fitting doors and bases usually follows the laying of the floor covering. The final work of interior finishing is the attaching of hardware. Much of the hardware is fitted but not installed until after the painting has been finished.

Interior Wall Covering

The introduction of many new materials and the desire to create new effects has brought about many changes in the wall finish of residences. Lath and plaster still holds a place in the construction business but has been replaced to a great extent by other materials, particularly in residential work. The extensive use of gypsum wallboard, wood paneling, hardboard, and other materials has broadened the field.

When plaster is used, the carpenter is concerned only with providing the necessary plaster grounds, which serve as guides for the plasterer, making it possible for him to build straight and true surfaces. All of the other materials mentioned are applied by the carpenter. (Some of the materials come under the work of other trades in certain areas.)

Wood as Interior Finish

Wood has become popular as a wall covering material, particularly in living, dining and recreational areas of the house. The number of different species of hardwood now available with a wide range of color and finish makes many choices possible. Some woods are light, others dark, some have imperfections such

409

as burls, knots and markings which make them attractive. Some, such as pecky cypress or cedar, have deep fissures caused by insects or fungi.

Others are sandblasted to show a swirl of hard and soft grain, or machined to give a striated effect. Much of the wood for wall paneling pur-

Fig. 1. Wood paneling is used effectively for wall covering. It has beauty, durability, and requires a minimum of maintenance. (National Forest Products Assoc.)

poses comes pre-finished, thus saving the builder much of the cost of decorating. See Fig. 1.

A second consideration worth noting is the fact that wood makes a practical wall covering. Many of the woods are hard and resist rough treatment very well. If the surface becomes damaged it can be repaired and refinished. There is a certain amount of insulating value and a reduction in sound transmission in the use of wood as wall covering. Not only is wood durable, but it is easily installed. Little preparation is needed except for the furring of the walls. Board paneling which is available in long pieces, and plywood sheets which come in large pieces, can be installed with a minimum of cutting and labor.

Installing Wood Board Paneling. Paneling of pine, fir, and cedar comes in random widths of 4, 6, 8, 10 and 12 inches with a dressed thickness of approximately ¾ of an inch. The lengths are from 6 to 16 feet. The boards are tongue and

groove and usually have a **V** joint or a more elaborate molded edge pattern. See Fig. 2.

When the paneling is applied horizontally, no furring strips are required because the paneling is applied directly to the studs. Inside corners are made by trimming the boards to the exact length and butting them flush against the paneling for the other wall. If random-width paneling is used, the boards on each wall must match in width. The tongue and groove permits blind nailing. When paneling is placed in a vertical position on the wall, furring is required at the top, middle, and bottom of the wall, at the corners, and around doors and windows. If a baseboard is used, the base is furred out so that its face is flush with the paneling. See Fig. 3. An alternative method of applying vertical boards requires the use of 2 × 4 headers between studs. See Fig. 4. Masonry walls must be furred before applying boards. A cove or crown molding is used at the ceiling. A

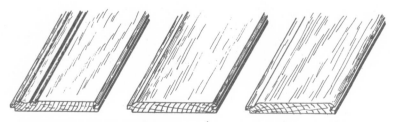

Fig. 2. Wood board paneling is available in several patterns with tongue and groove joints.

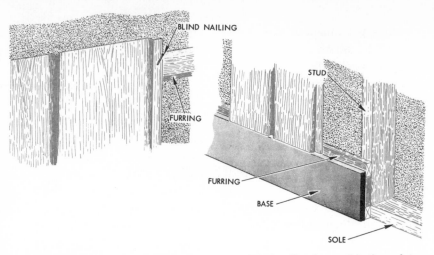

Fig. 3. Board paneling is easily installed over furring. Blind nailing is possible through tongue. Furring behind base provides good nailing.

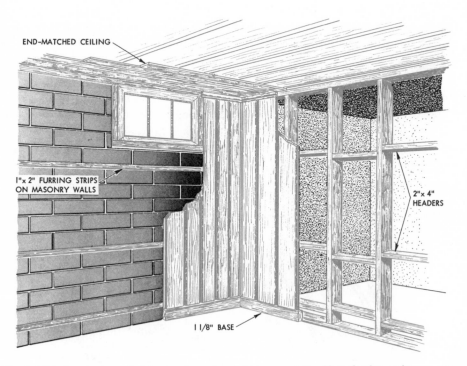

Fig. 4. Boards may be nailed to headers placed between studs. Note furring strips on masonry walls.

Fig. 5. Many novel effects can be obtained by installing paneling in different directions.

number of interesting effects can be produced with board paneling when it is installed vertically, horizontally, or diagonally. See Fig. 5.

Installing Plywood Paneling. The plywood panels used for finished wall covering are generally 3 ply ¼ inch or 5 ply ⅜ inch. They come in several sheet sizes, thus providing the greatest economy of material. In general, panels are available in 48 inch widths and in lengths of 7 and 8 feet. Some are available in 10 feet lengths. Longer lengths may be ordered. The face plies of the panels are chosen to be as uniform in grain and color as possible, and when prefinished they match very well. Beautiful hardwoods are usually chosen for this purpose. Oak, elm, walnut, cherry, birch and pine are some of the more common native woods used. Exotic and foreign veneers are also available. The carpenter must use good judgment, however, as he decides

on the location of each sheet, so that it blends with the sheets adjacent to it. He must also see to it that the best spacing possible is achieved at corners, doors and windows. The face ply of the plywood is usually cut with **V** grooves or channels in a random plank effect. This feature permits the joints between panels to remain unnoticed. See Fig. 1.

Plywood is placed in a vertical position in most applications. The furring strips are placed vertically on 16 inch centers. The panels are then cut to reach from floor to ceiling and the backs of the panels marked approximately where the furring strips occur. The next operation is to apply two coats of contact cement to the furring and to the backs of the panels where marked, allowing each coat to dry thoroughly. Then the plywood is put in place carefully and pressed against the furring strips to insure contact. The panels can be tacked at the top and bottom where nail holes will be covered by trim. Some carpenters use 4d finishing nails along studs to reinforce the cement bond. Nail holes are countersunk and filled with matching putty. A variety of moldings such as casing and trim, window stool, base, cove, inside and outside corners, etc., is available to match the factory finished panels.

Manufacturers have perfected clips which are completely hidden as each piece is put in place.

Hardboard as Interior Finish

Hardboard is made by exploding wood chips into a fibrous state and then pressing them in heated hydraulic presses until they form a very dense, rigid board. It has a hard, smooth surface, great structural strength, and excellent wearing qualities; it takes finish readily, is easily worked with ordinary tools, and can be bent with comparative ease into curved shapes.

Hardboard is prepared for wall applications with a great variety of wood grain finishes simulating fine woods. Grooves are provided at random widths so that the finished wall has the appearance of a series of planks. One type resembles marble, other types have plain surfaces in many colors. A very durable plastic coating over the surface makes hardboard paneling highly wear resistant.

Most of the hardboard paneling is supplied in 4 × 7, 4 × 8 and 4 × 10 foot panels which are ½ inch thick. It may also be obtained in 16 and 24 inch planks, 7, 8 and 10 feet long. Ceiling blocks 16 inches square and ¼ inch thick with tongue and groove edges are available for glueing to old ceilings or for fastening to furring strips with staples.

One precaution suggested by the manufacturer is that the panels be exposed, by standing them up around the room where they are to be installed, for 48 hours in order to adjust to the moisture conditions. All panel edges must be supported for nailing. Intermediate studs should be on 16 inch centers so that nails fall on the grooves in the panels. Color matched nails are available. If ordinary finishing nails are used they should be countersunk and matching color putty used to conceal the hole. Nails should be spaced 4 inches apart on the panel edges and 8 inches apart on intermediate supports.

Many builders prefer to apply the sheets by using adhesives. One type of adhesive is applied to the studs or the wall surface in a bead and allowed to dry 2 to 3 minutes. The sheet is pressed in place and fastened at the top with 2 or 3 nails. Using the nails as a hinge the sheet is pulled away long enough to let the adhesive become tacky, about 8 to 10 minutes. It is then pressed in firmly. See Fig. 6.

A series of matching metal or plas-

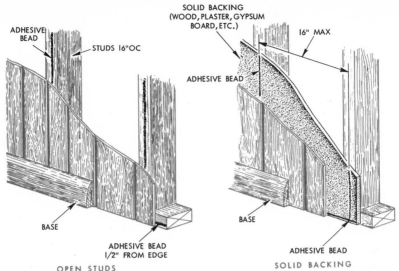

Fig. 6. Hardboard panels are fastened to the studs with adhesive. (Masonite Corp.)

tic moldings is provided to cover up inside corners, outside corners, and panel edges where panels end and where they join. Wood moldings are provided for base, cove and also for inside and outside corners.

Gypsum Wallboard

Several features basic to drywall application have been discussed in Chapter IV, Rough Framing. The information was in regard to the structural systems using wood and metal studs for drywall base, and the manner of achieving fire resistance and reducing sound transmission.

Gypsum wallboard is made of a core of gypsum which is molded while in a plastic condition between two sheets of tough protective paper. The edges are either square, slightly beveled, or tapered. The ta-

pered edges are made so that a slight depression is provided for the tape and joint compound. The sheets are $\frac{1}{4}$, $\frac{3}{8}$, $\frac{1}{2}$ and $\frac{5}{8}$ inch thick, 4 feet wide, and from 6 to 14 feet in length. There are several types of wallboard designated for special use. Among them are fire resistant wallboard which has a core of special ingredients along with the gypsum, such as vermiculite and fiber glass reinforcement. Insulating wallboard has aluminum foil laminated to one side to provide reflective insulation. Backer board is used as a base for a two layer application. Moisture resistant wallboard is used as the base for tile in bathrooms. A 1 inch core board is available to form the base for a 2 inch solid partition. In addition to these standard products, decorative vinyl-surfaced wallboard may be obtained in a number of colors and textured surfaces, including beautiful wood effects with random plank grooves.

Application. Gypsum wallboard is applied either with one or two thicknesses. The double thickness adds greater sound deadening and fire resistant qualities and prevents nail popping because the second layer is fastened with adhesive. Single layer applications use ½ or ⅝ inch wallboard (¼ inch thickness is

recommended for use over old wall surfaces only).

Single Layer Method. Ceilings are applied first. The sheets are placed at right angles to the joists. Side walls follow. The sheets may be placed vertically or horizontally. Horizontal application usually brings about fewer joints to be taped later. Nails should be spaced not to exceed 7 inches o.c. on ceilings and 8 inches o.c. on side walls. They should be between ⅜ and ½ inch from the edge of the sheet. Fig. 7

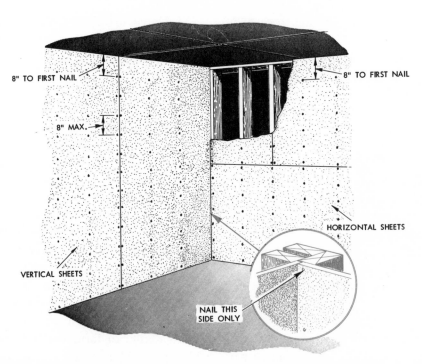

Fig. 7. One layer application of gypsum drywall shows nailing pattern for horizontal or vertical sheets. (United States Gypsum Co.)

shows the nailing pattern of what is called a floating interior angle system. This simply means that one sheet at each interior angle is not nailed, thus permitting the sheet to move slightly when the wood framework of the building dries out. Annular ring nails are suggested for best nail holding value. (See Fig. 58, Chapter IV.) Screws may be driven using a power screw gun.

The single layer wallboard may be applied to the studs by using adhesive nail-on method also. Beads of adhesive are applied to the studs. Permanent nails or screws are re-quired at 24 inch intervals along the perimeter of each board. No nails or screws are needed away from the edges. Prefinished wallboard is applied vertically by the adhesive method with screws on 24 inch intervals top and bottom only. Temporary bracing is used to maintain contact with adhesive until it is dry.

Double Layer Method. The first layer may be regular gypsum board or backer board nailed or screwed to the studs in the conventional manner. Special lamination adhesives are spread on the surface of the wallboard with a mechanical spreader.

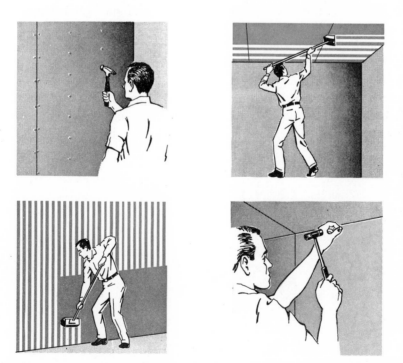

Fig. 8. Double layer drywall application is applied by nailing the base layer and using adhesives for the second layer. (National Gypsum Co.)

See Fig. 8. The finished layer is applied at right angles to the first layer. Joints need not fall on studs but should be off set at least 10 inches from parallel joints in base layer. It is held in place with double headed nails until the adhesive sets. Temporary bracing may be used instead of nailing for prefinished panels.

Application to Metal Studs. Fig. 62 Chapter IV shows a drywall application using metal studs. The procedure is similar to that using wood studs. Self tapping drywall screws are required spaced 8 inches o.c. on vertical edges and 12 inches o.c. in the field when the sheets are applied vertically. They are to be spaced 12 inches o.c. on the edges as well as in the field when the sheets are applied in a horizontal position.

Moldings and Accessories. Moldings are provided to be used with prefinished gypsum wallboard which have the same color and finish.

They serve to cover up the exposed ends of sheets and joints between sheets. Other moldings provide finished inside and outside corners. See Fig. 9.

Other accessories for regular wallboard application are available such as corner beads and metal trim where wallboard panels stop at doors and windows. They are installed over the wallboard in the course of application. See Fig. 10.

Taping Operation. The taping operation is not done by the carpenter. However it is important that he do his work of applying the wallboard so that the taper who will follow him has good joints to work with. Each joint is buttered with compound and the tape applied full length pressing it into the compound with a broad knife or tape applicator. Internal angles at wall corners and at the ceiling are treated in the same way. Nailheads are coated with

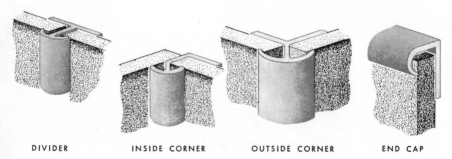

DIVIDER   INSIDE CORNER   OUTSIDE CORNER   END CAP

Fig. 9. Moldings for prefinished drywall panels present a finished appearance. (United States Gypsum Co.)

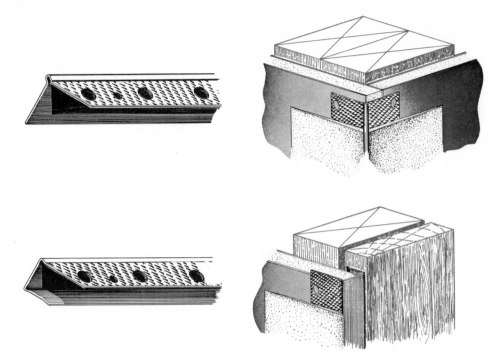

Fig. 10. Metal trim helps finish gypsum wallboard corners and edges. (United States Gypsum Co.)

compound. After the first coat is dry a second coat is applied to the joints and nailheads. The edges are feathered out. When the second coat is dry it is lightly sanded. A finish coat is then applied and after 24 hours it is sanded smooth.

Finishing Ceilings with Tile or Lay-in Panels

Ceilings may be covered with acoustical and decorative tile made of fiberboard or incombustible mineral fiber. The pieces are ½ or ¾ inch thick and are 12 inches square.

A flange is provided on two edges for stapling and a groove on the other two sides to provide a means to interlock them and conceal the staples. See Fig. 11. Tiles may be stapled to furring strips applied at right angles to joists on 12 inch centers. It is considered good practice to arrange furring strips and tile to begin with the center of the room. Metal channel runners may be used instead of furring strips. The flanges on the tile engage the runners and the previously installed tile. Two methods

419

Fig. 11. Acoustical and decorative tile may be fastened by stapling to furring strips or by the use of runners. (Celotex Corp.)

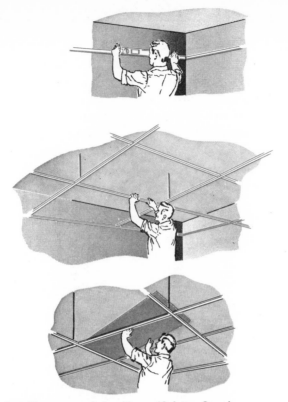

Fig. 12. Steps in installing suspended ceilings. (Celotex Corp.)

may be used over flat surfaces. The tile may be stapled over a gypsum board ceiling or may be fastened by adhesive to any sound flat ceiling. Butt edged tile (without flange) is used for application with adhesive. A pat of adhesive is placed at each corner of the tile and another pat on the ceiling at the center of each location.

A suspended ceiling may be used in new homes where provisions have been made for it and in the remodeling of old homes with high ceilings. Wall angles are fastened level around the room at the desired height. A series of T iron members are fastened to the wall angles and are hung from the ceiling with wire. They form a grid into which the 2 × 4 foot panels are dropped in place. Luminous panels of rigid plastic are used to provide a lighted ceiling with fixtures and wiring concealed. See Fig. 12.

421

Interior Trim

The various trim members used in finishing the interior of a building are the casings around the doors and windows, the baseboard with its base and shoe molding, and the cornice molding. There should be a definite architectural relation in the design of all these members to that of the doors, windows, and the general architecture of the building. Generally the architect chooses or designs the trim to be used. Where a carpenter must make the selection of trim he can use stock moldings available at the lumber yard.

Many varieties of wood are used for interior trim, such as birch, oak, mahogany, walnut, white and yellow pine, fir, larch, gum, and tupelo.

The trend in all trim members is to make them as simple in design as possible. See Fig. 13 for details of

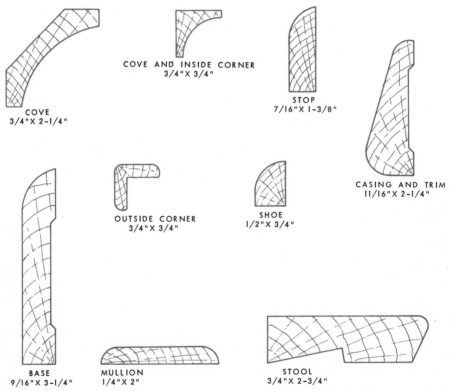

Fig. 13. Moldings for general use have been reduced to a few simple shapes. (Georgia Pacific Corp.)

trim members. They are easier to install and paint and have a pleasing appearance. The carpenter still has an opportunity to show his skill because poor fitting is more noticeable when the moldings are plain.

The carpenter should be familiar with the names, uses and application of many special moldings which he may be required to use in traditional houses or where special problems must be solved. The use of the right molding enhances the beauty of the finished home. The highlights and soft shadows which result from the suble curves and sharp breaks in the surface make them attractive. There are a great number of moldings available in different sizes and shapes. Fig. 14 shows examples of each general classification. Two moldings are often combined to make the effect more ornate. In order to have them fit tightly against the flat surface of the wall a recess of about $\frac{1}{16}$ inch is cut from the back of some moldings. Note the casing and base moldings in Fig. 14, *H, I* and *J,* and *K* and *L.*

Trim members used with windows are the casing, stool and, when two windows are placed side by side, a mullion casing. See Fig. 14, *H, I, J, N* and *Q.* A stop is used to hold the sash in place. See Fig. 14, *O* and *P.* Moldings used at the ceiling are the ceiling molding (often called a crown molding), bed molding, and cove molding. See Fig. 14, *A, B* and *C.* Those used at the floor are the

base molding and base shoe molding. See Fig. 14, *E, K* and *L.* A batten is used to cover a joint between two boards or sheets of paneling and a panel molding is used to surround a wall panel. See Fig. 14, *G* and *M.* The quarter round and corner guard are utility moldings used to cover internal and external angles. See Fig. 14 *D* and *F.*

Some of the moldings shown in Fig. 14 are used for exterior trim also, such as the ceiling molding which becomes a crown molding on a cornice; and the bed molding which is also a cornice trim member. The brick mold (molding) is used with a wood window in a masonry wall. See Fig. 14, *R.* The drip cap may be used over a window or door or as a member of a water table. See Fig. 14, *S.*

Interior Molding

The baseboard, shoe molding, and molding trim at the ceiling are generally continuous trim members extending around a room. The baseboard and shoe molding are among the last of the trim members to be put into place because they usually have to be fitted against other work, such as door casings, and cabinets. These trim members present the problem of joining in the corners of the room so that the joints will be tightly closed and all members of the moldings properly aligned. Either the miter or the coped joint is used for joining such trim mem-

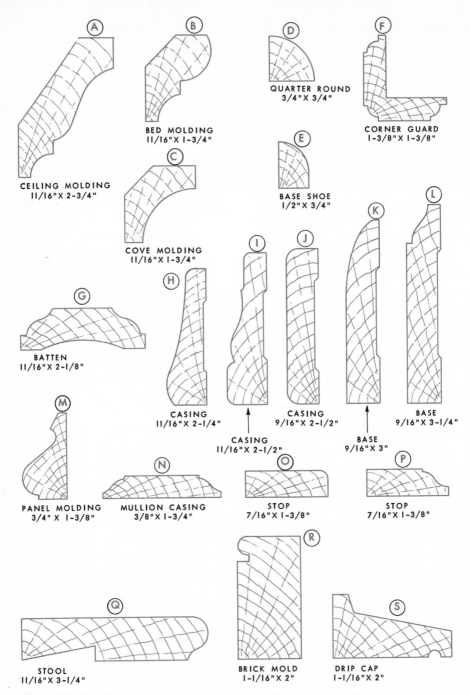

Fig. 14. Traditional moldings come in a variety of shapes to serve particular purposes.

bers, depending upon the nature of the corner in which the joint is to be made.

The internal corners, as shown at *A*, Fig. 15, formed by the side walls of a room, should be made with coped joints. The coped joint is bet-

ter for interior corners because it will not open while nailing the trim into place against the wall and if the wood on such joints should shrink, the opening will not be noticeable. External corners such as *B*, Fig. 15, formed by chimneys or any other

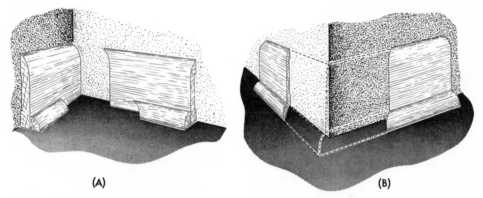

(A)   (B)

Fig. 15. Moldings at internal corners are usually coped. Moldings at external corners are mitered.

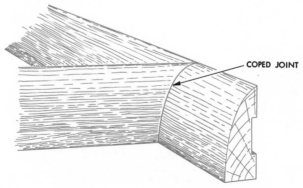

COPED JOINT

Fig. 16. One piece of a coped joint is cut to fit the profile of the other piece.

corners projecting out into a room, should have the trim members mitered.

Coped Joints. Coping consists of shaping the ends of a molding or board so that it will fit with a butt joint against an adjacent member as shown in Fig. 16. The coped joint is used in fitting moldings on internal or inside corners. To cut a coped joint proceed as follows.

PROCEDURE

1. Place the piece of molding in a miter box in the same position that it will be when in place against the wall or other surface, as shown in Fig. 17. The vertical side of the molding when in place should be against the back of the miter box. A 45 degree miter will give the correct outline on the face of the molding for a right angle or 90 degree corner. The outline or profile formed by this miter cut is the cutting line which is to be followed with the coping saw to get the correct cut in making a coped joint.

Note: The angle of the miter must always be one-half of the angle of the corner to which the moldings are to be fitted.

2. Place the molding on a saw-

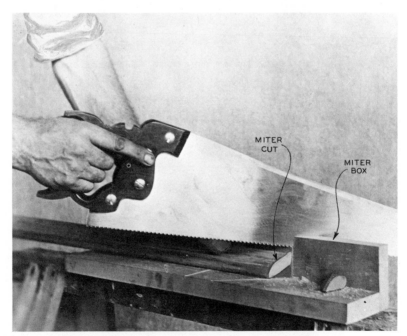

Fig. 17. Miter cut will give the profile or cutting line for a coped joint.

horse with the vertical side down (the side which was against the side of the miter box), Fig. 18.

With a coping saw follow closely on the waste side of the cutting line formed by the miter cut, holding the saw as illustrated, the teeth of the saw pointing down.

Note: The coped end should be slightly undercut. This will permit the front edge to fit up tightly while the back edge is free.

3. Try the joint against the other member which is nailed in place. If necessary, improve the cut by trimming it with a jackknife.

4. The coping line for wide boards usually is scribed with a pair of scribers or dividers instead of mitering to get a profile.

Miter Joints. The angle of the cut on the molding or board for a miter joint is equal to one-half of the angle of the corner around which the molding is to be fitted. The angle of the miter cut for a square corner is 45 degrees. The two pieces should be carefully cut in a miter box. As they are cut the pieces must be held in the position they will take when applied to the wall. When the corner is not 90 degrees a T-bevel should be used and the angle bisected.

Fitting Baseboards. A trim member usually is provided at the

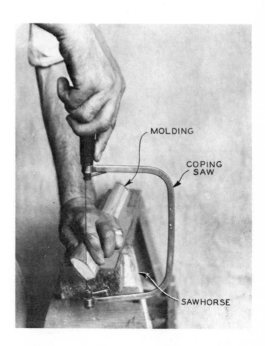

Fig. 18. Coping saw is used to follow profile of miter cut to make coped joint.

junction of the wall and the floor, called the *base*. This base usually consists of only one board and a base shoe, as shown at *E* and *L*, Fig. 14. The baseboard is nailed against the wall and fitted with a coped joint for internal corners, and a mitered joint on external corners, as shown in Fig. 15.

When fitting baseboards, the following method may be used.

PROCEDURE

1. Clean out the corners of the room. Drive in any nails protruding on the grounds and sweep the floor clean along the edges, where the base is to be fitted in place.

2. Locate all wall studs and mark them on the floor with a light pencil mark.

3. Square both ends of a piece of base molding to the correct length and fit it into place along the longest wall of the room. A tight fit can be insured by cutting the board 1/16 of an inch longer than the length of the wall, and springing the board into place against the wall. However, care must be exercised not to break the plaster or gypsum board in the corners. Nail the board in place with two 6*d* finish nails to each stud, holding the board down tightly against the floor.

Note: Sometimes two or more pieces of base molding are required for the length of a wall; if this is the case, the joints should be made on a stud where each of the boards can be securely nailed and the surface block sanded.

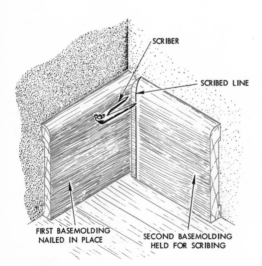

Fig. 19. Scribe base molding before coping.

FIRST BASEMOLDING NAILED IN PLACE SECOND BASEMOLDING HELD FOR SCRIBING

SCRIBER

SCRIBED LINE

4. Select a second piece of base molding of the approximate length of the adjacent wall, hold it in position and scribe the end against the first board as shown in Fig. 19. Set the scriber for the thickness of the base molding.

5. Cope the end of the board, undercutting slightly to insure a tight fit on the surface.

6. Cut the second piece to the correct wall length, measuring from the face of the first baseboard to the plastered wall in the other corner. Then nail the second piece in place.

7. The base molding should be fitted against door casings.

8. Complete base molding pieces around the room using coped joints.

9. The base shoe molding should be fitted the same as the base molding, using coped joints. Hardwood flooring manufacturers suggest that the base shoe molding be nailed to the base molding rather than the finished floor so that the flooring may expand and contract.

10. The mitered corners on the base molding for external corners should be laid out on the board when it is in position, as shown in Fig. 20. Use the baseboard to draw a mark on the floor (Fig. 20, left). Then, with the baseboard fitted in place, draw a mark from the corner to the mark on the floor (Fig. 20, right). This procedure will take care of any irregularities of the walls or floor and will help to insure a satisfactory joint.

Wood Trim at Interior Doors. The trim at interior doors is gener-

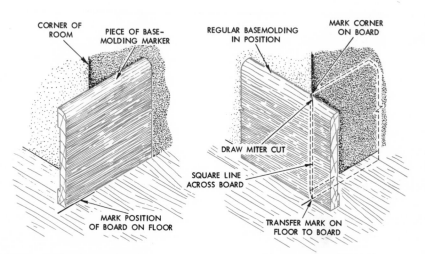

CORNER OF ROOM

PIECE OF BASE-MOLDING MARKER

REGULAR BASEMOLDING IN POSITION

MARK CORNER ON BOARD

DRAW MITER CUT

SQUARE LINE ACROSS BOARD

MARK POSITION OF BOARD ON FLOOR

TRANSFER MARK ON FLOOR TO BOARD

Fig. 20. An easy method of laying out a miter cut for baseboard on external corner is to mark face of board on the floor.

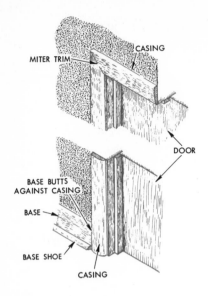

Fig. 21. Simple trim is preferred in modern homes.

ally a simple casing mitered at the corners and cut to fit squarely against the finished floor. The casing is held back $5/16$ inch from the face of the jamb. The base is cut to butt against the casing. The base shoe is cut on an angle away from the casing. See Fig. 21.

Windows

The installing of sash and the trimming of windows usually is done before the finished floor is laid. In cold weather the sash is usually in place so as to close the building so that heat can be applied before and during the wall covering process.

Fitting and Hanging Double-Hung Sash.   In outside walls, windows and doors must be properly fitted to prevent a great loss of heat and an infiltration of cold air. The windows and doors should have a $1/16$ inch clearance on each side. This will insure easy movement, but will also provide a reasonably close fit. Modern windows are either delivered with the sash in the frames or the sash is prefitted and ready for installation. The carpenter may have to make minor adjustments, particularly in the installation of the sash balance devices, so that the windows operate smoothly. It is his job in some instances to install the sash balance. Careful instructions have been worked out by the manufacturer to give the step-by-step procedure.

Patent Sash Balances. There are several patent sash balance devices on the market which have been accepted as satisfactory by home builders. Some of them operate on the principle of a spring which winds up as the sash is raised, thus providing tension. Some of them operate on a friction principle. Some of them are adjustable so that the tension on the spring counter-balances the weight of the sash. They are installed quickly. Because they eliminate the need for the space for window weights, the rough opening need be no more than that required for a casement window, thus permitting the use of narrow trim. The sash balance and weatherstrip shown in Fig. 22 is a metal jamb liner fastened to the jamb, replacing the usual wood parting stop and containing springs which permit the sash to remain open in any position. This type combines the value of a sash balance with a weatherstrip feature.

Several manufacturers have de-

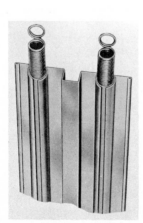

Fig. 22. Sash balances use springs to counterbalance the weight of the sash. (Zegers Inc.)

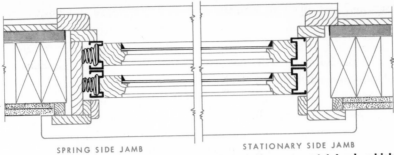

SPRING SIDE JAMB STATIONARY SIDE JAMB

Fig. 23. Plan view through jambs. Removable windows have a metal jamb which compresses to permit the removal of the sash. (R. O. W. Window Corp.)

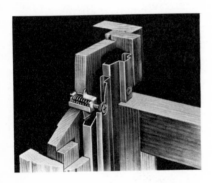

Fig. 24. Detail view of adjustable side jamb. (ARB Window Sales Co.)

veloped windows with a "take out" sash. One of the jambs is equipped with a metal or plastic jamb liner that rests against springs, which compress to permit the sash to be removed. A few extra precautions are needed such as: (1) setting the frames so that the jambs remain plumb and straight, (2) trimming the window so that the jamb liner is not bound but can move when the jamb is pressed, and (3) painting so that the spring feature is not hampered. The result is a smooth operating window which can be removed for cleaning. See Figs. 23 and 24.

Trimming a Double-Hung Window. Before beginning to trim the opening for a window, you should make sure that all necessary members have been selected and placed conveniently near the opening. When mitered joints are used, trim may be fitted in place as in Fig. 25.

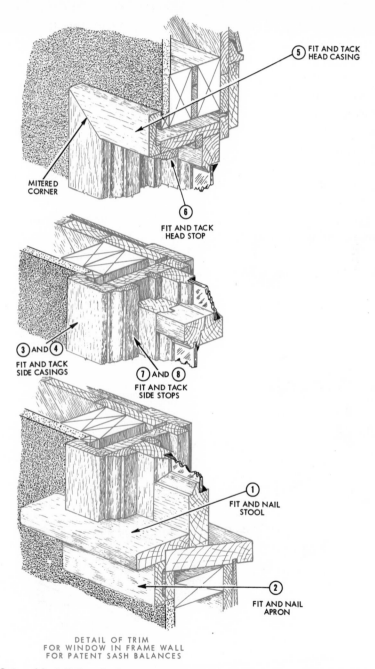

FIT AND TACK
HEAD CASING

MITERED
CORNER

6
FIT AND TACK
HEAD STOP

3 AND 4
FIT AND TACK
SIDE CASINGS

7 AND 8
FIT AND TACK
SIDE STOPS

1
FIT AND NAIL
STOOL

2
FIT AND NAIL
APRON

DETAIL OF TRIM
FOR WINDOW IN FRAME WALL
FOR PATENT SASH BALANCES

Fig. 25. Cut and install the stool, apron stops, and casings in the suggested order.

PROCEDURE

1. Set a pair of scribers to the width of the rabbet on the window stool, as shown at A, Fig. 26.

2. Place the window stool against the opening at the height it will be when fitted. With a square held in the position shown at C, Fig. 26, draw the lines X and Y. Scribe the lines m and n on top of the stool, holding the scribers against the wall, as shown at B.

3. Carefully saw along these lines and remove the wood from the corners of the stool.

Note: When making a finish cut on the trim, always cut on the waste side of the cutting line, leaving part of the line; this will insure a snug fit against the casing.

4. Raise the lower sash and place the stool in its correct position. Bring the sash down and mark a line on the stool along the edge of the sash. Plane to this line and fit the stool with a $\frac{1}{16}$ inch clearance between the stool and the sash.

5. The dimension from the casing to the end of the stool Y Fig. 27 is usually made equal to dimension X. Sand the stool and nail it in place.

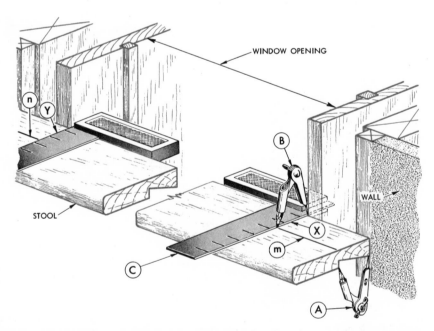

Fig. 26. Simple steps are suggested for laying out the stool for a double-hung window.

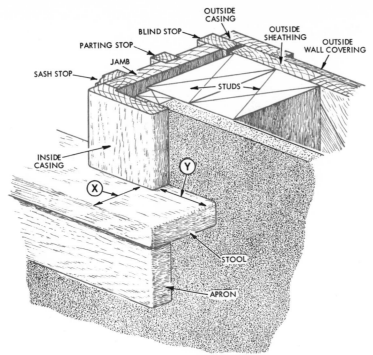

OUTSIDE CASING

BLIND STOP

PARTING STOP

JAMB

SASH STOP

INSIDE CASING

OUTSIDE SHEATHING

OUTSIDE WALL COVERING

STUDS

X

Y

STOOL

APRON

Fig. 27. The stool and apron fit snugly. X and Y are made equal.

The stool when in position is shown at 1. Fig. 25.

Note: When nailing the trim, unless the wood is unusually soft, always drill holes for the nails first, to prevent the splitting of the wood.

6. Fitting the apron under the stool.

(a) Mark the position of the side casing on the stool. The distance from the outside of one casing to the outside of the other casing will give the length of the apron. In other words, the ends of the apron are in line with the outside edge of the casings. When the apron is simple in design, cut it to the proper length and finish the ends. See Fig. 27.

(b) When the apron is molded, take a small piece of apron material and draw a pattern for the return of the apron on one end, as shown at A, Fig. 28. Measure the length from point 1 and draw the return on the other end in the same way.

(c) Then cut out with a coping saw, and sandpaper both ends of the apron.

7. Nail the apron in position under the stool with 8d finish nails by

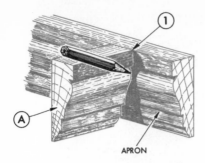

Fig. 28. Mark the apron to be cut to return to the wall. This is a molded stool.

nailing into the solid header of the rough opening, as shown at *2*, Fig. 25.

8. Cut and fit the top window stop *6*, Fig. 25, in the opening, using square end cuts. Raise the bottom sash and nail the stop with *4d* finish nails, allowing a $\frac{1}{16}$ inch clearance between it and the sash. Fit the bottom of the side stops *7* and *8*, Fig. 25, to the stool. Cut them to the correct length and cope them to fit against the head stop. Nail the side stops with *4d* finish nails. Allow space so that the sash will have easy movement.

9. When starting the casings, all pieces should be left about 1 inch longer than required. Put a left and right hand miter on the two side casings and a miter on one end of the head casing, *3*, *4* and *5*, Fig. 25.

10. Place the head casing *5*, Fig. 25, in position with the end which has the miter on it in line with the corner of the jamb. Mark the other

end, miter it, smooth the cut, put it back in place and nail it.

11. The side casings, *3* and *4*, Fig. 25, have already been mitered. Turn the miter upside down so that it rests on the stool and mark the other end at the top of the casing. Cut the side casing pieces *3* and *4* square on the line. With a block plane dress down to the line, making the surface of the cut smooth and square with the face of the casing. Put it in position and nail it, using *4d* finish nails to fasten the casings to the jambs, and *8d* finish nails to fasten the outside of the casings to the wall. Make sure that the *8d* nails pass into the studs.

12. Drive all the nails home and set them with a nail set. Sandpaper the high points on the joints.

Trimming Casement and Other Windows

Wood windows (other than double hung), such as casement, horizontal sliding, hopper and awning types, may be trimmed with wood casing, stool, and apron in a manner similar to that described for the double-hung window. Fig. 29 shows an awning type window with typical trim including casing, stool, and apron. Windows may be trimmed with casing members on all four sides, as in Figs. 72, 76 and 77, Chapter VI.

Some metal windows are trimmed with casing, stool and apron, other windows have features which permit the elimination of conventional trim.

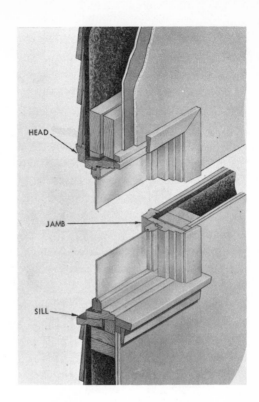

Fig. 29. An interior view of a wood awning type of window shows how it is trimmed with casing, stool and apron. (Note that the exterior view of this window is shown in Chapter 6, Fig. 78.) (Andersen Corp.)

See Fig. 84, Chapter VI (jambs, sill and apron of wood to be provided by the carpenter). Fig. 85, Chapter VI, shows the dry wall returning into the opening on the top and sides to stop against the metal frame of the window. The stool and sill are similar to that used for wood windows.

Doors

Two main classes of doors are the flush door and the panel door. Flush doors have one large flat surface on each side. Panel doors are made of vertical members called stiles and horizontal members called rails. Panels which have raised surfaces on them are held between the stiles and rails. Both flush and panel doors are used as interior and exterior doors. Exterior doors are generally 1¾ or 1⅜ inches thick. A few of the styles are shown in Fig. 30. The doors are chosen by the architect to be in keeping with the design of the house. Panel doors are generally used with

FLUSH
ONELIGHT

GOTHIC-HEAD
V JOINTED

OUTSIDE COLONIAL DOORS

ONE-LIGHT
CROSS PANEL

FRENCH

REGULAR
5 PANEL

COLONIAL
6 PANEL

COLONIAL
8 PANEL

SIX-LIGHT
2 PANEL

NINE-LIGHT
CROSS RAIL

FLUSH

FOLDING
LOUVERED

STOCK DOORS

Fig. 30. Designs of stock doors.

traditional architecture. Flush doors are almost always used with contemporary structures.

Two types of flush doors are man-

ufactured, the solid core and the hollow core. Solid core doors are usually used as exterior doors. They are heavier and can withstand weather

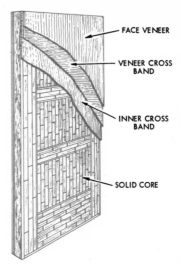

FACE VENEER

VENEER CROSS BAND

INNER CROSS BAND

SOLID CORE

Fig. 31. A solid core flush door is made up of many small blocks glued together and covered with layers of veneer.

better than hollow core doors. The solid core door is made up of many small soft wood blocks which are glued together. Two layers of veneer are glued to the faces of the door with the face ply chosen carefully for its beauty. If the door is to be given a transparent finish the edges are covered with the same type of veneer as the face. If it is to be painted, only hardwood edges are required. See Fig. 31.

Hollow core doors are lightweight and quite satisfactory for inside use. They are made up of strips of wood forming a frame and a core of interlocking strips. There are several different ways of arranging the parts of the core. The various features of the door are shown in Fig. 32. Vent openings, which provide for ventilation

and equilization of temperature and humidity, are shown at *A*. Wide top and bottom rails of sufficient width to permit cutting down 2 inches in height, to be cut equally from top and bottom, are shown at *B*. The edge strips can be faced with hardwood to match the door faces, as shown at *C*. A grid core of wood, mortised and framed together for strength and to insure against swelling, shrinking, or sagging, is shown at *D*. The lock area, measuring $4\frac{5}{8}$ inches by 20 inches on both edges of the door, insures ample lock space no matter how the door is hung, and is shown at *E*. The woven-wood core, overlaid with veneers of plywood (usually 3 ply), is shown at *F*. The veneer may be of several kinds of wood.

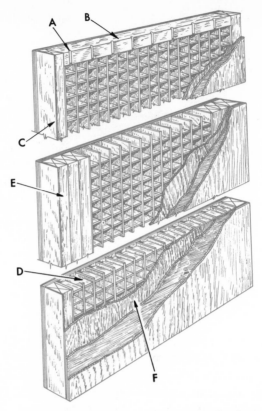

Fig. 32. The hollow core door is lightweight and resists warping because of the construction of the core.

Hanging a Door

The common methods of hanging a door are by hinges on the edge or side of the door, or by hanging the door from a track.

The usual type of hinge used is called a butt hinge or a butt. See Fig. 33.

The round central portion of the butt hinge, shown in Fig. 33, is known as the *knuckle*. It is ordinarily divided into five sections. It is then called a *five-knuckle butt hinge*. The flat parts of such a hinge are known as the *leaves* or *flaps*. The two flaps are held together by a pin running through the knuckle. Door butts usually are made so the pin may be taken out, and are then known as *loose-pin butts*. When the pins are not removable the butts are called *fast joints*. The thickness and width of the door determine the size of the butt hinge required.

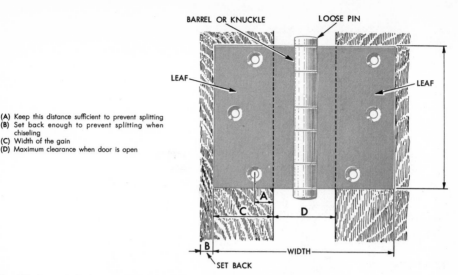

BARREL OR KNUCKLE   LOOSE PIN

LEAF   LEAF

(A) Keep this distance sufficient to prevent splitting
(B) Set back enough to prevent splitting when chiseling
(C) Width of the gain
(D) Maximum clearance when door is open

A
C   D
B
WIDTH
SET BACK

Fig. 33. Loose-pin butt mortise hinges vary in size according to use.

Sliding Doors or Roll-Away Type. The sliding door, hung from a track and operating on rollers, has regained its popularity. This type of door requires only the regular 2 × 4 wall thickness. It is a complete sliding-door unit with a track and rollers built into one package, as shown in Fig. 34. The frame unit is set into the wall opening and covered with the regular interior wall finish. Any door, with a thickness of 1⅜ inches, can be hung to the rollers, to match the interior trim. The frame for this type of sliding door, set up complete with the door hung and finish hardware installed, is shown at left, Fig. 34. When this door is placed in the wall any type of interior wall finish can be applied over the spreaders.

Many manufacturers make sliding door hardware to serve many purposes; right, Fig. 34, shows a typical track arrangement for bypassing doors.

Folding doors also are used extensively in modern home building. They are used on closets, to enclose laundry areas or kitchenettes, and as room dividers. An efficient track system permits long, satisfactory service. See Fig. 35.

Setting Inside Door Jambs

That part of a doorway trim which forms the lining of the door opening is called the *door jamb*. The jambs, together with the casings, complete the unfinished wall around the door opening. To close the opening, the

441

 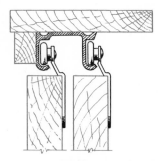

Fig. 34. Pocket roll-away door fits into 3½ inch wall space. Sliding doors use simple hangers and track. (Sterling Hardware Mfg. Co.)

Fig. 35. Folding doors prove practical as room dividers.

door is fitted and hung on these jambs. Inside door jambs are ⅞ of an inch in thickness, and of the same kind of wood as the interior trim. The inside distance between the side jambs should be equal to the width of the door, but the height should be ¼ inch more than the height of the door to allow the door to swing freely; carpet thickness or a threshold may require more space. The head jamb should be housed into the side jambs as shown at *A*, Fig. 36.

PROCEDURE

1. Door jambs usually are delivered to the job with all parts assembled and ready to install. It is advisable to check the width of the jambs with the wall thickness; also, to check the length of both the head and side jamb with the door and the squareness of the corners. Cut off part of the lugs if necessary.

2. If the finish floor has been laid, place the jambs in position, and see that the head jamb is perfectly level. If the finish floor has not been laid, set the jambs on blocks to bring them to finished floor level. If the head jamb is not level, raise the lowest side jamb and cut it off to fit the door. This should bring the head jamb into a level position.

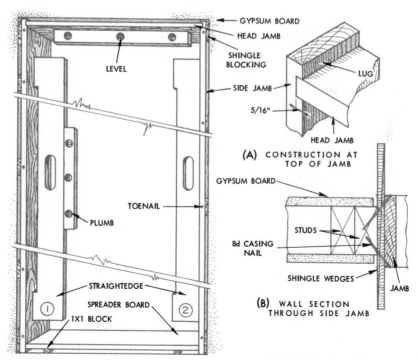

Fig. 36. Shingles are used as blocking to hold jamb in place. Jamb must be made plumb and level.

3. Take a piece of 1×6 and cut the ends square to fit snugly between the jambs at the head, thus forming a spreader which should be placed on the floor betwen the jambs at the lower end. See Fig. 36.

4. Consult the working drawings to determine which way the door is to swing. Then mark the hinge jamb on the edge of the jamb to which the hinges are to be fitted.

5. The door thickness is usually $1\frac{3}{8}$ or $1\frac{3}{4}$ inches. Measure the thickness of the door. Gage a faint pencil line $\frac{7}{8}$ of an inch more than the thickness of the door from the edge of the jamb on which the door hinges. This line will be the *center line* for nailing. This line will later be covered by the door stop which will hide the nail holes.

6. Set the jambs as near as possible to the center of the opening, holding the jambs in place with double-shingle wedges on each side at the top, in line with the head jamb. Wedge the bottom in the same way.

7. Plumb the hinge jamb with a straightedge and level, holding the straightedge as shown at *1*, Fig. 36. Check the edge of the jamb with the wall finish line. Then fasten the jamb with an $8d$ casing nail at the top and bottom. Place each nail back $\frac{1}{2}$ inch from the pencil line. *Do not* drive the nails home until the other jamb has been adjusted and secured. Before nailing the second jamb, the shingle wedges should be brought up tightly against the second jamb at the top and bottom.

8. Complete the blocking by placing three more wedge blocks back of each jamb. On the hinge jamb, the blocks are placed with one block in the middle and the other two at the hinge location, which is 5 inches down from the top and 10 inches up from the bottom of the jamb. (Some carpenters use 7 inches down and 11 inches up). On the lock side, one block should be placed 36 inches up from the floor and the other two blocks should be placed midway between this block and the blocks above and below. Each jamb should be checked with the back of the straightedge as shown at *2*, Fig. 36, while placing the blocks and nailing the jambs in position. Each block should be fastened with two nails, staggering the nails $\frac{1}{2}$ inch on each side of the pencil line.

9. Complete the nailing of the jambs by toenailing down the edges into each block, as shown at *B*, Fig. 36. The nails should be set back at least $\frac{5}{16}$ of an inch from the face of the jamb, so they will be covered by the casings.

Trimming a Door Opening

A door opening is trimmed by fitting and applying the casings, shown in Fig. 37. This trimming work is done after the jambs have been set and the floor laid, but before the fitting of the baseboards. Many car-

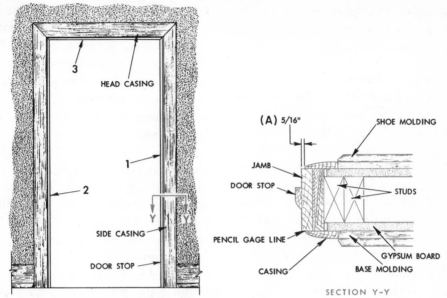

Fig. 37. Castings are carefully fitted around door jambs.

penters will fit and hang the door before applying the trim so that they can still make minor adjustments in the jamb. After the casings are in place, this cannot be done. To trim a door opening, proceed as follows:

PROCEDURE

1. Select the necessary pieces of trim for the door opening and place these pieces conveniently near to the opening.

2. Gage a light pencil line on the edge of the jamb, $5/16$ of an inch back from the face, as shown at A, Fig. 37. The inside edge of the casings should be set to this line.

3. Lay out, cut, and fit the top of the side casings and both ends of the top casing in the same way as for window trim.

4. Fit the bottom end of the side casings shown at *1* and *2*, Fig. 37, to the finished floor.

5. Nail the casings in place with $4d$ nails, nailing into the jambs. Along the outer edges, use $8d$ nails, nailing into the studs.

Note: Sometimes casings must be scribed and fitted to the wall surface if it is uneven or rough. However, the painter usually is expected to fill any minor openings between the wall surface and casings.

6. Cut, fit, and tack the door stops

445

in place. The stops should not be nailed in place until after the door has been fitted and hung.

Fitting the Doors

A door must be handled with care so that it may not be damaged. When delivered to the job, the doors should either be stacked carefully on the floor or set against the wall. If the doors are set against the wall, special care must be taken to prevent warping and to make sure that the wall surface is not marred. Before attempting to fit and hang a door, the following preliminary precautions should be observed.

1. Consult the working drawings and building specifications regarding the type of door required for a particular opening, the hardware specified, and the direction the door is to swing.

2. Mark the door jamb which is to receive the hinges.

3. Check the size of the door with the opening size.

4. Gather all necessary tools and the equipment required to fit the door. Besides the usual small tools, such as the plane, saw, hammer, and chisel, it will be necessary to have a pair of sawhorses and a door jack to hold the door while working on the edges. To fit the door, proceed as follows:

PROCEDURE

1. Mark the hinge stile on the door and fit the door against the hinge jamb, planing the edge if necessary to conform to the shape of the jamb.

Note: The hinge edge usually should be square, although a slight bevel at the back has an advantage.

2. Measure the width of the opening (distance between the jambs) at the top and bottom with an extension rule, or two sticks to take the place of an extension rule, and transfer the dimensions to the door lying on the sawhorses. Draw a cutting line on the door, making the door ⅛ of an inch narrower than the width of the opening.

Note: A well-fitted door should fit to the shape of the door opening and have a clearance of $\frac{1}{16}$ of an inch on each side and on top. The bottom clearance should be from ⅜ to ½ inch, unless a threshold is used, in which case a $\frac{1}{16}$ inch clearance should be allowed between the door and the threshold. The threshold should be fitted in place after the door has been hung. Carpeting presents a similar problem.

3. Plane the second edge of the door to the cutting line.

Note: To insure uniform clearance, check the jamb for straightness before planing off the entire amount to be removed.

4. Place the door in the opening, check the fit and insert a wedge, as shown at *X*, Fig. 38, in place. Scribe the top edge of the door to the top jamb. (*Scribing* means drawing a line parallel with an existing surface.)

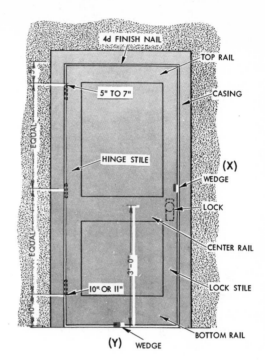

Fig. 38. The door must be made to fit the opening with 1/16 of an inch clearance. Lock and butts are located at a uniform height.

The scribing can be done with a pair of dividers or a regular scriber. This operation is unnecessary when both the door and jambs are square.

5. Plane the top edge of the door to fit the top jamb.

6. Bevel the lock edge of the door. The side-hinge door forms an arc as it swings, and the lock side must be beveled so the point on the door shown at *A*, Fig. 39, will clear the edge of the jamb shown at the point *B*. The amount of bevel required will depend upon the thickness and width of the door and the width of the hinge. This bevel can be obtained by drawing a diagonal line on the top edge of the door from one corner to the theoretical pin center of the hinge. The bevel line *AB* Fig. 39, is at a right angle to the line *AX*. Set the T bevel to the line *AB* and the side of the door to find the correct angle of the bevel. Plane edge to this angle.

7. Remove the sharp edges of the door with the plane and sandpaper all edges until they are smooth.

447

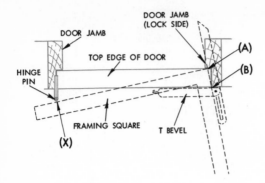

DOOR JAMB (LOCK SIDE)

DOOR JAMB

TOP EDGE OF DOOR

(A)

(B)

HINGE PIN

FRAMING SQUARE

T BEVEL

(X)

Fig. 39. A framing square can be used to determine the amount of bevel needed on the lock stile.

Note: Edges of hardwood doors sometimes are hard to plane smooth and free from checks due to cross grain. A well sharpened scraper will help to smooth such edges.

Installing Hinges

The size and weight of the door will determine the length of the hinge you should use. The width of the hinge and the amount of the setback will depend upon the thickness of the trim shown in Fig. 40. Sufficient clearance must be allowed to permit the door to swing back parallel to the wall. To hang a door proceed as follows:

PROCEDURE

1. Place the door in the door opening, then force the door against the hinge jamb with a wedge shown at X, Fig. 38. Place a 4d finish nail on top of the door and force the door up against the nail with a wedge shown at Y.

2. Mark the hinge location on both the jamb and the door stile with a knife or sharp pencil and make a cross mark to indicate the side of the line the hinge should be gained.

Note: The hinge location may vary according to the decision of the architect or the contractor. However, standard procedure is to place the top of the hinge 5 inches down from the top of the door, and the bottom of the lowest hinge 10 inches up from the floor. Some western states use the figures 7 and 11 as shown in the illustration, Fig. 38. When there are three hinges, these figures generally are used. The third hinge should be centered between the top and the bottom hinges, as shown in Fig. 38.

3. Scribe the bottom of the door to the floor before removing the door. If a threshold is used, measure the thickness of the threshold and add to this figure $\frac{1}{16}$ of an inch for clearance. If no threshold is to be used,

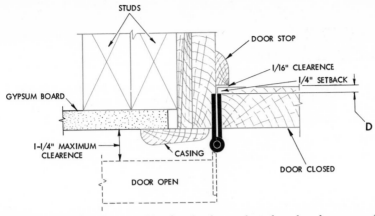

Fig. 40. Method of hanging door provides for clearing casing when door is swung wide open.

then a ⅜ inch to ½ inch clearance is usually made.

4. Place the door in a door jack and with a knife and a butt gage mark the width of the hinge on the edge of the door. Square the lines across the edge of the door with the butt gage, as shown in Fig. 41.

Note: The detail of the gain for the jamb is shown at *A*, Fig. 42, and the detail for the door is shown at *B*.

5. Set the butt gage to the width

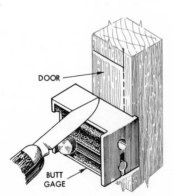

Fig. 41. Knife and gage are used for squaring lines for width of gain.

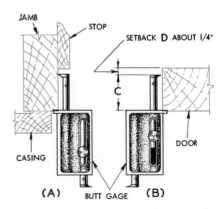

Fig. 42. Width of gain is determined by width of hinge and clearance required.

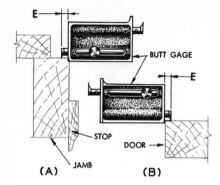

Fig. 43. Method of setting the butt gage for depth of gain.

of the gain as shown at *B*, Fig. 42. This width will be determined by the casing clearance required and the width of the hinge as shown in Fig. 40. Gage the width of the gain on the door as at *B*, Fig. 42.

Note: The depth of the gain on the jamb is shown at *A*, Fig. 43, and the depth of the gain on the door is shown at *B*, Fig. 43.

6. Gage the depth of the gain for the hinge as shown at *B*, Fig. 43.

Note: The depth *E*, Fig. 44, will depend upon the construction of the hinge. Butts for large doors are swaged as at *A*, Fig. 44, small butts for cupboard doors are straight and

the gage is set slightly less than half the thickness of the barrel shown at *B*, Fig. 44.

7. The gain layout is shown at *A*, Fig. 45. With a sharp chisel notch the two ends of the gain, as shown at *B*, Fig. 45, by setting the chisel with its bevel toward the gain. Score the rest of the gain and clean out by paring with a chisel, Fig. 45, C.

8. Place the hinge in the gain so the loose pin will be up when the door is in position. Drive the screws toward the back of the hinge holes so the hinge will be drawn tightly into the gain against the setback shown at *D*, Fig. 40.

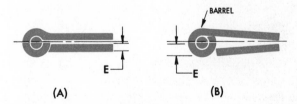

Fig. 44. Depth of gain depends upon hinge: (A) swaged hinge, (B) straight hinge.

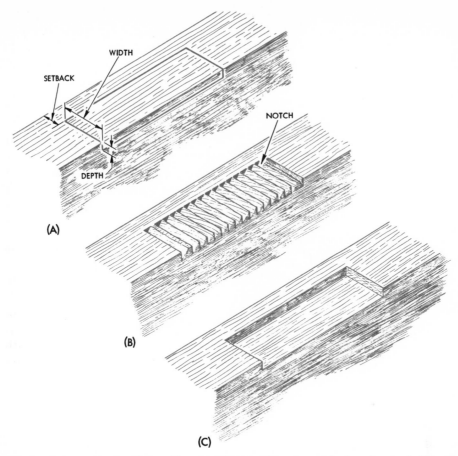

SETBACK

WIDTH

DEPTH

(A)

NOTCH

(B)

(C)

Fig. 45. Making gain for hinge: (A) gain laid out, (B) gain notched and scored, (C) gain cleaned out by paring with chisel.

9. Lay out and mortise the gain into the jamb as shown at *A*, Fig. 42, the same as in the door. Pull out the loose pin and screw the free leaf of the hinge into place on the jamb with two screws.

10. Hang the door in place on the hinges and check the door for proper clearance, with should be $\frac{1}{16}$ of an inch on each side.

Note: If the door has more than $\frac{1}{16}$ of an inch clearance along the hinge jamb, the gain should be deepened slightly. If the door binds against the jamb, place a strip of cardboard behind the butt in the gain. Then drive all screws in place securely.

11. Adjust the door stops. The stop on the hinge jamb should have

1/16 of an inch clearance between it and the door. The stop on the lock side should hold the door flush with the outside edge of the jamb. The top stop should be held in line with the side stops. Nail the door stops securely with 4d finish nails.

Tubular and Cylindrical Lock Sets

Locks which require the boring of two holes and the cutting of a small mortise for the face of the lock are used extensively in new work because they are easily installed and very satisfactory. They are manufactured to serve many purposes both for exterior and interior doors. The manufacturers provide templates for the location of the holes. See Fig. 46.

Jigs are manufactured which clamp on the edge of the door and which make the correct boring of the holes a fool proof operation. See Fig. 47. A mortising tool is also available which permits cutting the mortise to the correct depth for the face of the lock. Tubular lock sets are used mainly for interior doors, for bedrooms, bathrooms, passages, and closets. They can be obtained with pin tumbler locks in the knob on the outside of the door and turn button or push button locks on the inside. There are several variations to this arrangement. See Fig. 48.

Cylindrical lock sets are sturdy heavy duty locks, designed for maximum security for installation in exterior doors. See Fig. 49. Manufacturers' instructions supplied with the locks should be followed carefully.

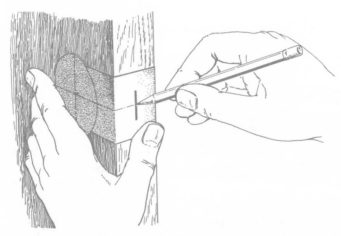

Fig. 46. Paper templates are provided by the manufacturers to help the carpenter locate holes accurately. (Yale and Towne Mfg. Co.)

Fig. 47. A jig is fastened to the edge of the door to give accurate location for the holes. (Kwikset Sales and Service Co.)

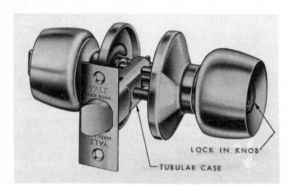

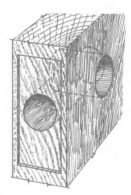

Fig. 48. Tubular latch set is installed by drilling 2 holes and mortising lock face. Locks of this type are supplied for several different interior door applications. (Yale and Towne Mfg. Co.)

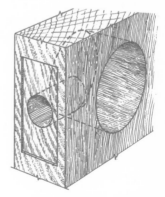

Fig. 49. Cylindrical lock sets are used for heavy duty on exterior doors. (Yale and Towne Mfg. Co.)

Mortise Locks

The following detailed information is for the installation of the ordinary mortise lock.

Right-Handed or Left-Handed Doors or Casements. Locks are not always made so they can be reversed or changed to suit doors hinged on either the right-hand or left-hand side, or for doors opening in or out. Therefore, chiefly for the purpose of buying door hardware, it is necessary for the carpenter or builder to have some knowledge of the standard rules regarding locks intended for right-hand or left-hand doors or casements.

1. Whether a door is to be right-handed or left-handed is always determined from the *outside*.

2. The *outside* of a door is the street side of an entrance door and the corridor side of a room door. The *outside* of a communicating door, that is from one room to another, is the side from which the butts or hinges are not visible when the door is closed. The *outside* of a closet,

cupboard, or bookcase door is the room side, thus reversing the rule which applies to other doors.

3. When you stand *outside* a door, if the butts are on your right it is a right-handed door; if the butts are on your left it is a left-handed door. If, when standing outside, the door opens from you, or inward, it will require a lock with a regular bevel bolt and the lock is described as either *right-handed* or *left-handed*, depending upon whether the butts are to your right or left. A lock with a regular bevel, for a right-handed door, is shown at *A*, Fig. 50. A lock with a regular bevel, for a left-handed door, is shown at *B*, Fig. 50. If, when standing outside the door, it opens toward you or outward, the door will require a lock with a reverse bolt and the lock is described as a right hand reverse bevel or left hand reverse bevel, depending upon whether the butts are to your right or left. A right-hand reverse bevel lock is shown at *A*, Fig. 51. A left-hand reverse bevel lock is shown at *B*, Fig. 51.

Fig. 50. When doors open away from you, they are right handed or left handed, depending on which side has the butts.

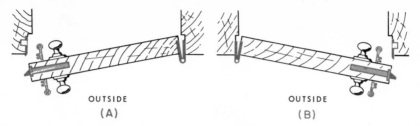

Fig. 51. When doors open toward you, they are right handed or left handed, depending on which side has the butts. A lock with a reverse bolt is required.

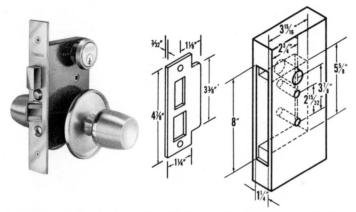

Fig. 52. A modern mortise lock provides high security. (Sargent and Co.)

A large percentage of the locks installed in new buildings are of the cylindrical or tubular types shown in Fig. 48 and 49. There are still enough mortise locks used, however, to make it necessary for the carpenter to have the skill of installing them. Fig. 52 shows a modern mortise lock with a cylinder lock. They are generally used in front entrance doors.

Installing the Mortise Lock. Fig. 53 illustrates a simple mortise lock which will serve to outline the procedure to be followed.

PROCEDURE

1. Unpack the package containing the lock and examine each part in order to become familiar with the installation requirements.

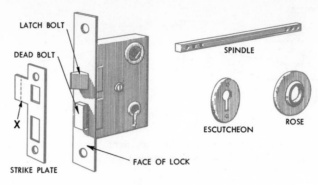

LATCH BOLT

DEAD BOLT

X

STRIKE PLATE

FACE OF LOCK

SPINDLE

ESCUTCHEON

ROSE

Fig. 53. Various parts of a basic mortise lock.

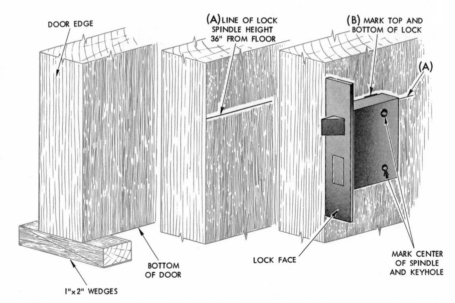

DOOR EDGE

(A) LINE OF LOCK
SPINDLE HEIGHT
36" FROM FLOOR

(B) MARK TOP AND
BOTTOM OF LOCK

(A)

BOTTOM
OF DOOR

LOCK FACE

MARK CENTER
OF SPINDLE
AND KEYHOLE

1"x 2" WEDGES

Fig. 54. Mortise lock layout: wedging the door, laying out spindle height, locating spindle and keyhole.

2. Open the door to a convenient working location and block it with two wedges under the front edge as shown in Fig. 54.

3. Measure up 36 inches from the floor, the usual knob height, and square a line for the lock spindle from the edge of the door, as shown at *A*, Fig. 54.

4. Place the lock on the side of the

door with the face of the lock flush with the edge of the door and the spindle-hole center on the line *A*, Fig. 54. Mark the spindle location and the center of the keyhole. Also mark, near the edge of the door, the location of the top and bottom of the lock as shown at *B*, Fig. 55.

5. Square the top and bottom lines indicated by *B*, Fig. 55, across the edge of the door and gage a center line between them, as shown at *C*. (A deep gage line here will help to center the auger bit.)

6. Bore a ¾ inch hole for the spindle and another for the key.

Note: Continue to bore the hole until the screw of the bit shows on the opposite side of the door, then bore back from that side of the door. This will avoid splitting the wood. When small escutcheons are furnished, it is advisable to bore two small holes for the key and clean out these holes with a pocket knife instead of boring a ¾ inch hole. This will insure coverage of the hole by the escutcheon.

7.Select an auger bit 1⁄16 of an inch larger than the thickness of the mortise lock and bore holes into the edge of the door, as shown at *1* and *2*, Fig.

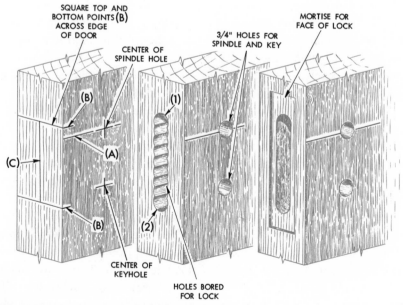

Fig. 55. Making mortise for lock: gaging center line, boring holes for mortise, mortise for lock face.

55. Then continue to bore a series of holes, one overlapping the other, to avoid excessive chiseling.

Note: In boring these holes, sight both sides of the door in order to drill holes in the correct direction.

8. Clean out the mortise with a chisel and try the lock.

9. Insert the lock with the face pressed tightly against the edge of the door. Line up the lock with the spindle and keyhole, then draw a line with a knife around the edge of the lock face.

10. Remove the lock and chisel out the mortise to the depth of the thickness of the lock face, as shown in Fig. 55.

11. Replace the lock and fasten it with screws.

12. Assemble the rose, escutcheon, spindle, and knob on the door and fasten them in place with screws. Adjust the knob and tighten the setscrew in the knob.

Note: A careful check should be made to see that the spindle is straight in the lock and the knob is free in the rose to insure freedom of action. The rose and escutcheon must be in line vertically for the sake of appearance, if for no other reason.

13. Remove the wedge from under the door, and partly close the door. Mark the top and bottom of the latch bolt on the door jamb with a pencil.

14. Mark the relation of the strike plate to the lock by holding the plate against the face of the lock; also hold the plate against the side of the latch bolt and draw a line as shown at X, Fig. 53, along the edge of the door with a knife.

15. Mark the location of the strike plate on the jamb with a knife, holding the plate so the line X is in line with the edge of the jamb and the latch bolt marks on the jamb center in the strike plate hole.

16. Remove the strike plate and chisel out the mortise to a depth equal to the thickness of the strike plate. Screw the plate in place.

17. Chisel out the wood to a depth of $\frac{1}{2}$ or $\frac{5}{8}$ of an inch through the strike plate openings, to allow the latch and dead bolts to enter the strike plate.

Metal Doors and Frames

Metal doors used for the interior of a house are generally $1\frac{3}{8}$ inches thick, 6 feet 8 inches high, and one of the following widths: 1'-6", 2'-0", 2'-4", 2'-6", 2'-8" or 3'-0". The doors are made up of steel sheets with stiffeners, reinforcing plates, and a honeycomb core to make them rigid. They may be obtained prefinished with baked-on enamel or with a vinyl laminated surface. Doors are provided with recesses for butts.

The metal frames which accompany the doors, or which may be used for wood doors, are made to fit several wall thicknesses. They are shipped knocked-down and are quickly assembled and fastened to

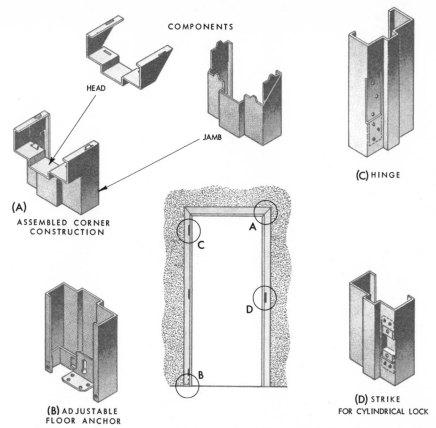

COMPONENTS

HEAD

JAMB

(A)
ASSEMBLED CORNER
CONSTRUCTION

(C) HINGE

(B) ADJUSTABLE
FLOOR ANCHOR

(D) STRIKE
FOR CYLINDRICAL LOCK

Fig. 56. Metal door frames are assembled on the job. Hinges and lock strikes are positioned accurately. (The Ceco Corp.)

the framework of the partition. Fig. 56, *A* and *B*. Lock strikes and hinge rabbets are prepared so that the installation of hardware is easy. Fig. 56, *C* and *D*. Several devices for fastening them to different types of partitions are available. Fig. 56 shows the manner in which the door frames are assembled, and a typical floor anchor.

The great emphasis on dry wall has brought about the use of metal door frames for use with metal studs. A number of different door frames and anchoring devices have been invented. Fig. 57 gives information on

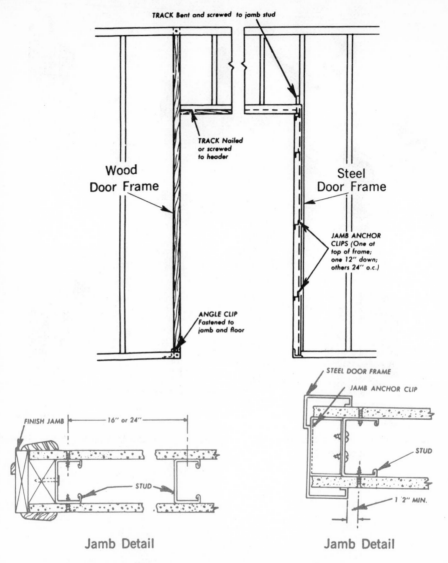

TRACK Bent and screwed to jamb stud

TRACK Nailed
or screwed
to header

Wood
Door Frame

Steel
Door Frame

JAMB ANCHOR
CLIPS (One at
top of frame;
one 12" down;
others 24" o.c.)

ANGLE CLIP
Fastened to
jamb and floor

STEEL DOOR FRAME

JAMB ANCHOR CLIP

FINISH JAMB

16" or 24"

STUD

STUD

1 2" MIN.

Jamb Detail

Jamb Detail

Fig. 57. Metal and wood door frames are provided for use with metal studs for drywall application. (National Gypsum Co.)

wood or metal door frames to be used in a metal stud partition. A piece of track, such as used on the floor, is fastened over the door to receive the crippled studs. The jamb anchor clips are fastened with screws.

Floors

Laying Finished Floor

Wood for finished floor is selected because of its durability to withstand wear and for its appearance. The woods most commonly used for finish flooring include oak, both plain and quarter sawn, hard maple, beech, birch, pecan, fir and yellow pine. Finish-flooring material is usually matched; that is, the boards have a tongue and groove to produce a tight smooth floor.

Hardwood flooring comes in $\frac{3}{8}$, $\frac{25}{32}$ and $\frac{1}{2}$ inch thicknesses, in $1\frac{1}{2}$ inch, 2 inch, $2\frac{1}{4}$ inch, and $3\frac{1}{4}$ inch face widths. It is bundled in lengths ranging from 2 feet to 16 feet. Oak flooring also is made in random widths of 3 to 8 inches with square edges to give a traditional floor effect. This is called plank flooring. It may be stained in cherry, black walnut and teak also.

Formerly, maple was used extensively for kitchen floors. Today, however, most kitchen floors are covered with resilient flooring, which requires a plywood subfloor or hardboard underlayment. Maple is used for finished floors in other parts of the house because it is very durable. A good serviceable floor at lower cost can be made from either 4 inch vertical-grain fir or yellow pine.

Another type of wood floor, called block flooring, is now gaining in favor with builders and contractors. It is made of hardwood squares of oak,

Fig. 58. Block floor may be laid in mastic. (E. L. Bruce Co.)

maple, and elm laid in mastic (a quick drying cement) over a concrete slab. It can also be nailed to a subfloor. The squares are $7\frac{1}{2}$ or 9 inches in size, and are made up of several pieces of $2\frac{1}{4}$ inch face flooring glued together; or can have a single ply face. The squares are laid so that the direction of the boards will alternate with each square. See Fig. 58. Flooring may be obtained prefinished. Block flooring has the appearance of historic parquet flooring which has been revived in very expensive residential work where a true traditional flavor is desired. In real parquet flooring each strip in the square is a separate piece. Strips may be laid in herringbone and other interesting patterns also.

Before any finished floor is laid, it is necessary for the rough floor to be thoroughly cleaned, all plaster removed, and loose nails driven down. If the floor is placed over a basementless space, special precautions must be made to control moisture. Fifteen pound asphalt felt is placed over the subfloor before the floor is laid. The same is true when flooring is laid over a concrete slab. Two layers of asphalt felt or polyethylene film are laid over the slab, followed by mastic in which the screeds that support the floor are embedded. Flooring manufacturers generally agree that in ordinary flooring applications, waterproof felt should be used between the rough floor and finished floor.

Furring strips are used under the finished floor to provide for conduit when necessary, and to provide an air space. The furring strips should be spaced 12 or 16 inches on center (o.c.), and be well nailed through the rough floor into the joists with $10d$ common nails to prevent the strips from working loose. When laying a finished floor directly on the rough floor, the boards of the finish floor should be laid so that they will run in the opposite direction from the boards of the rough floor. Following this procedure will insure a smoother floor. When diagonal rough floor or furring strips are used, the finished flooring may be laid in either direction; that is, parallel or at right angles, to the joists. Plywood is often used instead of boards for rough flooring.

PROCEDURE

1. Before the actual work of laying the floor is begun, a careful study of the floor plans should be made to determine the kind of flooring which is to be laid in the different rooms and the relations of the rooms to each other. First, select the *key room*, that is, the room which because of its size and importance determines the direction the boards of the finished floor should be laid. Then study the relation of the other rooms to the key room to see if the boards of the flooring in the key room will extend into any other room. See Fig. 59.

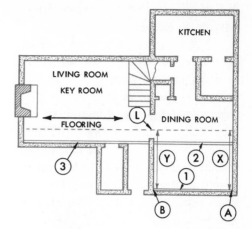

Fig. 59. Flooring is laid in relation to base line (L).

2. Check the walls of the key room to see if the opposite sides are parallel to each other.

3. Establish a straight line, as *L*, Fig. 59, by snapping a chalk line on the building paper or on the rough floor. This line should be parallel to the longest wall of the key room, and should extend into the adjacent room.

Note: If, through an error in construction, the walls are not exactly parallel to each other, it will be necessary to adjust the line so the difference will be divided equally on both sides of the room.

4. When laying the first flooring board shown at *1*, Fig. 59, proceed as follows:

(*a*) Select a long straight piece of flooring, the full length of the room if possible.

(*b*) Place this piece of flooring in position, with the grooved edge toward the wall. A space of about 1 inch should be allowed for expansion. (Less than the combined thickness of base and shoe moldings.)

(*c*) Face nail the board at *A* with an 8*d* finish nail, but *do not* drive the nail home.

(*d*) With a stick, measure the distance *X* from the face of the first board to the chalk line *L*. Transfer this distance to *Y*, and set a nail at *B*. The board *1* will then be parallel to the chalk line *L*, and also will be parallel to the main wall in the key room.

(*e*) Check the edge of the board *1* for straightness; this can be done with a straightedge, a line, or by sighting. Then face nail the board every 12 inches with 8*d* finish nails, nailing as near to the wall as possible. Set all nails with a nail set.

5. Continue to cut, fit, and nail the flooring until the board marked

2, Fig. 59, has been reached, proceeding as follows:

(a) First, cut and fit a number of boards (about 6 or 8), and lay them in order on the floor ahead of the nailing, as shown in Fig. 60. Use different lengths, matching them so they will reach from wall to wall. Never allow the joints in successive courses to come together. All joints should be broken after every course. Begin with piece *1*, Fig. 60, and follow with pieces *2* and *3*. The part which is cut off from *3* should be used for piece *4* of the next course. In this way, there will be no waste of flooring material. Move the loose boards to the starting board for installation.

(b) Blind nail all boards after the first one. Nail three or four pieces then place a short length of straight edge hard wood against the tongue edge of the outside piece and drive

the unit up snugly. This operation is repeated after every three or four pieces are laid. Table I, Nailing Schedule, gives information on nails and spacing. Always drive the nails through the tongue of the board at an angle of about 50 degrees to the floor, as shown in Fig. 61.

(c) While nailing, stand with your feet on the board to be nailed, as shown in Fig. 62. The man with the hammer is standing on the board he is nailing. If you will follow this method of procedure, you can hold the board in position while it is being nailed. By standing on your feet, you can deliver a straight blow with the hammer to the nail with an easy motion. A standing position also permits quick and easy body movements. When the head of the nail reaches the board, you should raise the handle of the hammer. This will permit the face of the hammer to

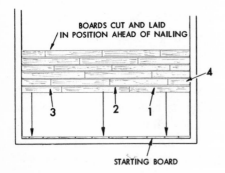

Fig. 60. Boards are cut and laid loose, then moved to starting board.

Table I   Nail Schedule: Oak Flooring

Tongued and Grooved Flooring Must Always Be Blind-Nailed, Square-Edge Flooring Face-Nailed.

Size Flooring	Type and Size of Nails	Spacing
(Tongued & Grooved) 25/32 x 3¼	7d or 8d screw type or cut steel nail*	10-12 in. apart
(Tongued & Grooved) 25/32 x 2¼	Same as above	Same as above
(Tongued & Grooved) 25/32 x 1½	Same as above	Same as above
(Tongued & Grooved) ½ x 2, ½ x 1½	5d screw type or cut steel or wire nail	10 in. apart
Following flooring must be laid on wood sub-floor:		
(Tongued & Grooved) ⅜ x 2, ⅜ x 1½	4d bright casing nail — wire, cut or screw nail	8 in. apart
(Square-Edge) 5/16 x 2, 5/16 x 1½	1-in. 15 gauge fully barbed flooring brad, preferably cement coated	2 nails every 7 in.

*Machine-driven barbed fasteners of the size recommended by the manufacturer are acceptable.

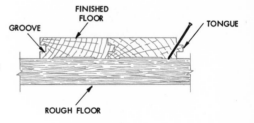

Fig. 61. Blind nailing drives flooring up tight and hides nails.

strike the tongue of the board instead of the edge, when the nail is given the last blow. Tongue and groove finish flooring is also nailed with a manual or pneumatic nailing machine. See Fig. 63.

6. When the finish floor has been laid up to the line 2, Fig. 59, the

Fig. 62. The carpenter must have the correct stance in laying finish flooring.

Fig. 63. Nailing machines make floor laying much easier. (Rockwell Mfg. Co.)

starter board *3* in the key room should be laid. The front edge of this board should be the same distance from the chalk line *L* as the front edge of the board *2*. This will insure the boards coming out right at the door opening where the flooring passes from one room to the next.

7. Continue laying the finish floor until the flooring is within 2 or 3 boards from the opposite wall of the room. Then cut and fit the last few boards to be laid. With a rabbet plane, open up the groove of each board. Place the boards in position and draw them together tightly with

a pinch bar, then face nail them in place.

Note: In using the pinch bar, be sure to protect the wall finish against bruises by placing a strong piece of board between the bar and the wall.

8. When there are no projections in the key room, and the finish floor-ing boards do not extend into any adjacent room, laying the finish floor becomes a simple matter. The start-ing board is nailed as close as pos-sible to one of the two longest walls of the room, starting along one wall and running parallel to the two long-est walls.

Cabinets

Cabinets are generally made in a mill or cabinet shop by another member of the carpenter trade who is a specialist in this field. They are delivered to the job, where they are installed by the carpenter. Kitchen cabinets make up much of this work, but an increasing number of ward-robes, chests of drawers, and a vari-ety of other built-ins are being used. The installation work requires some degree of skill to insure that the cab-inets are installed plumb and level and fitted tightly against the wall or other cabinet work. The carpenter must work with care to keep from damaging them. Many are made of very fine woods and some are pre-finished. See Fig. 64. The following method of installing cabinets may be used.

PROCEDURE

1. Set the cabinet in place on the floor and in the position where it is to be installed.

2. Level the top both ways as shown at *1* and *2*, Fig. 65. If the floor should not be level, it will be neces-sary to use wedges, as shown, to bring the cabinet to a level position. After the top has been leveled, plumb the sides as shown at *3* and *4*. If the cabinet has been carefully built so that all faces are square, then the sides will be plumb when the top is level.

3. Scribe the bottom edge of the cabinet to the floor. This is done by setting the scribers *A*, Fig. 65, to the widest space, and then drawing the pencil line *a* with the scribers parallel with the floor.

4. Turn the cabinet over on its side or back and remove the excess amount of wood to the lines just scribed. Any amount more than ¼ of an inch is more quickly removed with a saw. However, the plane is commonly used for this job.

5. Again place the cabinet into the position where it is to be in-stalled, pushing it tightly against the walls and level the top a second time as a check.

6. Set a pair of scribers *B*, Fig.

Fig. 64. Counter top ranges and built-in ovens are features of modern kitchens. (Kitchen Kompact)

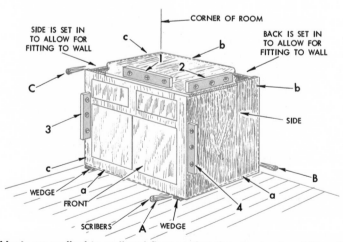

Fig. 65. Cabinets are scribed to wall and floor so that they are level and fit perfectly.

65, to the widest opening between the back of the cabinet and the wall, then scribe a line *b* along the end and the top of the cabinet.

Note: Cabinets should be designed with excess material along the edges of the outside faces by setting the back and the side of the cabinet from ½ to ¾ inch back from the edges, as shown in Fig. 65.

7. Set the scribers *C* to the widest opening along the front edge and scribe the lines *c* along the front and the top.

8. Remove the excess wood with either saw or plane to the lines just scribed, undercutting slightly to insure a tight fit on the face side.

9. Place the cabinet back into position and check all edges for a good fit. Improve the cuts if necessary.

10. Fasten the cabinet into place as the design requires. In some cases provision for fastening to the floor and the wall are made inside the cabinet.

Other Built-Ins

A great area of interest to the carpenter is the trend toward including more built-ins. Kitchen cabinets of wood with counter tops, ranges and biult-in ovens have been accepted

Fig. 66. A counter top lavatory with a cabinet below is an interesting and practical feature of a modern bathroom. (Rheem Mfg. Co.)

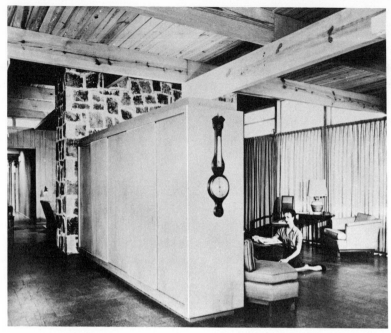

Fig. 67. A built-in closet wall serves as a room divider. Note the plank and beam construction. (Southern Pine Assoc.)

by housewives as features of a modern kitchen. See Fig. 64. Cabinet lavatories or vanities are included in modern bathrooms. They are cabinets for storage with the lavatories recessed into the counter tops. See Fig. 66. Closet walls between bedrooms, and cabinets which serve as room dividers, are useful for many purposes. They are often made in a cabinet shop and installed after finished flooring is in place. See Fig. 67. Built-in furniture such as wardrobes in bedrooms, china cases in dining areas, and book cases, serve the functional needs of the home.

Stair Construction

The staircase, when carefully designed and built, adds dignity and charm to a home. The quality of craftsmanship displayed reflects the character of the entire interior of the building.

In general, stairwork is considered a special field of carpentry. The main stairway, which may have several artistic features that are difficult to make on the job, is usually made in a mill and assembled at the house. Stairs which are usually built by the carpenter on the job include the porch and other stairs on the outside of buildings, and less important stairs within a building. It is essential that every carpenter have the necessary information regarding the general principles involved in stair building, as well as knowledge of the layout and construction.

Types of Stairs. The staircase in a building is one means whereby one may travel from the level of one floor to another. The ease with which a stairway can be traveled depends upon the proper proportioning of the riser and tread of each step and the number of steps in one series or flight. The design of the building and the space allowed for stairs will control the type of staircase which may be built.

Straight-Flight Stairs. A stairway commonly known as a *straight-flight stair*, shown in Fig. 68, is the simplest to build, but not necessar-

ily the most desirable. Furthermore, the layout of a building does not always permit the use of a straight flight stairway. A staircase with a long flight, consisting of more than fifteen steps, is tiring because it affords no opportunity for a pause in ascent. For this reason a landing should be introduced somewhere in the flight, usually at the halfway point, as shown in Fig. 69.

Landings also have another function, that of changing the direction of the stairs, as shown in Fig. 70. The staircase returning on itself, as shown in Fig. 71, is economical in

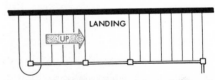

Fig. 69. A straight-flight stair is broken by a landing when the floor to floor height is greater than normal.

Fig. 68. A straight-flight stair is very satisfactory if space permits its use.

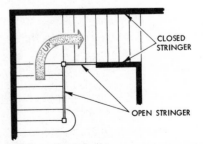

Fig. 70. A landing serves to change direction in a 90 degree stair change.

471

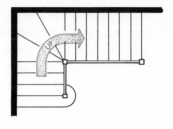

Fig. 71. An open newel stair provides an 180 degree change in direction.

Fig. 72. A 90 degree change stair with winders.

space, especially when there are a number of floor levels to be connected. In this case the stairs continue to wind upward.

Winder Stairs. Space limitations frequently demand a staircase with winders to bring about a change in direction. The three-winder stairway, illustrated in Fig. 72, is frequently used. It is not considered dangerous as long as the treads are approximately the same width on the line of travel.

Geometrical Stairs. The most complicated and most expensive stairways are those that are curved, commonly known as the *geometrical stairway*, Fig. 73. The geometrical stairway is a winding stairway, but it is so designed that the tread at the line of travel of all steps is the same width. These staircases may be circular as shown at *A*, or elliptical as at *B*, Fig. 73, and often are designed with landings to insure ease in ascending them.

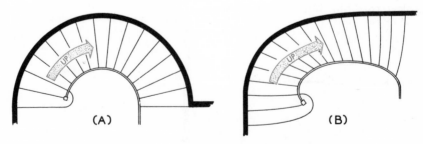

Fig. 73. Two types of geometrical stairs: (A) circular stair, (B) elliptical stair. Geometrical stairs provide an elegant touch to a building.

472

Safety Precautions in Stairway Building

Statistics compiled by the National Safety Council show that stairways are the cause of the greatest number of accidents in the home. These accidents can be attributed to various factors; some, of course, are beyond the control of those who design and build the stairways. However, there are far too many accidents due directly to faulty construction. The carpenter can make a worthwhile contribution toward accident prevention if he plans and does his work well.

The Safety Engineering Department of the National Workmen's Compensation Service Bureau has set up the following standards as suggestions to stair builders to help remove some of the causes responsible for many accidents.

1. Stairways should be free from winders.
2. The dimensions of landings should be equal to or greater than the width of stairways between handrails (or handrail and wall).
3. Landings should be level and free from intermediate steps between the main up flight and the main down flight.
4. All treads should be equal and all risers should be equal in any one flight.
5. The sum of one tread and one riser, exclusive of the nosing, should

not be more than 18 inches nor less than 17 inches. (Stair ratio.)
6. The nosing should not exceed 1¾ inches.
7. All stairways should be equipped with permanent and substantial handrails 36 inches in height from the center of the tread.
8. All handrails should have rounded corners and a surface that is smooth and free from splinters.
9. The angle of the stairways with the horizontal should not be more than fifty degrees nor less than twenty degrees.
10. Stair treads should be slip proof, firmly secured and with no protruding bolts, screws, or nails.

Tread and Riser Relationship

Stairs must be adapted to meet many special requirements to fit into a particular building and rules have been established to make stairs as comfortable to use as possible. Unfortunately, rules must be overlooked occasionally at times in order to solve a problem. This is particularly true in remodeling work, but is also true when a house has not been well planned. However, a carpenter should know how to make choices which will result in the best stairs under the circumstances. He should be familiar with the building code which applies locally and should bend every effort to build stairs accordingly.

The stair ratio is a relationship between the tread run (width) and the riser height so that as one increases, the other decreases, and vice versa. A minimum tread run and a maximum riser height keep the stairs from exceeding the critical angle of the whole stair. See Fig. 74 and Table II. The economical use of material is also a factor. Good design often requires wider boards for treads than the carpenter would like to use if economy were the main consideration.

Some fundamental ideas on tread-riser relationships:

1. All risers in the same flight must be equal.

2. All treads in the same flight must be equal.

3. For residences, the maximum height of a riser shall be eight inches. (F.H.A. permits 8¼ inches.)[1]

4. For residences, the minimum tread run shall be nine inches exclusive of nosing.

5. The stair ratio: The height of a riser plus the width of a tread shall equal not less than 17 inches nor more than 18 inches.

Minimum R + T = 17

Maximum R + T = 18

The formula T + R = 17 to

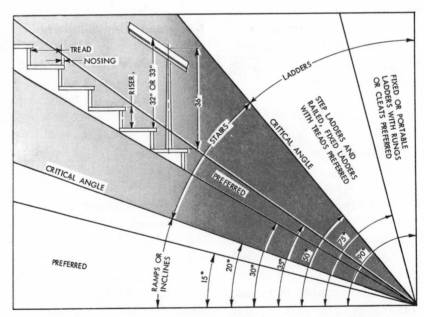

Fig. 74. Preferred and critical angles for stairs, ladders, ramps, and inclines.

---

1. Federal Housing Authority: *Minimum Property Standards for One and Two Living Units,* F.H.A. No. 300.

Table II Angles, Risers and Treads for Stairs*
(Tread + Riser = 17½ Inches)

ANGLE WITH HORIZONTAL		RISER IN INCHES	TREAD IN INCHES	
Degrees	Minutes			
22	00	5	12½	
23	14	5¼	12¼	
24	38	5½	12	
26	00	5¾	11¾	
27	33	6	11½	
29	03	6¼	11¼	
30	35	6½	11	
32	08	6¾	10¾	Preferred
33	41	7	10½	
35	16	7¼	10¼	
36	52	7½	10	
38	29	7¾	9¾	
40	08	8	9½	
41	44	8¼	9¼	
43	22	8½	9	
45	00	8¾	8¾	
46	38	9	8½	
48	16	9¼	8¼	
49	54	9½	8	

*Safety standards developed by Safety Department of National Workmen's Compensation Service Bureau.

18 is used by many carpenters because the calculations can be made mentally. Local building codes may have other tread and riser limitations and ratio requirements.

Treads. Material for treads is generally 2 x 10 or 2 x 12 inches (actual size 1½ x 9½ or 1½ by 11½ inches). See Fig. 75. The run of the tread is the distance from the face of one riser to the face of the one which follows it and is the same dimension as the cut on the stringer. When a 9 inch tread run is required, only ½ inch is left for nosing. When a larger tread run is required (either

by the code or by the use of the stair ratio formula) a board wider than a 2 x 10 will be necessary.

The tread is often cut so as to extend beyond the stringers at each side the same distance as the nosing extends in front.

Risers. Stairs without risers (open riser) are permitted for certain applications but are not considered good practice. Risers are usually made of 1 x 10 or 1 x 12 inch boards and are ripped to fit. The risers are placed behind the lower treads and snuggly fitted against the under side of the upper tread. See Fig. 75.

475

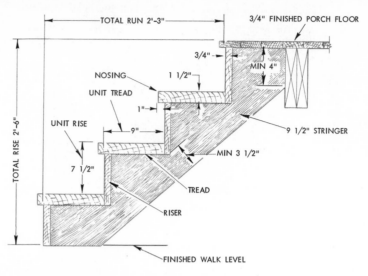

Fig. 75. The stringer must be laid out so that the unit rise and unit tread are the same for each step.

It is very important that all the riser heights on a flight of stairs be equal in order to prevent the danger of tripping or misstepping. Also, the riser height must be limited so that it is reasonably similar in all stairs. However, the board (not the unit rise) for the top riser and the bottom riser in a flight of stairs may vary in height in order to make up the difference in thickness of flooring, etc. See Fig. 75.

Stringer. The stringer is the most important of the stair parts. This is the cut out support for treads and risers. If the carpenter has made the correct layout and made the proper deductions, the stairs will be

perfect when installed. The material used is usually a 2 x 10 or a 2 x 12 in order that 3½ inches are left to carry the load after the cuts are made. Deductions must be made at the top and at the bottom of the stringer so that the bottom rise and the top rise of the finished stair may be equal. The thickness of the tread material must be deducted at the bottom and is added at the top unless the flooring and tread thickness are not the same. Further additions and adjustments are required, depending on the problem. See Fig. 76.

Adequate bearing (4 inch minimum F.H.A.) against the header must be provided so that the stringer may be well fastened.

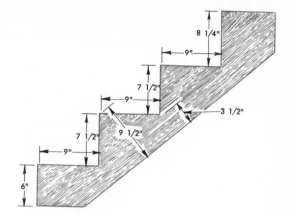

Fig. 76. The carpenter must learn how to make correct deductions. (This is for the stringer for Fig. 75.)

Calculations Necessary for a Straight-Flight Stair Layout

To help bring about a better understanding of how to go about laying out a stair stringer, let us consider laying out a stair which must have a total rise of 8 feet 4 inches. The stairwell, already established, is 11 feet 3 inches, as shown in Fig. 77.

Before any stringer can be laid out a study must be made of the plans, or stair location if the building is in progress, to determine the type of stair required. The limitations or restrictions must also be considered, such as a beam which may cut down headroom, a door opening at the bottom of the stair, or windows along the stair flight. Frequently such restrictions will determine the place where the stairs will start at the bottom, and may necessitate the shortening of the total run of the stair, thus changing the standard proportions between the riser and the tread.

When the principles involved in the layout of a simple stair with no restrictions are thoroughly understood, then problems which include variations can be solved satisfactorily. The straight flight stair shown in Fig. 77 will be considered as a typical problem.

Two methods may be used to find the exact riser height. One in which a story pole is used is time taking but accurate and the other uses simple mathematics.

Using The Story Pole to find the Unit Rise.

PROCEDURE

1. Take a story pole (any piece of lumber 1 × 2 preferred straight with

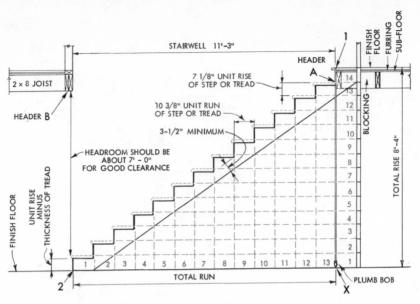

Fig. 77. Straight-flight stair problem showing the relation of riser to tread, total rise to total run, and desirable headroom.

square ends) and set it on the finished floor in the stairwell on the basement floor. Mark the location of the finished floor above, or first floor, as shown at *1*, Fig. 77. The distance *1—X* will be the total rise of the stair, in this case 8 feet 4 inches. Then place the story pole on two horses.

Note: If the finished floor has not been laid when the measurement is taken, a block of wood should be placed on the rough floor to establish the line of the finished floor, or allowance can be made for the thickness of the finished floor.

2. Set a pair of dividers to 7 inches (a permissible unit rise per step) and step off the total rise on the story pole, dividing the distance *1—X* into equal parts. If upon the first trial you find there is a remainder, adjust the dividers and try again. If the remainder is less than 3½ inches set the dividers to a setting larger than 7 inches. If the remainder is more than 3½ inches, set the dividers to a setting smaller than 7. Continue adjusting the dividers and stepping off the distance on the story pole, until the last unit is the same as all of the others. The dividers are now set to the unit rise which should be within the allowed

riser height requirements. Be careful not to disturb the divider setting.

Using Mathematics to find the Unit Rise. The unit rise per step can also be obtained by dividing the total rise in inches by 7 to find the number of risers (drop the fraction if any), then divide the total rise by the number found, to obtain the exact unit rise per step.

Total Rise = 8'-4" or 100 inches, 100 ÷ 7 = 14$\frac{2}{7}$ risers.
We must choose either 14 or 15 risers:
100 ÷ 14 = 7.143 inches or 7$\frac{1}{8}$ inches.

Finding the Unit Tread. The stair ratio is used to find the unit tread. There is a little leaway permitted the carpenter because he should choose a tread width which falls between the limits of the ratio:

T + R = 17 to 18.
The riser height has been determined as 7$\frac{1}{8}$ inches.

Minimum tread ratio: T + 7$\frac{1}{8}$ = 17, T = 9$\frac{7}{8}$ inches.

Maximum tread ratio: T + 7$\frac{1}{8}$ = 18, T = 10$\frac{7}{8}$ inches.

A midpoint would be 10$\frac{3}{8}$ inches.

Referring to Table II it will be noted that these dimensions, R = 7$\frac{1}{8}$, T = 10$\frac{3}{8}$, fall within the range of preferred angles.

Note: In laying out the stair, the nosing of a step is not considered a part of the tread and does not enter into stair calculation.

Finding the Total Run. To find the total run of the stair, multiply the width of the tread by one less than the number of risers. The reason for this can be found by studying Fig. 78, which shows that there is one less tread than the number of risers. In the foregoing problem, the width of the tread was found to be 10$\frac{3}{8}$ inches and the total number of risers 14. Subtracting 1 from 14 leaves 13, the number of treads; and 13 × 10$\frac{3}{8}$ gives 134$\frac{7}{8}$ inches, or 11

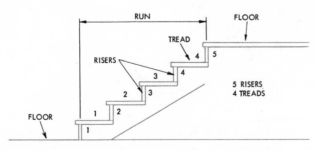

Fig. 78. To go up 5 risers, 4 treads are required.

feet 2⅞ inches (3 inches), the total run of the stairs.

To find the starting point of the stairs, locate point X, Fig. 77, on the basement floor by plumbing down from the header A in the stairwell. Then lay out the total run of 11 feet 3 inches (2⅞ inches) of the stair to locate the starting point as shown at 2, Fig. 77.

Finding the Headroom. In this particular stair the length of the stairwell is equal to the total run of the stair. The actual headroom would be the finished floor to floor height minus (1) one unit rise, (2) the thickness of the joist, and (3) the thickness of the flooring components:

Finished Floor	=	¾
Floor Furring	=	¾
Rough Floor	=	¾
Joist		=7½
Riser		=7⅛

$$16⅞'' \text{ or } 1'\text{-}4⅞''$$
$$8'\text{-}4'' - 1'\text{-}4⅞'' = 6'\text{-}11⅛''$$

A 6'-11⅛" headroom is very adequate.

Stairwells and Headroom. The length of the stairwell is usually determined by the designer of the plans so that a certain arrangement of partitions will result. He also fixes the location of the foot of the stairs so that the proper amount of space is provided between the lowest riser and adjacent walls or partitions. The carpenter must work within the limits shown on the plans.

Headroom should be measured vertically from the front edge of the nosing to a line parallel with the stair pitch. The dimension should be 6'-8" minimum for main stairs and 6'-4" minimum for basement or service stairs. (F.H.A.) A headroom of 7'-0" is preferred. Where a soffit develops, as shown on Fig. 79, particular attention must be given to provide adequate headroom in order to overcome the illusion of being crushed by the ceiling above.

When the carpenter runs into difficulty in making the stairs work out he should consult the owner and the architect. If he is on his own on remodeling work he may be able to change the header at the end of the stairwell or may be able to change the unit tread, unit rise, or number of risers to achieve a shorter total run.

Laying Out a Stair Stringer. In laying out the stair stringer illustrated in Fig. 77, the following method can be used.

PROCEDURE

1. Select a straight piece of 2 × 12 of sufficient length and lay it on a pair of sawhorses.

Note: The required length can be found by taking the unit rise per step (7⅛ inches) on the tongue of the framing square, and the unit run per step, or tread (10⅜ inches), on the blade. Lay the square on the edge of any straight stick at these measurements and draw the lines

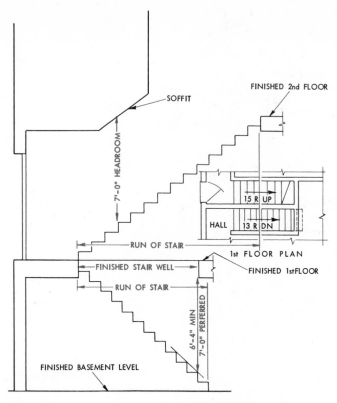

Fig. 79. Problems in head room arise in a two story dwelling.

AC and *CB*, Fig. 80. The distance *AB* will be the bridge measure per step. Multiply this bridge measure (12¾ inches) by the number of risers (14). The result will be 14 feet 10 inches, the approximate length required for this stair stringer. Allowance must be made because the board must be longer to connect to the header at the top.

2. Begin at the bottom of the stringer, lay the square in the posi-

tion shown in Fig. 80 (use framing-square clips if available). Take the unit rise (7⅛ inches) on the tongue and the unit run, or tread (10⅜ inches), on the blade. Draw the lines *1–2* and *2–3*.

3. Reverse the square and draw the lines *1–4* at right angles to *1–2*. The length of the line *1–4* is equal to the unit rise of the step (7⅛ inches). Shorten the rise of the first step from the bottom an amount

481

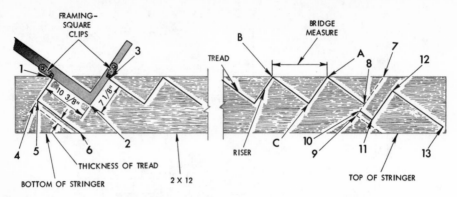

Fig. 80. The stair stringer is laid out in steps, using the unit tread width and the unit riser height on the framing square. The thickness of the tread is deducted at the bottom. Adjustments are made in the layout for support at the top.

equal to the thickness of the tread to be used. Draw the cutting line *5–6* parallel to *1–2*.

4. Continue to lay out from point *3*, along the edge of the 2 × 12, the balance of the steps required for the stair. Great accuracy is required in laying out the steps. Therefore, use a sharp pencil or knife and make the lines meet at the edge of the 2 × 12.

5. When the point *7* at the top of the stringer has been reached, extend the line *7–8* to point *9*, making *7–9* equal to the thickness of the first floor above (joist and flooring), at the stairwell.

6. The thickness of a tread was removed from the first riser at the bottom of the stringer; this will drop the stringer. Then this tread thickness *9–10* must be allowed at the top, if

the stringer is to fit up tightly against the joist header of the first floor. (The cut will be made on line *10–11*.)

7. Greater nailing support of the stringer at the top can be obtained by fitting the stringer around the header joist. Therefore, draw lines *10–11*, thickness of joist; also 11–12, height of joist; and *12–13*, top cut of the stringer.

Stair Widths

The width of staircases is determined by the necessity for two people to be able to pass comfortably on the stairs, and the fact that furniture will have to be carried up or down. If two people are to be able to pass on the stairs, the width should be three or three and one-half feet. The minimum set by some codes is 2 feet 8 inches for main stairs clear of handrails.

The width of stairs necessary for the passage of furniture depends upon the shape of the stairs and the kind of furniture which will have to be taken up or down the stairs. The straight flight stairway permits the movement of objects more easily than does the winder or platform type of stairs. When winding or platform stairways are open on one side, including open-well stairways, they will afford a better chance for moving large pieces of furniture, because such objects usually can be raised over the handrails and newel posts unless the articles are extremely heavy.

Handrails

Handrails should be provided on one or both sides of a stairs. The height of handrails should be 32 or 33 inches from the edge of the nosing to the top of the rail, or 36 inches from the center of the tread, as shown in Fig. 74.

Winding Stairs

Winding stairs perform the following functions:

1. They change the direction of travel of a stair.

2. They save room in some cases because not only is the direction changed but a rise is achieved at the same time.

3. They are used to provide an interesting architectural effect particularly when used for finished stairs. See Fig. 81.

When a plan requires that a stair start from one floor and make a quarter turn or half turn before reaching the floor above, either a platform or winders must be introduced. Wind-

Fig. 81. Full sized plan layout of winders is used to find dimensions and cuts. (Note solid lines represent riser faces not tread nosings.)

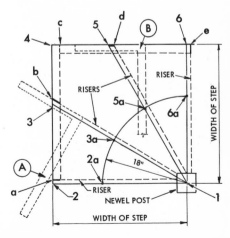

ers will help conserve space because the turns are used to raise the level also.

Winders are not considered as safe as straight stairs or straight stairs with a platform. The main reasons why they are less safe is because the tread width varies from almost nothing at the newel to a very wide space at the far end. To overcome this fault as much as possible, a line of travel with a radius which would approximate the line where a person would walk, is established. After the line of travel has been drawn, the risers are put in place in such a manner that they are spaced equally and also approximately equal in width to the spacing of the risers in the straight flights above and below.

The carpenter must not only bear in mind the need for safety but also the problems of cutting out the parts,

assembling them, and fastening them to the posts or supports. Stringers can either be nailed to the side of the posts or butt against them. When risers converge at posts they should be arranged so that good nailing is provided. Blocks may be used to back up or support the risers for nailing on carpenter-made stairs. The newel post is routed out to receive the risers on mill-made stairs. Outside stringers usually must be made in more than one piece, joining where the straight stair ends and the winders begin. See Fig. 82.

Three-Winder Stair. It is advisable when building a winder stair to first draw a full size plan view layout on the floor, showing size and shape of the treads, length of risers, and all angle cuts of both treads and risers. The stringers may also be laid out easily from the plan view. The

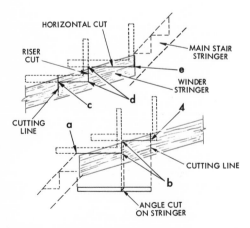

Fig. 82. The stringers for the winders are laid out using the same unit rise as the straight flight. The cuts for the tread length and riser angle cuts are taken from the full size plan layout.

following method may be used when building winders.

PROCEDURE

1. Draw a square *1–2–4–6* equal in width to that of the stair as shown in Fig. 81. Dotted lines show the thickness and location of the outside stringers.

2. Using an 18 inch line of travel, swing an arc with center at *1*.

3. Divide this arc into three equal parts *2a–3a*, *3a–5a*, and *5a–6a* and through these points draw the riser lines *1–3* and *1–5*. Draw in the back of the riser with a dotted line.

4. The width of the treads at their narrowest point is obtained by drawing the full size newel post in position.

5. The angle of the cuts for the stringer cutouts is obtained by laying the framing square on the layout as at *A*. The framing square held as at *B* will give the angle cut for the risers.

Layout of Stringer for Winders. The winder stringer is in two parts *a–4* and *c–e*, Fig. 81. The layout of each part is different and both stringers have a different angle of rise from that of the main stair as shown in Fig. 82.

The layout of the stringer is made along the edge of the board with the framing square, in the same way as shown in Fig. 80. The rise per step is the same as that of the main stair, but the run of each tread must be taken from the full size layout. Fig.

81. Dimensions *a–b*, *b–4*, *c–d*, and *d–e*, in Fig. 82, are taken from the layout, Fig. 81.

The angle cut for the riser on the stringer should not be laid out until the horizontal cut for the tread has been made on the stringers. The angles for these cuts are taken from the full size layout by laying the square as shown at *A*, Fig. 81. Note: The cut for the upper winder will be different. Use the square in the same way on stringer *c–e* to get this cut.

The shape of the treads is obtained by laying out lines representing the nosing on the full size plan layout 1¼ inch in front of the riser face. The exact size, angles and cutout at the newel will be shown on the plan layout.

Riser lengths and angle cuts are also obtained from the layout; their heights are the same as the risers of the main stair.

Finished Interior Stairs

The job of making finished interior stairs and rails is generally that of a specialized carpenter called a stair-builder. However, every carpenter should have some knowledge about this part of the building of a house because he must prepare the stairwells, supports and walls for the stairs and under some conditions may be directly involved in assembling a stair. See Fig. 83.

Careful measurements must be taken at the job by the carpenter who will do the work. The stair parts

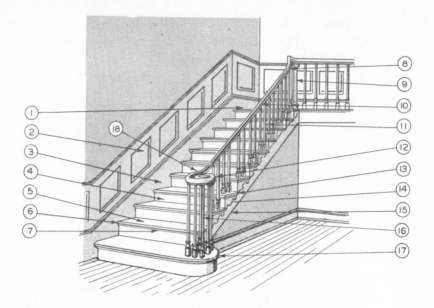

1. Landing
2. Raised-panel dado
3. Closed stringer
4. Riser
5. Tread
6. Tread housing
7. Cove molding under nosing
8. Goose neck
9. Landing newel post

10. Handrail
11. Baluster
12. Volute
13. End nosing
14. Bracket
15. Open stringer
16. Starting newel post
17. Bull-nose starting step
18. Concave easement

Fig. 83. The carpenter should know the names of the parts of a staircase.

are then usually made in a shop so that accurate woodworking machines may be used. When the stair parts are ready a stairbuilding carpenter goes to the job and installs the stairs making minor corrections as he proceeds.

Two distinct types are used: One type is the *open* or *mitered stringer*

stair which is used where the side of the stair is exposed to view. See Fig. 84. The other type is the *closed stringer* stair which is generally used along a wall. See Fig. 85. Many stairs have a closed stringer along the wall and an open stringer on the side toward the room. See Fig. 83. A closed stringer is used occasionally on the

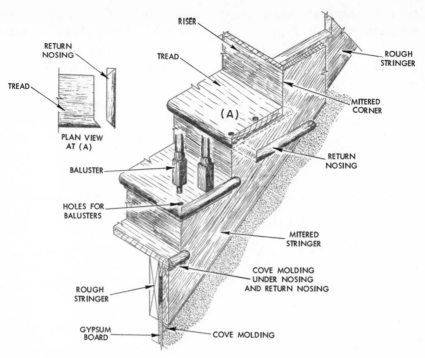

Fig. 84. A finished interior stair exposed to view. Stair may use a mitered string and stair parts made in a mill.

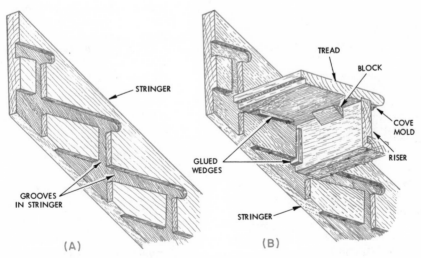

Fig. 85. The stringer is housed to receive the treads, risers and wedges. Glued blocks reinforce the center of the treads.

exposed side also to provide a special architectural effect.

In first class stairwork nails are used sparingly. All joints are housed or concealed in some way. Closed stringers are routed out to receive the ends of treads and risers. Treads are often routed out to receive the top edge of the risers. Wedges are glued and driven in place to make the stairs solid. Blocks are glued to the underside of the intersection of treads and risers to keep the joint from opening up. See Fig. 85.

Checking On Your Knowledge

The following questions give you the opportunity to check up on yourself. If you have read the chapter carefully, you should be able to answer the questions.

If you have any difficulty, read the chapter over once more so that you have the information well in mind before you go on with your reading.

DO YOU KNOW

1. What general types of material are used for interior wall finish?
2. How is gypsum wallboard applied to studs?
3. How are suspended ceiling panels hung?
4. What trim members are used at windows?
5. What are the check rail, stop, and brick mold?
6. Where are the following moldings used: cove, base shoe, batten?
7. What is the advantage of a coped joint?
8. When would a base molding be mitered?
9. What is a sash balance?
10. How may wood awning windows be trimmed?
11. What is a flush door? solid core? hollow core?
12. What is a panel door?
13. What is a pocket door?
14. What does the *hand* of a door refer to?
15. What is a loose pin butt?
16. How are shingles used in setting a door frame?
17. Where are butts located in relation to the floor and the top of the door?
18. What is a swaged hinge?
19. What is a tubular latch?
20. What is a cylindrical lock?
21. What is a mortise lock?
22. How is a metal door frame fastened to drywall metal studs?
23. What wood is used most for flooring? What other woods are used?
24. What is plank flooring?
25. What is block flooring? Parquet flooring?
26. What are some common built-ins?
27. When is a straight flight of stairs not advisable?
28. What stair ratio is suggested? What headroom?
29. Define *unit tread* and *unit riser*.
30. What is a closed string stair?
31. What are winders? Are they safe?

Appendix

Reference Material

The field of general carpentry has become so vast that no book or set of books can encompass all of the material. New products are reaching the market constantly and new techniques are being developed each year. Printed information covering most of these products and techniques, however, is available in one form or another. The person interested in following carpentry as an occupation should be alert to all of the material which is published.

Progressive manufacturers are generally very willing to supply information about their products and how they should be used correctly. They feel that it is to their advantage to have the carpenter know about them and how they should be applied. Manufacturers often join forces by forming associations or institutes. These organizations are formed to promote their products but also have the functions of research and information. Generally they are very helpful in supplying literature in answer to specific requests.

New textbooks, reference books, and books in related fields are reaching the market constantly. Some have a general broad purpose, others are written in depth in a limited field. The following pages suggest some of the more recent books worthy of study for the carpentry student.

There are several periodicals of interest also which should be studied each month. Some of them are trade magazines, and subscriptions are limited to builders and to architects but they may be available at libraries or kept on file by employers.

Associations and Institutes

American Concrete Institute
Post Office Box 4754, Redford Station
Detroit, Michigan 48219

American Hardware Manufacturers'
  Association
342 Madison Avenue
New York, N. Y. 10017

American Institute of Steel
  Construction
101 Park Avenue
New York, N. Y. 10017

American Institute of Timber
  Construction
1757 K Street, N. W.
Washington, D. C. 20002

Asbestos-Cement Products Association
509 Madison Avenue
New York, N. Y. 10022

Asphalt Institute, The
Asphalt Institute Building
University of Maryland
College Park, Maryland

California Redwood Association
576 Sacramento Street
San Francisco, California 94111

Douglas Fir Plywood Association
1119 A Street
Tacoma, Washington 98402

Forest Products Laboratory
U. S. Department of Agriculture
Madison, Wisconsin

Hardboard Association
205 W. Wacker Drive
Chicago, Illinois 60606

Hardwood Plywood Institute
600 S. Michigan Avenue
Chicago, Illinois 60605

Insulating Siding Association
1201 Waukegan Road
Glenview, Illinois

Insulation Board Institute
111 W. Washington Street
Chicago, Illinois 60602

Maple Flooring Manufacturers
    Association
35 E. Wacker Drive
Chicago, Illinois 60601

National Forest's Products Association
1619 Massachusetts Avenue, N. W.
Washington, D. C. 20036

National Hardwood Lumber
    Association
59 E. Van Buren Street
Chicago, Illinois 60605

National Mineral Wool Association
2906 Americas Building
Rockefeller Center
New York, N. Y. 10020

National Oak Flooring Manufacturers
    Association
814 Sterick Building
Memphis, Tennessee 38103

National Safety Council
425 N. Michigan Avenue
Chicago, Illinois 60611

Ponderosa Pine Woodwork Association
105 W. Monroe Street
Chicago, Illinois 60603

Portland Cement Association
5420 Old Orchard Road
Skokie, Illinois 60079

Small Homes Council
University of Illinois
Urbana, Illinois

Southern Pine Association
P. O. Box 1170
New Orleans, Louisiana 70104

Structural Clay Products Institute
1520 Eighteenth Street NW.
Washington, D. C. 20006

United States of America Standards
    Institute
10 East 40th Street
New York, New York 10016

West Coast Lumbermen's Association
1410 S. W. Morrison Street
Portland, Oregon 97205

Western Pine Association
510 Yeon Building
Portland, Oregon

Western Red Cedar Lumber Association
White-Henry-Stuart Building
Seattle, Washington

Reference Books*

Burbank, Nelson L. *House Construction Details*. Simmons-Boardman Publishing Corp. (30 Church St., New York, N. Y. 10007), 1969.

Burke, Arthur E. *Architectural and Building Trades Dictionary*. American Technical Society (848 E. 58th St., Chicago, Ill. 60037), 1955.

Durbahn, Walter E. *Fundamentals of Carpentry: Tools, Materials and Practices, Vol. I*. American Technical Society, 1967.

Feirer, John L. *Cabinetmaking and Millwork*. Charles A. Bennett Co., Inc. (237 N. E. Monroe St., Peoria, Ill. 61602), 1967.

Feirer, John L. *Woodworking for Industry*. Charles A. Bennett Co., Inc., 1963.

Groneman, Chris H. and E. R. Glazener. *Technical Woodworking*. McGraw-Hill Book Co., (330 W. 42nd St., New York, N. Y. 10036), 1966.

Hepler, Donald E. and Paul Wallach. *Architecture: Drafting and Design*. McGraw-Hill Book Co., 1965.

Hammond, James J., et al. *Woodworking Technology*. McKnight & McKnight Publishing Co., (29 E. 10th St., New York, N. Y. 10003), 1966.

Hornung, William J. *Reinhold Data Sheets*. Reinhold Publishing Corp. (430 Park Ave., New York, N. Y. 10022), 1965.

Jones, Raymond P. *Framing, Sheathing and Insulation*. Delmar Publishers, Inc. (Mountainview Ave., Albany, N. Y. 12205), 1964.

Kidder, Frank E. and Harry Parker. *Architects' and Builders' Handbook*. John Wiley & Sons, Inc. (605 Third Ave., New York, N. Y. 10016).

Lloyd, William B. *Millwork: Principles and Practices*. Cahners Publishing Co. (221 Columbus Ave., Boston, Mass. 02116), 1966.

McDonnell, Leo P. *Hand Woodworking Tools*. Delmar Publishers, Inc., 1962.

McDonnell, Leo P. *Portable Power Tools*. Delmar Publishers, Inc., 1962.

Merritt, Frederick S. *Building Construction Handbook*. McGraw-Hill Book Co., 1965.

Muller, Edward J. *Architectural Drawing and Light Construction*. Prentice-Hall, Inc. (70 5th Ave., New York, N. Y. 10011), 1967.

Oberg, Fred R. *Heavy Timber Construction*. American Technical Society, 1968.

Portland Cement Association and the National Ready Mixed Concrete Association. *Concrete Technology*. Delmar Publishers, Inc. 1965.

---

* The address of the publisher is only shown once.

Fundamentals of Carpentry

Ramsey, Charles G. and H. R. Sleeper. *Architectural Graphic Standards.* (5th Ed.) John Wiley & Sons, Inc., 1956.

Smith, Ronald C. *Materials of Construction.* McGraw-Hill Book Co., 1966.

Smith, Ronald C. *Principles and Practices of Heavy Construction.* Prentice-Hall, Inc., 1967.

Spence, William P. *Architecture Design-Engineering-Drawing.* McKnight & McKnight Publishing Co., 1967.

Stegman, George K. and Harry J. Stegman. *Architectural Drafting: Functional Planning and Creative Design.* American Technical Society, 1966.

Steinberg, Joseph and Martin Stempel. *Estimating for the Building Trades.* American Technical Society, 1965.

Sundberg, Elmer W. *Building Trades Blueprint Reading, Part I.* American Technical Society, 1967.

Sundberg, Elmer W. and Rex Battenberg and W. Rahy Paul. *Building Trades Blueprint Reading, Part II.* American Technical Society, 1959.

Wilson, J. Douglas and S. O. Werner. *Simplified Roof Framing.* Mc-Graw-Hill Book Co., 1948.

Special References

Small Homes Council, University of Illinois, Urbana, Ill.
Booklets on house design, wood framing, kitchen planning, selecting lumber, windows, and many other topics.

Superintendent of Documents, U. S. Government Printing Office, Washington D. C. 10402: *Minimum Property Standards for One and Two Living Units,* FHA 300.

> Price list No. 72 covering government publications on homes construction, maintenance and community development.

United States of America Standards Institute, 10 E. 40th St., New York, N. Y. 10016. Standards for materials, safety codes.

Periodicals

Architectural Record. Monthly. McGraw-Hill Book Co. 330 W. 42nd St., New York, N. Y. 10036.

House and Home. Monthly. McGraw-Hill Book Co. 330 W. 42nd St., New York, N. Y. 10036.

Professional Builder. Monthly. 5 South Wabash Ave., Chicago, Ill. 60603.

Index

Numerals in **bold type** refer to illustrations.